Questions on German History

Paths to Parliamentary Democracy

Historical Exhibition in the Deutscher Dom in Berlin

The Exhibition, with the President of the German Bundestag as its patron, is organized by the German Bundestag.

Catalogue, 5th, completely revised edition

© Published by:
German Bundestag
Public Relations Division
53113 Bonn

Bonn 1998
English edition

Die Deutsche Bibliothek - CIP Einheitsaufnahme
Fragen an die deutsche Geschichte: Wege zur parlamentarischen Demokratie; historische Ausstellung im Deutschen Dom in Berlin / (die Ausstellung wird vom Deutschen Bundestag veranst. Hrsg. Deutscher Bundestag, Referat Öffentlichkeitsarbeit, Bonn).
19., neu bearb. Aufl. – Bonn:
Dt. Bundestag, Referat Öffentlichkeitsarbeit, 1996
Engl. Ausg. u.d.T.: Questions on German History
Franz. Ausg. u.d.T.: Interrogeons l'histoire de l'Allemagne

ISBN 3-924521-96-4
NE: Deutschland / Bundestag

The Exhibition is open from Tuesday to Sunday and on public holidays from 10.00 to 17.00 hours.

Guided tours of the Exhibition should be requested well in advance:
Tel.: (030) 227-32141
or Fax: (030) 227-36142.

Visitors may use an audio guide in English, French or German at a charge of DM 2.

Catalogue and cassette in English, French and German available from:
Historische Ausstellung im Deutschen Dom, Am Gendarmenmarkt, Berlin or
German Bundestag
Tel.: (0228) 16-25390
Fax: (0228) 16-26506

The nominal charge for the catalogue is DM 10.

Contents

Charts

Prussian Hegemony and Constitutional Change in the German
Empire after 1871

The Constitution of the German Empire of 1 August 1919

The National Socialist System of Rule

The Constitution of the Federal Republic of Germany –
the Basic Law of 23 May 1949

The Development of the Political Parties from 1981 to 1993

The Organization of Parliament

The Elected Parliament, Centre of Democracy

Foreword

The Exhibition "Questions on German History" opened in the Reichstag Building in Berlin in 1971 and was expanded a few years later. Its purpose was to afford the German public an opportunity to examine their past through a critical appraisal of the highs and lows of German history. The spirit of the Exhibition's very location drew visitors' attention to these central questions: the Reichstag Building stood next to the Berlin Wall, then the dividing line between freedom and dictatorship, and offered a clear view of the inhuman "death strip" beyond. Only a minute's walk away stood the Brandenburg Gate, so often at the centre of significant events in the course of German history. Once the gateway into Berlin's historic city centre, its was now in no-man's land – unpassable, indeed inaccessible. The Reichstag Building itself also embodied the spirit, and the questions, of those times: a building with a chequered history, under the terms of the Four Power Agreement it could no longer be used for sittings of Parliament. But it nevertheless housed a fully equipped plenary chamber large enough to accommodate all the members of parliament in a reunified Germany at any time – the symbol of a hope which was finally to be fulfilled in October 1990.

In November 1989, the Reichstag Building's location next to the Wall proved to be a happy coincidence for the Exhibition: following the opening of the Wall, thousands of East German citizens who for decades had been subjected to the communist party's distorted picture of the past, flocked there to inform themselves freely and thoroughly, for the very first time, about the course of German history in the 19th and 20th centuries.

Following the decision to renovate and convert the Reichstag Building, the Exhibition was moved to the Deutscher Dom in the former East Berlin where, having been substantially revised, it was re-opened in October 1996. This process was more than a symbolic gesture. Now that our country has overcome its political division, we live in a time of new challenges but also of new opportunities, both at home and abroad. The door to the future is once again open. This does not mean that the "questions on German history" have changed fundamentally. But there has been a shift in emphasis. No longer is our consciousness shaped by a sense of having reached history's final destination, where change becomes impossible; no longer is our memory shaped solely by the haunting recollections of all the failed attempts to resist violence and terror, embodied above all by the events of 20 July 1944 and 17 June 1953. The Peaceful Revolution of 1989 and 1990 has made us aware once again that history is a living process which can lead us to new and happier horizons. The courage of the men and women who risked their lives to demonstrate on the streets of Leipzig, Dresden, Halle, Berlin and so many other towns and cities in the former GDR against a state which flouted the rule of law showed us that, through their brave struggle for freedom and civil rights, people can take their history into their own hands – even after years of repression and violence.

This experience will, I am certain, reawaken interest in German history, and especially in the development of parliamentary democracy, liberty and human rights in our country – questions which are at the heart of this Exhibition. In contrast to the previous exhibition in the Reichstag Building, more emphasis has now been placed on juxtaposing the histories of the two Germanies between 1949 and 1990, and showing how and where they intersected. In the Deutscher Dom, the special features of the interior, while forcing the organizers of the Exhibition to focus their message, also gave them an opportunity to highlight with even greater immediacy the ceasuras and continuities of German history. It is to be hoped that the new concept underlying the Exhibition will succeed in demonstrating that, throughout our history, freedom has been a precious good, a good we have had to fight for and a good we must still defend today. If the Exhibition manages to convey the message that our history is not our destiny but a process we can actively shape ourselves, it will have served its purpose.

Prof. Rita Süssmuth
President of the German Bundestag

Introduction

by Lothar Gall

Those undertaking to organize an exhibition dealing with questions on Germany history over the last 200 years must first of all address a number of fundamental questions themselves. Most generally: How important is an understanding of the past for our perception of the present and our attitude towards the future? More specifically: What should the practical aims of such an exhibition be? And thematically: In an increasingly interdependent and interconnected world, does the choice of a national framework of historical analysis not narrow our perspective, thereby marginalizing central aspects of today's global reality?

These are legitimate questions. They go to the heart both of the purpose of such an exhibition and, more fundamentally, of the content of the knowledge and insights modern historiography can and must impart through such a medium.

To begin with, it is quite clear that the findings of historical research must be adapted to the nature of such a medium. Whereas the findings of historical research are essentially general and abstract, an exhibition achieves its impact by visualizing concrete events, by tracing specific processes and developments in their given context. The links between them, the factors which make apparently isolated occurrences characteristic of an entire period, are not immediately obvious; the visitor must be made aware of them by the combination of images and texts grouped around certain themes. The stories these images tell, at first sight only loosely related, must be woven into an overarching "history", thereby revealing their true meaning and significance. However, these images do not merely serve to illustrate more general, underlying currents; they are a means of historical discovery in their own right. Since they can be viewed from many different angles, they are also open to different perceptions and raise new questions. It is this very openness which constitutes the real appeal of any well-arranged exhibition. Such an exhibition, by reflecting the reality of life in all its diversity and immediacy, will in turn ensure that the chosen framework does not narrow the perspective.

Anyone embarking on the task of designing and preparing an exhibition must take into account, but also build upon, the autonomous quality of this particular medium. The "Questions

on German History" over the last two centuries since the
epochal upheavals of the French Revolution, and in particular
the questions concerning the development of parliamentary
democracy in this country, must be posed and answered, within this framework, in the form above all of images. In doing
so, however, it is important to avoid an approach which
amounts to nothing more than a superficial reporting of
events which, as everyone knows from television, is also most
easily performed using images.

The decision to avoid such superficiality determined the
design of the Exhibition. It was closely linked with other important decisions on content, in particular on the creation of
focal areas within the Exhibition and on the weighting to be
given, in visual terms as well, to individual factors. The first of
these focal areas, namely the history of the development of
parliamentary democracy in Germany, has already been men-
tioned. As a second focal area, it was decided to emphasize
the transformation of life in Germany wrought by this country's emergence as a modern industrial society. The aim was
not only to illustrate as effectively as possible the driving
forces behind this process as such, but also to highlight its social and political consequences, thereby providing a realistic
impression, in visual terms too, of each historical situation –
its specific problems, contradictions and challenges. On this
basis, a third focal area was defined, namely the history of the
decisive turning points in the political development of Germany in the nineteenth and twentieth centuries. The objective
was to shed light on the causes and short- and long-term
repercussions of each in turn: the upheavals of the years from
1806 to 1815; the revolution of 1848; the major constitutional
conflict in Prussia and the founding of the German Empire in
1871; the revolution of 1918 and the creation of the Weimar
Republic; the latter's collapse and the seizure of power by the
National Socialists, the mortal enemies of liberal parliamentary democracy and the governmental, societal and economic
pillars on which it rested; the successful reestablishment and
modernization of the parliamentary system in the western
part of Germany after 1945, accompanied in the east by the
founding and development of a second dictatorship; and, finally, the overthrow of this dictatorship by those under its oppressive rule in an act of revolutionary self-liberation, and the
unification of the two territories, separated since 1945, in a
parliamentary and democratic process. This concentration on
the major turning points of German history made it possible

to divide the Exhibition into large sections which are, in a certain sense, self-contained and can therefore be viewed individually. This also made it possible to integrate some of the influences from the fields of art, literature and science – that is from the world of culture in its broadest sense – which shaped the face and intellectual mood of each period but which in retrospect are often not seen in direct correlation with it.

This form of structural accentuation does of course pose a whole number of problems. Some aspects which the individual visitor might find important receive less emphasis, and others, which are difficult to visualize, can only be addressed in supplementary texts. Some major causal relationships can only be touched upon, and certain loose ends inevitably remain. The periodization, which has been revised in terms of content and is oriented not only to outward caesura but also to phases which undeniably witnessed decisive transformations, is no doubt open to criticism on various grounds. However, it must be borne in mind that, in addition to the fundamental considerations outlined above, the organizers also had to take into account a number of practical considerations, such as in particular the "staying power" of visitors not overly familiar with the subject and, not least, the amount of time they can be expected to spend in the Exhibition. Hence, in order to make it possible for visitors to choose for themselves what they wish to see in line with their own special interests, it was necessary not only to create as clear a structure as possible but also to highlight thematic links and to locate the events in easily comprehensible time frames.

In an exhibition intended to shed light on history from the point of view of issues rather than events there were of course limits to such an endeavour. However, given that the primary objective of such an exhibition is to sharpen awareness of the complexity of the factors and conditions which determine political action, these limits can also act as an incentive for visitors to draw their own conclusions, to make their own analyses, to find their own answers to the questions raised. Despite all the aids to orientation offered within the Exhibition, in terms both of content and of structure, this obviously places not inconsiderable demands on the individual visitor. However, they are no greater than those placed on each and every citizen in making political judgements, and helping to shape the political will by exercising their right to vote, in a well-functioning democratic polity. There is indeed an indissoluble link between the two. Keenly aware of this link, those responsible for organizing this exhibition took it as a guideline in deciding what could realistically be expected of visitors in terms of their capacity for concentration and their ability to make critical judgements of their own.

In this context, it was decided to prevent the past from being used in any conceivable way as a direct argument for or against a particular policy in the present. This applies to the exhibition as a whole, but in particular to those sections linked most directly with the present day, that is those dealing with the history of Germany since 1945. With regard to recent events, the sources permitting a balanced historical judgement are still very fragmentary. The organizers therefore practised extreme restraint: rather than attempting to offer a definitive classification and evaluation, they gave clear precedence to providing detailed information and documentation.

This may well be viewed by some as unsatisfactory, and might prompt debate and criticism. From the point of view of the individual citizen, called upon to engage in the daily process of political decision-making, such criticism is of course quite legitimate, indeed welcome. However, it is one thing for an individual to draw on the most recent past in making political judgements, thereby giving these events an additional perspective and dimension – a task this Exhibition wishes to facilitate – and quite another for the organizers of such an exhibition, by providing certain historical judgements, to suggest certain political conclusions. Moreover, wherever the findings of academic research and debate allow, visitors will find no lack of clear judgements. And, on the basis of the underlying concept outlined above, it goes without saying that these judgements go beyond naive but well-meant picture-book portrayals which do no more than celebrate the victories of the alleged forces of good and bemoan their defeats; rather, they seek to explore all the aspects of each conflict, the real interests and ideas involved, and the actual room for manoeuvre of decision-makers, and are not restricted to what might have been desirable in each case. Here, too, there will be objections, and here, too, such objections are as welcome as they are legitimate. Indeed, these objections will be a barometer for the Exhibition's success in inducing visitors to form opinions of their own on historical and political events, and in enlivening the debate on the character of major turning points of the past and the impact they have had down to the present day.

There is one question which the organizers of this Exhibition would like to see at the centre of this debate, and whose topicality and complexity cannot be denied: the question of the historical conditions which fostered but also impeded the development of liberal parliamentary democracy in Germany. What obstacles were there to the introduction of such a system? Which forces fought for democracy, and which fought against it? What are the conditions for establishing parliamentary democracy, and why did Germany fulfill them relatively late and, for a long time, only partially? Why was parliamentary democracy in Germany not only vulnerable to threats from outside but also beset during its emergence by internal crises and a tendency towards self-destruction? And why has the authoritarian state, the very opposite of democracy, continued to hold a fascination in Germany down to the present day? All these questions are explored in depth in this Exhibition. The answers which it attempts to provide are set in the specific context of each historical period. But, if one looks closely and is not distracted by superficial parallels, which all too often prove misleading, one can see that they are of relevance for the political debate today. This is especially true of one aspect which, if overlooked, could pose a fundamental threat to the system of liberal parliamentary democracy as a whole; namely that each period decisively shapes some of this system's external features and forms of organization, as well as some of its foundations, functions and mechanisms, which however make up less of its actual substance than one is occasionally led to believe. Here in particular, historical analysis can contribute to enhancing the general public's ability to distinguish between form and substance, and, going one step further, to recognize where and when, under changed conditions, form and substance can in fact become contradictory. If this Exhibition succeeds in providing an impetus in this direction by encouraging visitors to adopt a genuinely historical attitude to the past – one which overcomes the rigidities and ossification of traditional patterns of thoughts and opens them up to new development from within – it will have found a deeper justification than in any fashionable call to dismantle the allegedly false perceptions of history which one side imputes to the other.

Central Europe at the end of the eighteenth century

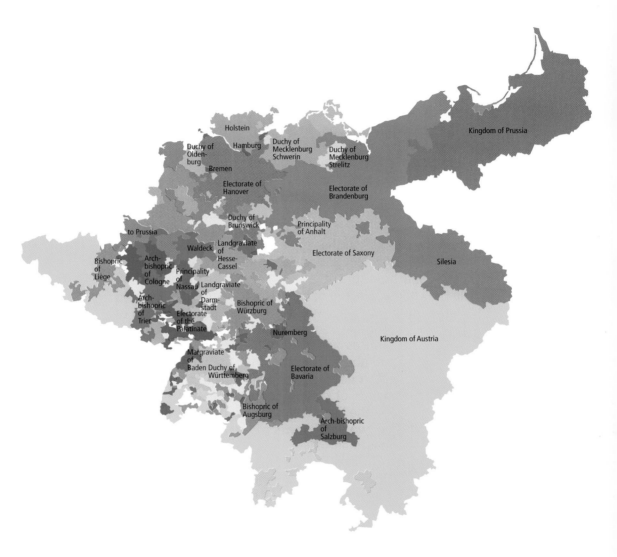

From the World
of Estates to the World
of the Bourgeoisie

I. From the world of estates to the world of the bourgeoisie

At the turn of the nineteenth century, Germany's political and social system plunged into crisis. The Empire's rapid collapse under the onslaught of the French revolutionary armies exposed, above all, the lack of internal – as well as external – cohesion which was symptomatic of the old Holy Roman Empire of the German Nation. In victorious France, contemporaries were witnessing the emergence of a politically self-confident nation: the revolution of 1789 had swept away all divisions between classes – or "estates" – and citizens' legal equality was now anchored in a constitution. By its own efforts, and under the leadership of a economically invigorated and enlightened bourgeoisie, the French nation had freed itself from the shackles of the *ancien régime*. Against this background, Germany's political and social conditions seemed hopelessly anachronistic.

The Holy Roman Empire of the German Nation, fragmented into hundreds of territories, was merely a loose association of states which lacked any central political authority. Germany consisted of its princes and their subjects, who were ruled through a system of absolutistic authority. The traditional concept of empire was in decline, kept alive only in smaller territories or in the minds of certain constitutional lawyers. The political situation in the Empire was largely determined by the rivalry between the two great powers, Prussia and Austria.

Within the states themselves, rigid divisions between estates – nobility, bourgeoisie and the peasantry – stifled social and economic development. Subjects and princes alike lacked any political consciousness of nationhood: the former had no political rights and the latter were primarily concerned with dynastic power struggles. Only in cultural life did an awareness of a nationhood which transcended social divisions begin to emerge in the second half of the eighteenth century; in Schiller's words, "The German Empire and the German nation are two separate notions ... as the political Empire shakes, the spiritual realm becomes ever more steadfast and complete."

Given the absence of a strong bourgeoisie in an economically underdeveloped Germany, the French Revolution, whilst arousing intense intellectual excitement, initially had little practical political impact in Germany. The French Revolutionary Wars merely revealed the weakness of the old political and social order. Under the onslaught of the French revolutionary armies, the absolutist states crumpled; Austria and Prussia, the great powers, were defeated, and after Napoleon's territorial simplification of Germany, the Empire was dissolved in 1806.

In this hour of utter defeat, a few political thinkers recognised that the causes of the catastrophe lay above all in the deep rift between state and society. What was required, they argued, was a bourgeois society based on the principles of liberty and equality, in order to create a new foundation for the institutions of state and ensure the liberation of the Fatherland. Reforms of the institutions of state would lead to the political emancipation of citizens and awaken their interest in state and nation.

The Prussian reformers' objective was ultimately to introduce a "representative system" ... "which ensures the effective participation of the nation in the legislative process, in order thus to establish a solid and durable foundation for public spiritedness and the love of the Fatherland." The failure to uphold this commitment following the adoption of reactionary policies after 1815 robbed the Prussian social reforms of their political meaning. At the same time, the adverse effects of the reforms on social conditions were becoming apparent as large numbers of peasants and artisans fell victim to the liberal economic order and were impoverished. Education and wealth continued to be enjoyed by only a privileged minority.

The social reforms introduced in the Confederation of the Rhine under Napoleon were superficially similar to the Prussian reforms but focussed on a different objective. Class divisions were dismantled, the economy was modernised and citizens' equality before the law was ensured. Initially, however, there were no moves to grant political rights, for the reforms were primarily designed to promote the establishment of a centralised administration.

In Prussia, the pledge to introduce a representative system remained unfulfilled. However, this type of system was introduced after 1815 in the southern German states, where political emancipation in the *Vormärz*, or "pre-March" period prior to 1848, progressed further than in Prussia. Austria, meanwhile, remained in thrall to its absolutist system.

The national ideas of the Prussian reformers fell on fertile ground, not least on account of the oppressive French occupation. However, despite the sense of nationhood engendered by the victory over Napoleon's armies, patriotic hopes were doomed to disappointment. At the Congress of Vienna, the re-shaping of Germany was again determined by the interests of its princes. In the German Confederation, as in the majority of its constituent states, there was no popular representation. What was created in Germany was not a nation-state but a loose confederation of principalities. It soon became clear that its main purpose was to persecute all those who displayed lib-eral and national sympathies and were audacious enough, even after the triumph of the forces of reaction, to demand constitutions, a national assembly and press freedom. In terms of foreign policy, the German Confederation and its largest member states were integrated into the system of the Holy Al-liance and the pentarchy, the group of five powers – Russia, England, France, Austria and Prussia – which dominated Eu-rope. Its purpose was to shore up the traditional political and social order. The monarchs remained the only sovereigns. De-spite its strengthened economic position, the bourgeoisie was still at the beginning of its struggle for political influence.

In the decades between 1815 and 1848, during the *Vor-märz*, or "pre-March" period, which preceded, in the broad sense, the outbreak of revolution in March 1848, numerous reform movements emerged in opposition to the system em-bodied by the German Confederation. Supported by various social groups with different objectives, and varying also in their political methods, all these movements were nonetheless united in their belief that a fundamental transformation of the economic, social and political system was required. On the ba-sis of parliamentarianism, they sought to create a nation-state which would draw together Germany's fragmented social and political forces and sweep away archaic political structures.

Nor were these aspirations confined to Germany. During this period, nationalism was a revolutionary force throughout Europe. The popular uprisings in Greece, Spain, Italy and Poland kindled the sparks of German nationalism. In 1830, the July Revolution in France triggered a wave of nationalist revolutionary uprisings across the entire continent of Europe. The German nationalist movement now began to express its demands more vociferously than before. Much of the impetus behind the movement for national unity came from Ger-many's economic sector. After the onset of industrialisation, Germany's political and economic fragmentation – symbol-ised by a multiplicity of customs barriers, coinages, weights and measures – proved a major obstacle to the development of commerce and industry. Customs barriers separated not only the German states but even the provinces and cities. Having supported the wars of liberation against Napoleon and proclaimed the ideal of national unity, the bourgeoisie now had sound economic reasons to demand the political unification of the German states as well.

A first step towards economic unity was the abolition of internal customs barriers in Prussia in 1818. As a successor to the Central German Customs Union and Prussia's customs agreements with central and southern German states, the German Customs Union (*Zollverein*) came into existence in 1834. Led by Prussia, it included most of the states of the German Confederation, with the notable exception of Austria. At the same time, the building of railways, roads and canals created the conditions required for a free trade area. Whereas the purpose of the Customs Union was primarily to expand the unified economic area, some observers – notably the economist, Friedrich List – were motivated above all by political considerations. The economic upswing enjoyed by the countries belonging to the Customs Union proved highly attractive to other states. After the formation of an economic association, political union seemed to be the next logical step.

Initially, however, the national idea drew its real impetus from the tradition of the wars of liberation, which flourished primarily among the students. Prior to 1830, the patriotic student fraternities, or *Burschenschaften*, came together throughout Germany to form the vanguard of the nationalist movement. At the "Wartburg festival" in 1817, they staged the first public demonstration for German unity, burning reactionary symbols and writings in a display of opposition to traditional authority. Indeed, their radical wing – known as the "Giessen Blacks", or *Giessener Schwarzen*, – saw its ultimate goal as the creation of a republic, which they believed could only be achieved through the violent overthrow of the princes.

By contrast, the proponents of political liberalism – the most important opposition movement of this period – sought to achieve their objectives by legal means, firstly within the individual states. Their common goal was to achieve personal and political liberty for all subjects, i.e. to guarantee civil rights and freedoms – such as freedom of expression, press freedom and freedom of association – and the participation of citizens in the political decision-making process. They favoured the system of government exemplified by the constitutional monarchies of England and France. The constitutions adopted in the central and southern German states after 1815 formed the basis for the liberals' work, and they had some success in implementing individual reforms in these states. Even here, however, their attempts to introduce more far-reaching changes foundered on entrenched monarchist support, individual states' claim to sovereignty, and the unrelenting efforts of the still semi-absolutistic governments to reduce press and parliament to mere instruments of the executive.

The restrictions on freedom in the German states strengthened the liberals' nationalist agenda. In the state parliaments, or *Landtage*, the demonstrations for national unity became increasingly frequent, the most notable example occurring in the Baden lower house when Karl Theodor Welcker tabled a motion calling for the creation of a pan-German parliament. This was a classic example of the way in which the concept of nationalism arose out of the demand for greater liberty. Popular assemblies, press and civic associations in which liberals of all political hues worked together were the focus of agitation for the nation-state. The demands of the "radicals" for social and political reform went further than those expressed by the majority of the other liberals. Rather than merely calling for citizen participation, they demanded self-government by the "people". Furthermore, over and above the free development of natural talents and learned skills, they actively promoted the concept of social equality. In their view, this meant the elimination of all outward differences and all patronage and privilege, thus bringing about an improvement in the social and political status of the disadvantaged.

An essential aspect of the radicals' position derived from the mass impoverishment which followed the emancipation of the peasantry and industrialisation. "Pauperism" was the central problem of social development during the *Vormärz*, and the radicals responded by voicing the most far-reaching political demands. "The nation's lower classes must be elevated to a state of human dignity: only as a means to this end do the free political institutions have any purpose" (Johann Jacoby).

Shortly before the outbreak of the 1848 revolution, the main demands of the political opposition – the moderate liberal factions and the more radical democratic movements – were published in two manifestos, known as the Heppenheim and Offenburg programmes. They set out the various possible approaches to a new social and political order, which was ultimately to be decided by revolution.

I/1
Emperor Francis II,
painting by Leopold
Kuppelwieser

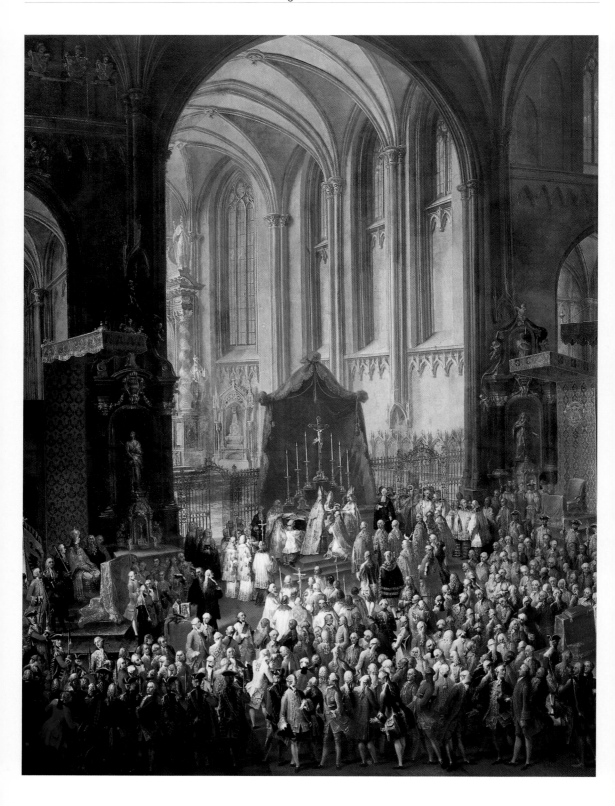

1. The Old Empire

By the end of the eighteenth century, the Holy Roman Empire of the German Nation, unlike its more centralised neighbours, was simply a loose association of numerous territories and fiefdoms which lacked any genuine central political authority. Real power, exercised through a system of absolutistic authority, lay with the individual states, headed by the two European great powers, Austria and Prussia.

offered a measure of protection against the arbitrary actions of the princes. All attempts to create a more powerful central authority foundered on the resistance of the individual estates of the realm. Their divergent interests also increasingly paralysed the representative assembly of the estates – the Imperial Diet, or Reichstag, in Regensburg.

Despite many attempts at reform by their absolutistic rulers, most of

I/3

Arrival of envoys to the Imperial Diet, or Reichstag, at Regensburg City Hall, 1729

The Empire's central institution, and the outward expression of its enduring unity, was the imperial crown. Yet the Emperor's power rested less on his position as head of the Empire than on his possession of the Habsburgs' hereditary lands.

The Empire lacked both a central administration and a standing army. Only its common body of law

the Empire's territories lagged behind the countries of Western Europe in both economic and social terms. The medieval economic and social structure, which guaranteed the nobility the most influential positions, was still virtually intact. A rigid hierarchy of "estates", with entrenched divisions between nobility, bourgeoisie and the peasants, stifled any further progress.

I/2 (opposite)
Coronation of
Emperor Joseph II
in Frankfurt Cathedral in 1764

The Constitution of the Holy Roman Empire

"The Holy Roman Empire would undoubtedly still be the most formidable power in the whole of Europe if its estates, especially the most powerful ones, were united and paid greater heed to the common good than to their private interests", wrote the German constitutional lawyer, Johann Jacob Moser, in 1745. Indeed, the real weaknesses of the Holy Roman Empire of the German Nation were its fragmentation into hundreds of small, virtually autonomous fiefdoms, the discord between electors, princes, imperial knights and imperial cities, and the never-ending conflict between Roman Catholic and Protestant estates. Unlike its European neighbours, the Empire was merely a loose federation of autonomous particularistic authorities. Due to their conflicting interests, they rarely presented a united front to the outside world.

A glance at the map of Europe on the eve of the French Revolution reveals the diversity of the Empire's territories. The existence of over 1790 autonomous principalities and fiefdoms rendered joint political action well-nigh impossible. Even in a tiny area such as the Swabian district there were 92 fiefdoms and imperial cities. Furthermore, the territories often lacked geographical cohesion, since – for example, in the case of the Archbishopric of Mainz – the individual possessions were scattered across the entire Empire. Only the extensive possessions of the great powers, Austria and Prussia, had some measure of territorial integrity. Their lands, of course, stretched far beyond the borders of the Empire.

From 1663 until the dissolution of the Empire in 1806, the Imperial Diet, or Reichstag, met in Regensburg. This permanent congress of ambassadors from the three estates – the electors, the princes and the imperial cities – met to deliberate

I/4
The Reichstag in session in Regensburg, 1663

on the affairs of state. As a college of envoys bound by the instructions of their respective estates, the Reichstag cannot be compared to a modern Parliament. Debates followed strict procedures, and were conducted separately by the three estates along confessional lines. Owing to its cumbersome procedures and the conflicting interests of the individual estates, the Reichstag lost more and more of its political significance. The "long bench", on which items were laid in preparation for apparently endless debate, was to become proverbial.

The concept of Empire was supported most vigorously by the minor estates of the realm, to whom the Empire appeared to offer a measure of protection against the larger territories' claims to power, and by a number of constitutional lawyers, whose aim was to implement reforms with its assistance. As the Empire had virtually no executive powers, its common body of law was the chief mechanism protecting the interests of its members. This legal unity was embodied by the Empire's two supreme courts: the Aulic Council in the imperial residence in Vienna, and the Imperial Cameral Tribunal in Wetzlar. Whereas the Imperial Cameral Tribunal, whose seat after 1689 was the tiny imperial city of Wetzlar/Lahn, was largely considered an institution of the estates, the Aulic Council was the Emperor's highest court of appeal and often represented imperial interests in its rulings. Yet despite the slow-moving wheels of justice – especially at Wetzlar, where a number of cases lasted over 100 years – the two imperial courts offered a measure of legal protection, above all against the arbitrary rule of the princes.

Since 1512, the Empire had been divided into ten districts whose original purpose was to maintain

internal peace. Gradually, however, they began to assume other functions, such as economic and transport policy. In fragmented southwest Germany in particular, the estates worked closely together within the framework of these districts. Furthermore, institutions representing the estates also existed in many individual states. Despite all its shortcomings, the tradition of estates established an important basis for the emergence of modern parliamentarism in the nineteenth century.

The economic and social structure of the Old Empire

By the end of the eighteenth century, Germany lagged far behind England and western Europe in its economic and social development. Its society was still characterised by rigorous stratification of the es-

I/5
"Audience" at the Imperial Cameral Tribunal in Wetzlar, around, 1735

tates. The pyramid structure of society, with entrenched divisions between estates, symbolised the hierarchical and God-given social order in which everyone was born into a

I/6

Allegorical depiction of the pyramid of estates, dating from the seventeenth century

particular estate and was generally bound to his or her social station for life. The various estates were strictly separated through language, clothing and conduct. Any tendency to relax this system was vigorously resisted by the princely or municipal authorities through the introduction of precise regulations.

The Old Empire was an agrarian society. Four fifths of the population lived on the land. Agriculture remained the most important sector of the economy. Its frequently fluctuating yields directly affected the living conditions of virtually all classes of society. In western and southern Germany, a manorial system of agriculture – known as *Grundherrschaft* – prevailed. Peasants worked their lands independently but were obliged to pay dues (tithes) to, and perform labour services (socage) for, the lord. By contrast, in the East Elbian territories, in particular, the Junker aristocracy used serfs and other dependent peasant labour to work their great estates. This system was known as *Gutsherrschaft*.

In the towns and cities of the Empire, two contrasting developments could be observed. The capitals and princely residential cities – some of

I/7

The unity of castle, city and village as a symbol of the feudal order of the Old Empire

I/8

Munich's Marien-
platz (St Mary's
Square) and Old
City Hall , around
1760

which had been newly established in the eighteenth century – were clearly prospering, as were some centrally located trading and commercial towns. Yet many once-great cities were experiencing stagnation or even decline. Even at the beginning of the nineteenth century, trades and crafts in the German cities were still organised to a great extent on the basis of guilds. These were determined to maintain their traditional privileges and suppressed open competition, thus hindering the development of a more liberal economy. Yet they also had a social function, ensuring that their members were adequately provided for. The guilds not only represented their members' economic interests but embraced all aspects of their lives outside the home and church.

Alongside the guild crafts, new forms of commerce emerged towards the end of the eighteenth century, often vigorously promoted by the princely authorities. They included manufactories – the largest pre-industrial commercial enterprises – which produced luxury goods in particular; and cottages industries, in which manufacturing work was distributed among large numbers of independent workers. Efforts to re-assert the economic sta-

tus of guild crafts in the face of growing competition from manufactories and cottage industries led to major social conflicts in many cities towards the end of the eighteenth century. In 1794, for example, an uprising by Augsburg weavers culminated in their occupation by force of City Hall.

I/9

Insurgent weavers
in front of Augsburg
City Hall, 1794

Trade began to increase gradually throughout the eighteenth century, although the many trade barriers still in existence meant that no fundamental structural change was yet in prospect. The development of trade was hampered by territorial fragmentation and a complicated system of tolls and tariffs. Virtually every individual territory had its own system of weights and measures and, in many cases, its own currency. In particular, merchants who made their fortune in wholesale and external trade increasingly emerged as an urban aristocracy towards the end of the eighteenth century. However, their political influence often continued to be restricted by the patrician nobility.

I/10
Leipzig's Marktplatz (Market Square) during the Fair, around 1800

2. Revolution and reform

The effects of the French Revolution triggered profound and far-reaching political, economic and social changes in Germany too between 1789 and 1815. Within a few years, the Old Empire collapsed under pressure from revolutionary, then Napoleonic France. Napoleon implemented an extensive territorial simplification of the patchwork geography of Central Europe, creating viable middle-sized territorial states, above all in southern Germany.

The decades of war in the late eighteenth and early nineteenth centuries coincided with a period of major reforms at domestic level.

The impact of Napoleon's policies, the rapidly escalating financial crisis and, in the southern German states, the need to integrate territories with very different structures into a single polity now led to a radical transformation of the political, military, economic and social system in Central Europe as well. In Prussia, the effects of military defeat also played a key role. The reforms finally spelled the end of the traditional feudal hierarchy based on a system of estates and removed many of the constraints on more liberal economic and social development. However, this was achieved exclusively through "reform from above", further strengthening the role and influence of the state.

The hopes of the national movement, formed during the wars of liberation against Napoleon, that a German nation-state would be created were shattered by the Congress of Vienna. Under Metternich's leadership, the German Confederation – which was merely a loose association of predominantly sovereign states – evolved into a instrument of pure repression, especially after the resurgence of the forces of reaction after 1819. In the southern

I/11
The Declaration of the Rights of Man and Citizen, in a German edition from 1792/93

German states, by contrast, the first modern constitutions were promulgated, creating new framework conditions and parliamentary institutions which the liberal bourgeoisie was keen to utilise in its efforts to fulfil its political aspirations.

tion finally erupted. The process of revolutionary change was soon irreversible and rapidly spread throughout France. In its Declaration of the Rights of Man and Citizen, of 26 August 1789, the French National Assembly expressed its commitment to the principles of po-

I/12
Meeting of the Mainz Jacobin Club in the Elector's Palace, 1792

Revolutionary France

The upheaval in France began with the revolutionary act of the deputies of the third estate – the commons – who proclaimed themselves the National Assembly on 17 June 1789 and took an oath, three days later, not to separate until a just constitution had been established for France. With the storming of the Bastille – the state prison which was the hated symbol of absolutism – on 14 July 1789, the smouldering unrest and resentment within large sections of the popula-

litical liberty and equality before the law as natural and inalienable rights of the individual. No other revolutionary text touched the people's hearts and minds as profoundly as this proclamation of the basic principles underlying every liberal social and political order.

The news of the revolutionary events in France quickly spread throughout Germany too, but failed to elicit any significant political response until the revolution entered its second phase after the proclamation of the First Republic in September 1792.

I/13 (opposite)
Landscape with tree of liberty, painting by Johann Wolfgang von Goethe, 1792

I/14
Napoleon and
his armies entering
Berlin, 1806

Influenced by the French Revolution, Germany's political public began to split into different factions in many areas. Along-side the Enlightenment movement, a new and more radical tendency with close links to the French Jacobins now emerged and adopted the republican agenda. Typically, however, German Jacobin activities centred largely on western and southern Germany, in the area of French rule and influence.

During the French occupation of Mainz, local Jacobins established the first, albeit short-lived, republic on German territory in 1792/93. However, it was supported by only a minority of the city's population and collapsed after French withdrawal.

The revolutionary wars

Soon after the outbreak of revolution, a first wave of political refugees streamed out of France into the neighbouring territories of the Empire. The majority of these emigrés were aristocrats, whose often arrogant behaviour failed to endear them to the population. Their calls for the European monarchies to take military action against revolutionary France went unheeded at first. However, the outbreak of the War of the First Coalition in April 1792 marked the onset of over two decades of war and military conflict in Europe, interrupted by only brief and occasional interludes of peace. Following the revolutionary armies' first and unexpected victories, the theatre of war quickly spread into the Empire. On 30 September 1792, French troops under General Custine seized the town of Speyer.

Under Napoleon, the task of defending the revolution finally gave way to a war of conquest which was fought in the name of the revolution and its achievements. Within a few years, France ruled virtually the entire continent of Europe. The domestic and foreign policy structures of the *ancien régime* had collapsed completely. In the wake of Napoleon's military triumphs over Austria and Russia in 1805 and the territorial simplification of southern Germany, the campaign against Prussia began in autumn 1806. It culminated in Prussia's crushing defeat at the two simultaneous battles of Jena and Auerstedt on 14 October that year. Napoleon's march into Berlin through the Brandenburg Gate on 27 October 1806 set the seal on Prussian humiliation. In the peace of Tilsit of 9 July 1807, King Frederick William III was forced to cede all the Prussian territories west of the Elbe, as well as Prussia's recently acquired Polish possessions, and pay a heavy war indemnity. Even the Prussian absolutist state, considered a model of progress, proved hopelessly inferior to revolutionary France in both political and military terms.

The Napoleonic reforms

The Empire's defeat at the hands of Napoleon precipitated a fundamental transformation of the entire territorial and political structure of Central Europe. The rulers of those larger and secondary states which had lost territories through the ceding of the left bank of the Rhine to France were now to be given ecclesiastical territories and petty secular principalities as recompense.

The task of redrawing the map of Europe was given to a committee of princes, known as the Imperial Deputation, or *Reichsdeputation*, whose Principal Resolution, or *Reichsdeputationshauptschluss*, of 25 February 1803 signified the Empire's recognition of Franco-Russian plans for reform.

The Principal Resolution and the territorial upheavals of 1805/1806 stripped virtually all the minor imperial estates of their status as sovereign members of the Empire. The map of the Empire lost much of its patchwork appearance. Through a process known as "mediatization", bishoprics and abbeys, petty principalities and imperial cities were absorbed into larger territories. At the same time, secularisation – the removal of ecclesiastical rulers' politi-

I/15
"Memorandum of the transfer of the imperial city of Nuremberg" to Bavaria, 1806

I/16
The princes of the
Confederation of
the Rhine pay
homage to Emperor
Napoleon, 1806

cal powers and the expropriation of extensive tracts of ecclesiastical land – was a significant step in dismantling traditional feudal structures and the hierarchy of estates. The aristocracy lost many of its im-

portant sinecures, peasants and bourgeoisie acquired church lands and property, and modern commercial enterprises established themselves in former convents and monasteries.

I/17
Public burning
of English goods
by French troops
in Hamburg,
1810

The territorial simplification of the Empire gave rise, especially in southern Germany, to the emergence of viable medium-sized territorial states, notably the kingdoms of Bavaria and Württemberg and the Grand Duchies of Baden and Hesse-Darmstadt. In the interests of their newly acquired positions of power, their rulers felt a deep sense of allegiance to Napoleon and France. The creation of the Confederation of the Rhine by sixteen southern and south western German states on 12 July 1806 in Paris spelled the end of the Holy Roman Empire of the German Nation. On 1 August 1806, the confederated states pro-claimed their secession from the Empire. Five days later, Emperor Francis II announced that he was laying down the imperial crown and declared the Empire defunct. On 12 July 1806, the princes of the confederated states paid homage to the French emperor in Paris. The Rhine Confederation, an offensive and defensive alliance under Napoleon's protectorate, created a power-political counterweight to Prussia and Austria in Central Europe. Yet all attempts to expand the Confederation of the Rhine into a federal state by establishing common institutions foundered on the resistance of the larger member states.

On 21 November 1806, Napoleon announced a Continental Blockade in his Berlin Decree. It was an attempt to force Britain to its knees, both politically and economically, by cutting off its lifeline of trade with continental Europe. At the same time, France hoped that restructuring the economy in continental Europe would improve its own export opportunities and strengthen its position. The economic effects of the Continental Blockade – which France attempted to enforce with draconian measures – were extremely uneven. Whereas some sectors of the economy flourished once freed from British competition, others – predominantly agriculture and trade – suffered severely as a result of the restrictions.

Reforms in Prussia and the Confederation of the Rhine

In the newly created southern German states, the desire to implement a comprehensive programme of reforms arose primarily from the need to weld territories with quite diverse historical traditions and administrative structures into a single cohesive polity. Their often rather tentative first steps soon gave way, in most cases, to a strongly centralist approach to reform based on the French model.

In Prussia, the reforms were prompted above all by the painful experience of defeat at the hands of Napoleon. In his "Nassau Memorandum", of June 1807, Baron vom Stein devised a comprehensive strategy "... to breathe new life into the spirit of the community, to create a sense of civic responsibility ..." and thus release new energies for the Prussian state. However, his ideas soon came into conflict with the Prussian king's claims to power.

Heading the list of reforms in each case was a far-reaching restructuring of the machinery of government, administration and finance, designed to promote and complete the process of creating a modern state which had begun under absolutism. The other focal point of the reforms was to release society from its shackles by introducing a new system of civil law. The problems associated with this measure were reflected above all in the conflicts surrounding the introduction of the *Code Napoléon*, Napoleon's Civil Code of 1804, in the Confederation of the Rhine.

Perhaps one of the most striking examples of the transition from an authoritarian to a liberal state was the Prussian military reform. The removal of the aristocracy's monopoly on commissions in the army shook the most important institution of old Prussia to its foundations. Henceforth, all ranks – even officers – were to be selected solely on the basis of the bourgeois criteria of training and merit. The other key element of the Prussian military reforms was the introduction of general conscription. Military service was no longer to be regarded as a hated obligation but as a citi-

I/18, 19
Baron vom Stein's "Nassau Memorandum", June 1807. The first page in Stein's own handwriting

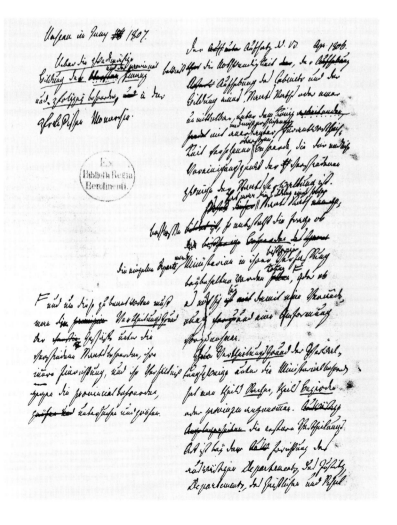

I/20
Friedrich Weinbren-
ner's design for the
new synagogue in
Karlsruhe, 1798

zen's patriotic duty, and the army was to become an integral part of bourgeois society.

One of the most important social reforms was the emancipation of the peasantry and the measures taken to accompany it. Serfdom was abolished, and the services and dues rendered by peasants to their landlord were replaced by monetary payments. Land became a freely disposable economic resource.

Closely linked to the economic and social reforms were the first legal steps to emancipate the Jews. The Prussian Edict of Tolerance of 11 March 1812 granted the Jews civic rights and the freedom to practise a trade and acquire land, although the civil service and officer corps remained closed to them. After centuries of mere toleration and sometimes life in the ghetto, and despite the persistence of many legal and practical restrictions, the way to equality and full civil rights was now opened to the Jews as well.

It was in his municipal ordinance of 1808 that Baron vom Stein came closest to realising his ideal of strengthening the Prussian state through the greater participation of its citizens. This ordinance granted municipalities extensive rights of self-government and placed local affairs into the hands of councillors who were elected by the citizens themselves. The restriction of civic rights to propertied merchants and tradesmen remained in place, however.

Yet the more far-reaching objectives which Stein and Hardenberg linked to the concept of self-government – i.e. representative and constitutional elements at the higher state levels, leading ultimately to a Prussian constitution – were not fulfilled.

As a result of the ceding of territories in 1807, Prussia had also lost its leading university in Halle. A concept for the establishment of a new university in Berlin was put forward by Wilhelm von Humboldt (1767–1835), appointed Prussian Minister of Education in 1809, in his letter of 24 July 1809 to the Prussian king. Humboldt's idea was based on the principle that academic research and teaching were inseparable elements of education, that scholarship need not necessarily have a practical application, and that learning should be supported and guaranteed by the state. In addition to university reform, Humboldt also restructured the Prussian school system, which was henceforth to consist solely of elementary schools for general basic education and a new type of classical grammar school for higher education.

I/21
Military parade
in Unter den Linden,
1837, painting by
F. Krüger

I/22
Mass for the
newly elected
Berlin city council-
lors in the Niko-
laikirche, 1808

I/23, 24
Wilhelm von Humboldt's letter proposing the establishment of the University of Berlin, 12 May 1809.
The first page in Humboldt's own writing

The wars of liberation

During the period of Napoleonic rule, philosophers and poets – such as Ernst Moritz Arndt, in his patriotic song "What is the Germans' Fatherland?" of 1813 – expressed their commitment to a "German nation" and called for the struggle against foreign domination. "Liberation" from the Napoleonic yoke was also to herald a new era of universal "freedom" within a constitutional nation-state.

In the German territories, resistance to Napoleonic rule steadily grew. The burdens of French occupation,

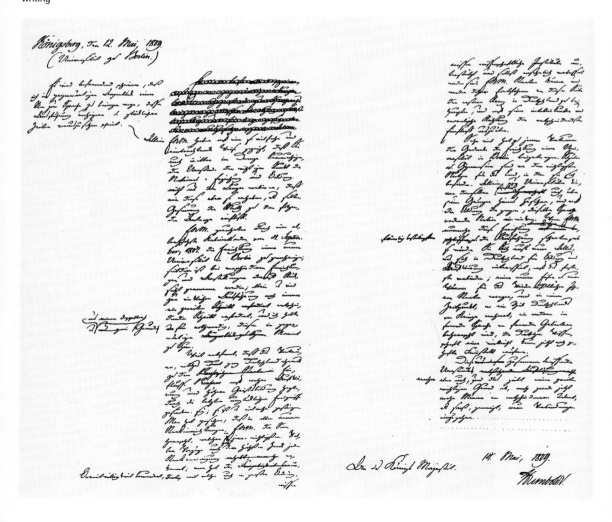

the levying of German troops and the misery of apparently never-ending warfare became increasingly oppressive. In Prussia, a somewhat reluctant King Frederick William III was propelled into war against Napoleon on a wave of enthusiastic nationalism. Resistance to Napoleon was soon supported by a broad-based volunteer movement from all sections of the population who organised themselves into the volunteer corps.

After Napoleon's defeat in Russia in 1812, the Prussian, Austrian and Russian allies secured decisive victory over the French at the Battle of

The Congress of Vienna

Following the victory over Napoleon, princes and ministers from Russia, Great Britain, Austria and Prussia – the allied great powers – and representatives of the other German and European states met in Vienna between September 1814 and June 1815, together with negotiators from defeated France, to redraw the map of Europe. On the one hand, the outcome of the Congress of Vienna – anchored in the Final Act of the Congress of Vienna of 9 June 1815 – was fully in line with the spirit of the Restoration:

I/25
The Battle of the
Nations at Leipzig,
16–19 October
1813

the Nations at Leipzig on 16–19 October 1813. Napoleon was forced to retreat with his armies to France, and the Confederation of the Rhine collapsed.

numerous borders and the balance of power between the five great powers were restored and the rights of forcibly expelled dynasties reinstated. On the other hand, a

I/26
Meeting of envoys
to the Congress of
Vienna in the State
Chancellery

complete return to the absolutistic structures of the pre-revolutionary period proved impossible. In a major territorial shake-up, many of Napoleon's changes to the map of Europe were reversed. Only the new territorial structure of Germany remained largely unchanged. The conservative eastern powers – Russia, Austria and Prussia – formed the Holy Alliance, ostensibly to renew Christian principles. In practice, its purpose was to maintain the existing dynastic order and ensure the violent suppression of all national liberation movements.

The German Confederation

Instead of fulfilling the liberal movement's hopes of a nation state, the Congress of Vienna merely created a loose confederation of states for Germany. The Confederation's main objective was to pre-serve the independence of its members, to secure the monarchy, and to stifle emergent political and social movements. The Confederation's supreme institution was the Federal Assembly, or Bundesversammlung, later known as the Federal Diet, or Bundestag, whose seat from 1816 to 1866 was the Thurn and Taxis Palace in Frankfurt/Main. Yet the Federal Assembly was not a representative assembly of the German people but a permanent congress of ambassadors of the German princes and free cities under Austrian chairmanship. In practical political terms, the federal organisation proved extremely cumbersome. One of the Confederation's achievements was to maintain peace at both domestic and international level for a considerable number of years. The price of this success, however, was the suppression of all efforts to bring about a more liberal political order.

The German Confederation initially consisted of thirty-seven states and four free cities. In the case of Prussia and Austria, only their former imperial territories were included in the Confederation, i.e. West and East Prussia and the non-German territories of the Habsburg monarchy were excluded. England, Denmark and the Netherlands also belonged indirectly to the Confederation by virtue of their German possessions.

within the individual states. While Prussia and Austria maintained their absolutistic system of government, the southern German states saw the introduction of modern representative constitutions as an opportunity to strengthen their sovereignty vis-à-vis the German Confederation.

For the first time, these constitutions granted citizens basic rights and freedoms, as well as opportunities for political participation

I/27
Session of the Federal Diet, the Bundestag, in Frankfurt/Main, 1817

The beginnings of the constitutional state

Article 13 of the Federal Act, or *Bundesakte*, which formed the legal basis of the Confederation, contained the vague promise that "constitutions based on the traditional provincial assemblies, (*landständische Verfassungen*) would be established in all states of the Confederation". However, this was handled in very different ways

through parliamentary assemblies, for the first time.

As the restrictions imposed by the Restoration tightened, Article 13 of the Federal Act was increasingly interpreted as an ban on the introduction of modern constitutions. In this respect, the Vienna Final Act of 15 May 1820 reaffirmed the monarchy as a form of government. South German liberals, in particular, responded by vigorously asserting their acquired rights.

I/28
Portrait of the King
of Bavaria, Maximil-
ian I, with the con-
stitutional charter

The Wartburg Festival

On 18 October 1817, at the behest of the Jena patriotic student fraternity, or *Burschenschaft*, some five hundred students gathered at Wartburg Castle in Thuringia. They intended to celebrate the tercentenary of the Reformation and the fourth anniversary of the Battle of the Nations at Leipzig, i.e. the political and the religious liberation of Germany. The Wartburg Festival drew the attention of the politically interested public for the first time to the new patriotic fraternities which had formed during the wars of liberation against Napoleon. The celebration also marked the beginning of the history of political demonstrations in Germany.

Around half of the participants were from Jena – the centre of the student reform movement – and the rest mostly from north German Protestant universities, although a few Catholic students also took part. The political tone was set above all in a celebratory address by a student named Riemann from Jena, who expressed sharp criticism of the German Confederation. However, it was the political aftermath of the Wartburg Festival which attracted the attention of the public: a small group of students from the circle of "*Turnvater*" Friedrich Ludwig Jahn – self-styled apostle of German physical culture – staged a ceremonial burning of "un-German" books and symbols of absolutism. The *Code Napoléon* and works by August von Kotzebue, including his history of Germany, and the ultra-conservative lawyer Karl Ludwig von Haller were thrown into the flames, together with a wig, a Prussian lancer's corset and a corporal's swaggerstick. The selection of items reveals the ambivalence of the student movement, in which liberalism was combined with elements of a nostalgic and reactionary nationalism.

I/29
Students' procession to the Wartburg, 1817

Metternich and his system

Resistance to the German Confederation's efforts to reimpose the old order first emerged within the universities and focussed on the student associations. Patriotic student fraternities, or Burschenschaften, and sports clubs led the struggle for a German nation state. The murder of the writer August von Kotzebue,

I/30
The murder of August von Kotzebue on 23 March 1819

a German noble in the employ the Russian legation, by the student Karl Ludwig Sand on 23 March 1819 in Mannheim – intended as a signal against the Restoration and in favour of the German nation state – heralded a period of intensified repression and political persecution. Sand was executed in Mannheim on 20 May 1820.

The Karlsbad Decrees of 20 September 1819, which remained in force until 1848, established a police state and a comprehensive system of surveillance designed to clamp down on the liberal and national movements.

A Central Investigation Commission was set up in Mainz to suppress "demagogic agitation" and "revolutionary associations". This notorious surveillance organisation drew up a list – the "Black Book" – of all persons who had been prosecuted for political offences within the territories of the German Confederation. For the period up to 1837, the list contained information on 1867 individuals.

The key instrument of the policies of repression, however, was press censorship. All printed material comprising less than twenty leaves had to be submitted to the censor prior to publication. The fledgling press attempted to protest against such intrusion by deliberately leaving "censor's gaps" in the texts, but this practice, too, was finally outlawed.

Many members and leading figures in the liberal and democratic opposition were persecuted and in some cases sentenced to lengthy periods of imprisonment.

I/31
Prisoners being transported to the Württemberg fortress of Hohenasperg

3. Society in upheaval

After the end of the eighteenth century, traditional society with its hierarchy of estates was increasingly in a state of flux. State-sponsored reforms, such as the emancipation of the peasantry and the introduction of freedom of trade in certain sectors, together with a general upturn in manufacturing and trade, transformed the economic system on which society was based. The beginnings of industrialtence. The new industries were still at too early a stage of development to provide employment for the masses.

Indeed, by increasing competition in certain sectors, they merely exacerbated the problems. The first half of the nineteenth century was therefore blighted by mass poverty and starvation, epidemics caused by poor sanitation, and emigration on a large scale.

isation, although varying widely from region to region, also played a role. These forces of change intensified the need to create a single economic area in Central Europe. This process was set in train with the establishment of the Customs Union, or *Zollverein*, in 1834 and promoted through the construction of roads, railways and canals.

These far-reaching changes were accompanied by major social problems. Agriculture and crafts – the traditionally dominant economic sectors – could no longer guarantee the rapidly burgeoning population an adequate level of subsis-

Yet at the same time, a new social structure began to take shape, especially in the cities. A self-confident bourgeoisie increasingly started to take its affairs into its own hands, initially at local level. A model of society emerged which was based on the principles of political self-determination, free association within voluntary clubs and societies, and economic prosperity. It rapidly acquired considerable momentum and sought to assert its demands at political level, both within the individual states and at national level, during the years of the *Vormärz*.

I/32
Merchants in the counting-house, around 1800

I/33
The Harkort factory
in Wetter Castle
around 1834, paint-
ing by Alfred Rethel

I/34
Munich's victuals market, painting by Domenico Quaglio, 1824

Economic transformation

The economic changes which took place in the first half of the nineteenth century were closely linked with the development of new technologies in manufacturing and communications. It was this technological change, in particular, which nurtured the optimistic belief in progress among the bourgeoisie. Agriculture, which employed well over 50% of the working population, was still the largest economic sector. Developments in the agricultural sector were due to a general improvement in production methods, which were now the subject of more systematic research. A network of agricultural associations, which were given sustained support by the state, ensured that information about new techniques in soil management, fruit cultivation and animal husbandry was made available on a wide scale.

The improvement in the economic fortunes of the urban bourgeoisie during the first decades of the nineteenth century was still based primarily on an increase in trade. Alongside agriculture, this sector attracted the highest level of capital investment and yielded the biggest profits. Trade was still dominated by the traditional type of merchant who often specialised in specific products, trading either direct or on a commission basis, and generally engaging in banking and the bill business as well. A further factor contributing to the growth of trade was the gradual dismantling of traditional barriers and restrictions. Prussia was at the forefront of these measures; its Customs Law of 1818 opened the way for a far more liberal policy on free trade. In 1833, eighteen states with a total population of 23 million people joined together under Prussia's leadership to form the German Customs Union, or *Zollverein*. The benefits of membership of this unified economic area proved so attractive that virtually all the remaining German states joined the Customs Union during the following years. Only Austria continued to cling to its protectionist policies. The economic unification of member states which was achieved when the Customs Union came into force on 1 January 1834 may be regarded in some ways as the precursor of the "Little German solution" to political union which came to the fore with the founding of the German Empire once efforts to form a nation-state had collapsed in 1848/49.

Construction of an efficient system of highways had commenced in the Napoleonic period, bringing about an improvement in the transportation system. There was a substantial rise in the volume of goods transported by road, while passengers were able to benefit from an

I/35
Bavarian coin commemorating the Customs Union of 1833

increasingly extensive stagecoach network. The development of the waterways opened up new opportunities, especially for the long-distance transportation of mass goods. Trade restrictions – such as customs and staples – were dismantled, rivers and canals were expanded and the advent of the steamship led to great improvements in the efficiency of water transport.

I/36
Railway, road and the Ludwig Canal at Erlangen, 1844

I/37
Opening of the Munich-Augsburg railway on 1 September 1839

I/38
Machine room in a
cotton mill, around
1830

However, the key element in the transition from old to new, from muscle-power to machine, was the advent of the railways. Railways transformed public and private life to a far greater extent than any other technological achievement. Their role in this process of economic transformation far outweighed their practical importance as a means of transport. They not only opened up entirely new trade routes, with far-reaching conse-

quences for the location of manufacturing industry, but also stimulated the production of iron and steel and machine-building to a crucial degree, thereby becoming the motor of industrialisation.

After 1830, industrial manufacturing of goods became increasingly established in Central Europe too. Whereas during the first phase of industrialisation the new production processes had generally been limited to the textiles industries, a

I/39
Converting pig iron
into wrought iron
using the puddling
process, around
1830

I/40
The Borsig iron
foundry at Oranien-
burg Gate, 1837

substantial upturn in iron and steel production and machine-building now occurred in parallel to the construction of the railways.

This new phase of industrialisation was symbolised by the Borsig Works in Berlin. After a carpentry apprenticeship and periods of study at the Royal Commercial Institute, Johann Carl Friedrich August Borsig (1804–1854) gained practical experience of industry, notably in a Berlin machine-building company and foundry, prior to setting up his own company at the Oranienburg Gate in Berlin in 1837. He initially employed just 50 persons. Ten years later, in the boom year of 1847, the Borsig Works had more than 1200 employees. Soon after its establishment, the factory began to supply components for use in railway construction.

By 1841, its experience of repairing English locomotives meant that the company had acquired sufficient

I/41
Borsig's "machine-
building works",
1847

expertise to manufacture locomotives of its own. Within a few years, the Borsig Works had become the largest producer of railway engines in Prussia and Germany, with an output of 67 locomotives in 1847 alone.

In many areas of the countryside, the emancipation of the peasantry did not lead to an increase in independent smallholdings. On the contrary, it primarily benefited the landed gentry. In Prussia, in particular, the rural underclass thus in-

I/42
The Silesian
Weavers: painting
by Karl Wilhelm
Hübner, 1844

Pauperism and social protest

During the first half of the nineteenth century, the population of Central Europe increased by over 60%. The high excess of births over deaths was due partly to declining mortality rates and partly to the rapid increase in marriages and births, especially amongst the lower classes as seigneurial or church restrictions on the right of the dependent poor to marry were abolished.

creased dramatically in numbers. It was from this group that the new social group of agricultural labourers was recruited, which often lived on the verge of abject poverty.

In the cities, the development of crafts in the first half of the nineteenth century varied very widely from sector to sector. Building, metal-working and some branches of the food industry underwent a period of expansion. In other craft sectors, however, the population explosion led to a sharp increase in the number of master craftsmen working without assistants, whose livelihood was precarious in the extreme. Many artisans – master craftsmen, journeymen and apprentices – thus drifted down the social scale, becoming part of the under-dominantly in textiles production. Competition in the labour market exerted such a downward pressure on the already low rates of pay that even a skilled worker's wages could not support a family. At the same time, traditional family struc-

I/43
Shoemaker's workshop on Sunday morning: caricature by Theodor Hosemann, 1845

class and barely managing to eke out an existence for themselves.

Children from both the rural and urban underclasses had to contribute to their families' incomes from an early age, either through begging or working long hours in manufactories and workshops. Initiatives which highlighted the health and social hazards of child labour and called for state-sponsored measures to protect children developed only very gradually. Women also formed a substantial part of the workforce. In Saxony, for example, women comprised 36% of the industrial workforce in 1846, pre-tures were crumbling. In both rural and urban areas, large sections of the underclass therefore no longer had any opportunity to earn an adequate income through paid work. Government policies to combat mass poverty were still inadequate. Indeed, in some cases – such as the highly unjust taxation system in Prussia – they merely exacerbated the suffering and deprivation of the lower classes. Furthermore, despite substantial increases in agricultural production, food crises continued to occur. In 1816/17 and 1846/47, in particular, poor harvests led to widespread famine throughout Eu-

I/44
Caring for impover-
ished and orphaned
children in the Ham-
burg workhouse,
around 1845

rope. Mass poverty, or "pauperism", thus resulted from a fundamental imbalance in the relationship between population growth
and food provision.

As a result of this social deprivation, there was a dramatic rise in
the number of people who left their
home country and emigrated elsewhere, not only to other German
states but also beyond German borders, above all to the United States.
This wave of emigration reached its
peak after 1845, with more than
60,000 people leaving their homes
each year. The majority of emigrants came from the regions of
Hesse, Franconia and the south
west where small-holdings predom-
inated.

In many towns and cities, the
growing population was accommo-

I/45
"New year celebra-
tions of poor men
around the world",
contemporary
woodcut

I/46
Emigrants from
Hesse on the way
to Bremen, 1824

dated in the confined space of existing housing stocks within the old city walls.

Population density and rate of occupancy increased dramatically, leading to a considerable rise in social problems and a sharp decline in standards of public health. With regard to water supply and sewage disposal, the technical means available at the time proved inadequate to deal with the needs of a growing population. Poor sanitation contributed to the spread of disease. The Great Fire of 5–8 May 1842 which destroyed almost all the densely populated old city of Hamburg was cited even by contemporaries as an example of the way in which traditional municipal structures had failed to find solutions to these new problems.

I/47
The Nikolaikirche
and Hopfenmarkt
during the Great
Fire in Hamburg,
1842

A new bourgeois society

It was in the cities that a new bourgeois society initially began to take shape. Even under the new structures which followed the period of reform, the urban bourgeoisie initially existed as a community of citizens who shared the same civic rights. It included every adult male who could prove that he had a secure income and who had acquired the civic rights of his local community. Together with their families, these citizens comprised between one-third and one half of the urban population. Following the establishment of institutions of self-government, elected by the citizens in line with the new municipal ordinances, the public became increasingly interested in assuming responsibility for municipal affairs. The municipal reform laws introduced in the Grand Duchy of Baden in December 1831 were regarded as particularly progressive. During the *Vormärz* period, this form of bourgeois self-government in towns and cities was the model upheld by the middle classes in their calls for greater participation in the affairs of state.

The transformation of society was associated with, and supported by, a newly emergent bourgeois public. Technological innovations in printing, such as the high-speed printing press and lithography, triggered a massive increase in journalism and publishing. Newspapers and journals, as well as the most important new literary publications, were read and discussed by the urban bourgeoisie in coffee houses and newly-established societies. After the turn of the century, social and civic associations, such as the "Casino", "Harmony", and "Museum" soci-

I/49
Frankfurt City Council swearing the oath on the Constitutional Amendment Act (*Konstitutionsergänzungsakte*), 1816

I/48 (opposite)
The Parochialkirche in Klosterstrasse in Berlin, painting by Eduard Gaertner, 1830

I/50
Meeting of Hamburg Council and Citizens' Convention in the Old Town Hall, 1834

I/51
Literary cafe in
Berlin: painting by
Gustav Taubert,
1832

ety, were set up in most larger cities; their members included leading figures from the nobility, public service and the urban bourgeoisie. Within these societies, the new bourgeoisie asserted its claim to social equality with the nobility and civil service. At the same time, through general education and debate, in the appreciation of arts and at social gatherings, the new bourgeois identity and sense of co-

hesion became firmly established. Music, in particular, as well as literature and fine arts played a key role in this process of shaping bourgeois identity. This was evident from the plethora of bourgeois associations devoted to music, song and the arts which emerged after 1830.

In the economic sector, too, the new bourgeois organisational structures became increasingly

I/52
Living room
in Berlin,
around 1820

well-established. In commerce, for example, the traditional guilds were supplanted after 1840 by artisans' and commercial associations. Building on the principles of self-administration and voluntary associations during the *Vormärz* period, the bourgeoisie, too, initially attempted to resolve the major social problems of the day.

However, the restrictive attitudes of the German Confederation prevented the associations from openly pursuing specific political objectives. The bourgeois liberal movement thus attempted to find other ways to discuss and coordinate their political agenda, e.g. by organising banquets for their Members of Parliament.

I/53
Banquet held by
a liberal citizens'
association,
around 1840

VERZ[...]

MITGLIEDER DER HAR[...]

VORSTEHER.	REPR.
Hr Polizeyrath Stark.	Hr Hofrichter [...]
„ Kollektor Hepp.	„ Hofgericht[...]
„ Oberbürgermeister Reinhardt.	
„ Amtmann Hofmeister.	
„ Buchhändler Fontaine.	

1. Hr Achenbach, Kreisassessor.	46. Hr Dietz, Kanzleyrath.	91. Hr Horn, Regiments-Chirurgus
2. Ahles, Pfarrer.	47. Disterweg, Professor.	92. Hout, Amtmann.
3. Akermann, Handelsmann.	48. Doel, Hofmedailleur.	93. Hünersdorf, Handelsma[...]
4. Andriano, Handelsmann.	49. Drais, Fhr. v. Oberhofrichter Exzell.	94. Hundheim, Fhr. v. Kam[...]
5. d'Angelo, Handelsmann.	50. Dykerhoff, Oberbaudirektor.	95. Hunzinger, Handelsmann[...]
6. Artaria, D. Kunsthändler.	51. Dykerhoff, Ingenieur.	96. Hutten, Rathsherr.
7. Artaria, G. M. Kunsthändler.	52. Dykerhoff, Architekt.	97. Jagemann, v. Stadtdirekt[...]
8. Bachers, Obereinnehmer.	53. Dykhut, Hofmusikus.	98. Joseph, Pfarrer.
9. Backhaus, Hofschauspieler.	54. Edel, v. Regierungsrath.	99. Jung, Hofrath.
10. Barochius, Doktor.	55. Ehrmann, Kreisrath.	100. Kaercher, Kaplan.
11. Barth, Handelsmann.	56. Einsmann, Prokurator Fisci.	101. Kaufmann, Buchhändler.
12. Bassermann, Rathsherr.	57. Ende, Freyherr v.	102. Katz, Hofprediger.
13. Bassermann, Handelsmann.	58. Erlach, Freyherr v.	103. Kessler, Kanzleyrath.
14. Baumbach, Fhr. v. Geh. Referendär	59. Esser, Lizentiat.	104. Kieser, Zuchthaus-Verwalte[...]
15. Beck, v. Hauptmann.	60. Fischer, v. Professor.	105. Kinkel, Freyherr v. Admiral[...]
16. Beck, v. Hauptmann.	61. Fischer, Kanzler.	106. Kirch, Dechant.
17. Behaghel, Handelsmann.	62. Foersch, v. Geh. Finanzrath.	107. Kladt, Rechnungsrath.
18. Bettinger, Amtmann.	63. Fontaine, Buchhändler.	108. Klengel, Hofschauspieler.
19. Beyerle, Doktor.	64. Frey, Hofmusikus.	109. Koester, Handelsmann.
20. Biermann, Rathsherr.	65. Friederich, Staats-Kassier.	110. Kolb, Obristlieutenant.
21. Bissel, Mahler.	66. Fries, Handelsmann.	111. Konold.
22. Bleul, Kanonikus.	67. Froehlig, Posthalter.	112. Krapp, Hauptmann.
22. Boeklin, Fhr. v. Obrist.	68. Fuchs, Raths-Verwandter.	113. Krauth, Reg. Quartiermeist[...]
24. Bomatsch, Lizentiat.	69. Gaum, Oberhofgerichts-Rath.	114. Kreyfeld, v. Handelsman[...]
25. Brand, Fhr. v. Obrist.	70. Gemmingen, Freyherr v.	115. Krippendorf, Oberhofger[...]
26. Braun.	71. Gemmingen, Fhr. v. Major.	116. Lamezan, Freyherr v. Präs[...]
27. Brentano, Rathsherr.	72. Gentil, Oberhofgerichts-Rath.	117. Lang, Rechtspraktikant.
28. Brentano, Handelsmann.	73. St. George, v. Hofgerichts-Sekret.	118. Laroche, Freyherr v. M[...]
29. Brüder, Hofrevisor.	74. Gerhardt, Rathsherr.	119. Laroche, Fhr. v. Kammer[...]
30. Bürmann, Direktor.	75. Gieser.	120. Laukhardt, Oberhofgerich[...]
31. Buzzini, Rath.	76. Graeser, Handelsmann.	121. Ledenbauer, Lizentiat.
32. Christ, Gastwirth.	77. Hammerer, Fhr. v. Präsident.	112. Leers, Amtsrevisor.
33. Courtin, Sen.	78. Hanselmann, Rathsherr.	123. Leibniz, Pfarrer.
34. Courtin, C. Handelsmann.	79. Hartleben, Kreisrath.	124. Lepique, Pfarrer.
35. Courtin, F. d. J.	80. Haub, Kreisrath.	125. Lerse, v. Regierungsrath.
36. Dachert, Lizentiat.	81. Heck, Hofschauspieler.	126. Lichtenberger, Rath.
37. Dahmen, Kreisrath.	82. Heim, Hofgerichtsrath.	127. Lindelof, v. Obristlieutena[...]
38. Dalberg, Herzog v. Exzellenz.	83. Hellwig, Hofkammerrath.	128. Loeffler, Buchhändler.
39. Dalberg, Fhr. v. Major.	84. Hepp, Kollektor.	129. Lorenz, Handelsmann.
40. Dalwigk, Fhr. v. Obrist.	85. Hertling, v. Hofgerichtsrath.	130. Lorenz, Kaffeewirth.
41. Darler, Handelsmann.	86. Heusch, v. Major.	131. Ludin, Gastwirth.
42. Dawans, v. Kreisrath.	87. Hessemer, Handelsmann.	132. Maehler, Lizentiat.
43. Dawans, v. Hofgerichtsrath.	88. Hieronimus, Handelsmann.	133. Maier, Oberhofgerichts-Rath[...]
44. Degenfeld, Fhr. v. Rittmeister.	89. Hofmeister, Amtmann.	134. Mathy, Professor.
45. Deurer, Handelsmann.	90. Hohnhorst, Fhr. v. Staatsrath u. Kanzl.	135. Matly, Hauptmann.

Gedrukt mit [...]

I/54
List of the members of the *Harmonie* association in Mannheim, 1815

CHNISS

NIE ZU MANNHEIM. 1815.

TANTEN.

nhardt Exzellenz.

er.

BIBLIOTHECARE.

Hr Pfarrer Lepique.

" Baron von Erlach.

. Hr Maubuisson, v. Hofkammerrath.	181.	Hr Rupprecht, Hofrath.	226.	Hr Walderdorf, Graf v. Kais. G.R.Exz.	
. Mayer, Kaufhausschreiber.	182.	Sachs, Handelsmann.	227.	Waldkirch, Graf v. Oberjägerm Exz.	
. Mayer, Handelsmann.	183.	Sachs, Professor.	228.	Walter, Rathsherr.	
. Mayer, Holzhändler.	184.	Sartori, Handelsmann.	229.	Walther, Sekretair.	
. Menges, Hoftheater-Tanzmeister.	185.	Schaaf, Handelsmann.	230.	Walz, Oberhofgerichts-Rath.	
. Messonier, Baumeister.	186.	Schachleiter, Hofgerichtsrath.	231.	Walz, Kreisrevisor.	
. Michel, Handelsmann.	187.	Schaefer, Kandidat.	232.	Wambold, Fhr. v. Domdechant.	
. Micheroux, Kreisassessor.	188.	Scharpf, Handelsmann.	233.	Weber, Hofgerichtsrath.	
. Minet, v. Hofgerichtsrath.	189.	Schies, Lizentiat.	234.	Weber, Hofgerichtsrath.	
. Moehl, Rathsherr.	190.	Schloesser, v. Rath.	235.	Wedekind, Doktor.	
. Moehl, Rath.	191.	Schmieg, Oberhofgerichts-Rath.	236.	Wedekind, Oberhofgerichts-Rath.	
. Moerdes, Hofgerichtsrath.	192.	Schoepf, v. General.	237.	Weikum, Professor.	
. Mohr, Lizentiat.	193.	Schuler, Hofrath.	238.	Weiler, v. Hofgerichtsrath.	
. Molliet, Handelsmann.	194.	Schumacher, Prof. u. Hofastronom.	239.	Wevelinchoven, v. Kammerherr.	
. Morgenstern, C. Handelsmann.	195.	Schumacher, Rathsherr.	240.	Wermerskirch, Gastwirth.	
. Morgenstern, P.	196.	Schweikhardt, Freyherr v.	241.	Werner, Hofschauspieler.	
. Müller, Hofrath.	197.	Schweikhardt, Fhr. v. L.C. Rath.	242.	Wilhelmi, Hofkammerrath.	
. Müller, Hofschauspieler.	198.	Seibold, Doktor.	243.	Woestenradt, Lizentiat.	
. Munz, Hofmusikus.	199.	Seiler, Professor.	244.	Wolf, Geh. Justizrath.	
. Newhouse, Handelsmann.	200.	Siegel, Staatsrath und Kanzler.	245.	Wolfinger, Doktor.	
. Nicola, Hofmusikus.	201.	Singer, Hofschauspieler.	246.	Yrsch, Graf v. Kammerherr.	
. Noll, Gastwirth.	202.	Soeldner, Amtmann.	247.	Ysenburg, Fürst v. Durchlaucht.	
. Nüsslin, Professor.	203.	Soiron, v. Postamts-Direktor.	248.	Zeroni, Doktor.	
. Otto, Geh. Referendär.	204.	Sperl, v. Hofgerichtsrath.	249.	Ziegler, Hofgerichtsrath.	
. Paine, Wm	205.	Speck, Oberlieutenant.	250.	Zyllnhardt, Fhr. v. Hofrichter.	
. Palm, Magazinverwalter.	206.	Stark, Polizeyrath.			Exzell.
. Pattberg, v. Premierlieutenant.	207.	Stengel, Fhr. v. Oberhofger. Rath.			
. Perglass, Fhr. v. Hofgerichtsrath.	208.	Stengel, Fhr. v. Kreisdirektor.			
. Pierron, v. Hauptmann.	209.	Stengel, Hofkammerrath.			
. Pistorius, Hofgerichtsrath.	210.	Stengel, Rechtspraktikant.			
. Pozzi, Professor.	211.	Stryk, Freyherr v.			
. Reinhardt, Oberbürgermeister.	212.	Stumm, Hofrath.			
. Reinhardt, Handelsmann.	213.	Sturmfeder, Fhr. v. Kammerherr.			
. Reinhardt, Gastwirth.	214.	Tannstein, v. General.			
. Renner, Gastwirth.	215.	Thurneisen, Handelsmann.			
. Renner, von Weinheim.	216.	Thürnagel, Hofschauspieler.			
. Renner, C. Handelsmann.	217.	Trau, Handelsmann.			
. Renner, Doktor.	218.	Türk, Hoftheater-Kassier.			
. Renner, L. Handelsmann.	219.	Ungern Sternberg, Fhr. v.			
. Richard, Schlossverwalter.	220.	Venningen, Fhr. v. ObRt Junker Exz.			
. Ritter, Apotheker.	221.	Verschafelt, v. Hofgerichtsrath.			
. Ritter, Kapellmeister.	222.	Vincenti, v. General-Lieut. Exzell.			
. Roddé, Banquier.	223.	Vogt, Handelsmann.			
. Rodenstein, Fhr. v. Kammerherr.	224.	Volz, Handelsmann.			
. Roeder, Handelsmann.	225.	Waechter, Freyherr v.			

pitals-Schriften.

I/55
A family concert,
painting by
Sebastian Gutzwiler,
1849

4. *Vormärz*

The decades − known as the Vormärz − which preceded the revolution of March 1848 were a time of political awakening. Throughout Germany and the rest of Europe, the rising middle class organised itself within the liberal and national movements, gradually preparing the ground for the revolution which swept Europe in 1848/49.

The bourgeois liberal movement's most important sphere of activity centred on the individual state parliaments which had been set up, primarily in southern Germany, on the basis of the constitutions issued after the Congress of Vienna. Alongside an upper house − representing the aristocracy, the church and other institutions − these constitutions provided for a lower house elected by citizens, albeit on the basis of more or less limited suffrage. Despite the parliaments' restricted powers, the liberals were successful in implementing a number of individual reforms within these states. At the same time, elections to the state parliaments, or *Landtage*, and parliamentary work prompted Members to organise themselves into parliamentary groups, to clarify their political objectives and thus prepare for weightier political responsibilities.

Outside parliament, too, the opposition movements − spurred on by the national and revolutionary upheavals now taking place in other European countries − joined forces against the reactionary political system of the German Confederation.

Phases of widespread political unrest, especially after the July Revolution of 1830 in France, alternated with renewed efforts to shore up the existing system. In the 1840s, the opposition split into different factions, despite continuing agreement on the broader national agenda. The left wing − the democrats − called for social reform and an extension of political rights to the lower classes. The liberal right wing, concerned at the prospect of social revolution, favoured a more cautious approach to reform.

I/56
Assembly House
of the Estates,
Dresden

I/57
Interior view of
the Chamber of
the Estates,
Munich, 1819

The beginnings of parliamentarism

On the eve of the Revolution of 1848/49, more than half the 39 states making up the German Confederation had modern parliamentary assemblies within the framework of a constitutional monarchy. The focus of parliamentary life lay within the southern German states which had been given their constitutions soon after the Congress of Vienna. In other states, especially in north and central Germany, parliamentary systems were introduced during a second phase after the July Revolution of 1830.

Most of the constitutions provided for a bicameral system, consisting of a conservative upper house drawn from the nobility, the churches, the universities and other institutions, and a lower house – the dynamic component of parliament – which was the real popular assembly. New buildings were often constructed for the chambers and a distinctive type of parliamentary architecture began to emerge.

In line with all the constitutions promulgated during the *Vormärz* period, elections to the lower houses were based on limited suffrage. The electoral law of the Grand Duchy of Baden was most progressive in this respect, for it granted all citizens of the municipality, as well as government officials, the right to vote. Other states limited the number of voters by restricting eligibility through stiff property qualifications.

The new parliaments' political powers were still limited. They could not introduce draft legislation or have a say in the formation of the government. Yet their rights of participation in to public finance and legislation, and their general right of petition – which they repeatedly used to initiate debates on current political issues – soon became major factors in public life.

PLAN

DES SITZUNGS SAALES DER IIten KAMMER

des Großherzothums Baden

Nebst Übersicht der zur vten Stände Versammlung (im Jahr 1831) gegenwärtigen Deputirten, der Wahlbezirke welche sie abordneten, der Sitze welche sie annehmen, und der Abtheilungen, in welchen sie sich zu den geheimen Verberathungen versameln.

I/59
Key Members of the
Baden lower house,
around 1847

During the course of the Vormärz period, "cameral disputes" frequently broke out between the monarchist government and parliament, focussing on the rights of the two chambers as well as on the assertion of the most important political basic rights. The Baden state parliament, whose debates attracted considerable interest amongst the liberal movement throughout Germany, played a key role in this respect.

I/58
(opposite)
Seating plan of the
Second Chamber
in Baden, 1831

Within the parliaments, a new class of political leaders – consisting of lawyers, scholars and officials, as well as a few members of the middle-class commercial community – gradually began to make its mark. Parliamentary practice equipped members with the knowledge and skills to challenge the nobility's and bureaucracy's claims to power. Throughout the Vormärz period, the urban bourgeoisie formed the social bedrock of parliamentarism, even in areas where, unlike Baden, the electoral law did not specifically favour the municipalities. In particular, the bourgeoisie's banquets and social gatherings in honour of their Members of Parliament strengthened liberal opposition to the authoritarian state.

I/60
Interior view of
the state parliament
in Stuttgart, 1833

The liberal movement

The first national uprising after the Congress of Vienna – the Greek revolt against Ottoman rule – triggered a wave of sympathy and support throughout Europe. On 6 February 1833 the first King of Greece, the Bavarian Otto I, arrived in Nauplia. The establishment of a Greek state was hailed, not only in Germany, as further confirmation of the irresistible advance of national-

ist principles and the liberal reforms with which they were associated.

After the July Revolution in Paris in 1830 against the restoration of Bourbon rule, much of Europe was gripped by revolutionary fervour. National uprisings against the existing régime shook the southern Netherlands and Poland. At the same time, revolutionary unrest often prompted electoral and constitutional reform in line with liberal principles, as was the case in Eng-

I/61
Handbill supporting
the Greek struggle
for independence

Griechenlands Befreyung vom Türkenjoche.

Jetzt oder nie!.. Des Schicksals Würfel liegen;
Jetzt gilt es, sterben oder siegen;
Euch ruft das Vaterland.
Ergreift die Waffen, Söhne der Hellenen!
Ein schöner Sieg wird eure Thaten krönen,
Des Nachruhms Unterpfand.

Jetzt oder nie __ zerbrecht die Sklavenketten.
Setzt alles dran die Freiheit euch zu retten,
Des Lebens höchstes Gut.
Hoch aufgelodert sind der Rache Flammen,
Sie schlagen über Mahmuds Thron zusammen.
Löscht sie mit Türkenblut.

Auf Stambuls Wälle pflanzt das Glaubenszeichen!
Der Halbmond muß dem Kreuze weichen,
Dem Griechen der Barbar.
Und wärn Ihrer auch wie Sand am Meere,
Euch bleibt der Sieg, Gott ist mit eurem Heere;
Drum muthig, tapfre Schaar!

I/62
The Kassel deputation to Elector William II, 1830

land and Switzerland. In Germany, those northern and central German states which had hitherto refused to introduce reforms now found themselves in the grip of revolution. During the night of 7 September 1830, for example, the reactionary Duke Charles II of Brunswick was driven off his lands and his castle was stormed, plundered and set alight. Following unrest in Leipzig and Dresden, conservative King Anton of Saxony abdicated in favour of his more reform-minded nephew Frederick August, under whose regency a liberal ministry was established and, a year later, a new constitution introduced on the south German model.

The political unrest of 1830 thus triggered a second wave of constitutional reform following the introduction of the southern German constitutions after 1818. The basic law introduced in the Electorate of Hesse-Cassel in January 1831 was

I/63
Attack on the main guard house in Frankfurt/Main, 3 April 1833

regarded as the most liberal of these new constitutions. It was issued by Elector William II on 15 September 1830 after urgent pleadings by a deputation from Kassel city council in the wake of violent popular unrest.

The general mobilisation of political forces in Germany was fostered, not least, by the Polish revolt of 1830/31. After the uprising was finally crushed by Russian troops in autumn 1831, patriotic Polish emigrés were fêted in many regions of Germany as champions of German liberation. In the course of a broad public debate on the fate of the Poles, solidarity associations sprang up in many areas. These Polish associations became key organisations in the liberal opposition.

In the Palatinate, the mobilisation of political forces, combined with more effective organisation, culminated in a mass meeting in the ruins of Hambach castle on 27 May 1832, attended by 20,000—30,000 people. It was one of the most significant liberal and national gatherings in favour of press freedom, constitutional reform and national unity for Germany.

Yet these political successes proved short-lived in the face of the reactionary measures implemented by the German Confederation during the period 1832–1834. The attempt by radical members of patriotic student fraternities to incite general revolution by storming the main guard house at the seat of the Federal Diet, or Bundestag, in Frank-

I/65
Demonstrators march to Hambach Castle, 27 May 1832

I/64 (opposite) Illustrations showing scenes from the revolutionary events of 1830

I/66
Gathering of
German journeymen
in Steinhölzli
near Berne,
24 June 1834

furt/Main met with little support and collapsed on 3 April 1833. The more radical opposition forces were generally forced to emigrate to neighbouring states. In Switzerland, in particular, the emigrants, ultimately numbering almost 40,000, joined together in artisans' associations and similar organisations. In Paris, representatives of the extreme left formed a secret society, known as the "League of Outcasts, in 1834; their Declaration of the Rights of Man and Citizen centred on the struggle against social inequality. From these beginnings, there emerged from the 1840s onwards range of socialist organisations.

The general politicisation of society also permeated the literature of the 1830s. Ludwig Börne, Heinrich Heine and the "Young Germany" group rejected Romanticism and introspection, regarding their task as writers as being to consciouls express political, democratic and radical criticism of existing conditions. The liberal movement's "Bible" during the *Vormärz* was the "*Staatslexikon*" – a popular and influential work of reference on political and social questions – published by the Freiburg constitutional lawyers Karl von Rotteck and Karl Theodor Welcker between 1834 and 1843. Its articles formulated a comprehensive political programme of liberalism which was rooted in constitutional law. In 1837, attention focussed on Göttingen Univer-

I/67
The "Göttingen Seven"

I/68
Celebratory procession at Cologne Cathedral

sity when seven of its professors publicly protested against the annulment of the 1833 constitution by the new Hanoverian King Ernst August. The "Göttingen Seven" – who included the Brothers Grimm, the historian Friedrich Christoph Dahlmann and the literary historian Georg Gottfried Gervinus – were stripped of their posts and driven into exile, instantly becoming national symbols of liberal resistance to a reactionary and authoritarian state.

In the absence of a unified nation-state, the German people's sense of nationhood was increasingly rooted in their common language, poetry, history and cultural unity. The Romantic transfiguration of the past, especially the Medieval period, was evident from the widespread public

Die Forderungen des Volkes.

Unsere Versammlung von entschiedenen Freunden der Verfassung hat stattgefunden. Niemand kann derselben beigewohnt haben, ohne auf das Tiefste ergriffen und angeregt worden zu sein. Es war ein Fest männlicher Entschlossenheit, eine Versammlung, welche zu Resultaten führen muß. Jedes Wort, was gesprochen wurde, enthält den Vorsatz und die Aufforderung zu thatkräftigem Handeln. Wir nennen keine Namen und keine Zahlen. Diese thun wenig zur Sache. Genug, die Versammlung, welche den weiten Festsaal füllte, eignete sich einstimmig die in folgenden Worten zusammengefaßten Besprechungen des Tages an:

Die Forderungen des Volkes in Baden:

I. Wiederherstellung unserer verletzten Verfassung.

Art. 1. Wir verlangen, daß sich unsere Staatsregierung lossage von den Karlsbader Beschlüssen vom Jahr 1819, von den Frankfurter Beschlüssen von 1831 und 1832 und von den Wiener Beschlüssen von 1834. Diese Beschlüsse verletzen gleichmäßig unsere unveräußerlichen Menschenrechte wie die deutsche Bundesakte und unsere Landesverfassung.

Art. 2. Wir verlangen Preßfreiheit; das unveräußerliche Recht des menschlichen Geistes, seine Gedanken unverstümmelt mitzutheilen, darf uns nicht länger vorenthalten werden.

Art. 3. Wir verlangen Gewissens- und Lehrfreiheit. Die Beziehungen des Menschen zu seinem Gotte gehören seinem innersten Wesen an, und keine äußere Gewalt darf sich anmaßen, sie nach ihrem Gutdünken zu bestimmen. Jedes Glaubensbekenntniß hat daher Anspruch auf gleiche Berechtigung im Staate.

Keine Gewalt dränge sich mehr zwischen Lehrer und Lernende. Den Unterricht scheide keine Confession.

Art. 4. Wir verlangen Beeidigung des Militärs auf die Verfassung.

Der Bürger, welchem der Staat die Waffen in die Hand gibt, bekräftige gleich den übrigen Bürgern durch einen Eid seine Verfassungstreue.

Art. 5. Wir verlangen persönliche Freiheit.

Die Polizei höre auf, den Bürger zu bevormunden und zu qualen. Das Vereinsrecht, ein frisches Gemeindeleben, das Recht des Volkes sich zu versammeln und zu reden, das Recht des Einzelnen sich zu ernähren, sich zu bewegen und auf dem Boden des deutschen Vaterlandes frei zu verkehren — seien hinfüro ungestört.

II. Entwickelung unserer Verfassung.

Art. 6. Wir verlangen Vertretung des Volks beim deutschen Bunde.

Dem Deutschen werde ein Vaterland und eine Stimme in dessen Angelegenheiten. Gerechtigkeit und Freiheit im Innern, eine feste Stellung dem Auslande gegenüber gebühren uns als Nation.

Art. 7. Wir verlangen eine volksthümliche Wehrverfassung. Der waffengeübte und bewaffnete Bürger kann allein den Staat schützen.

Man gebe dem Volke Waffen und nehme von ihm die unerschwingliche Last, welche die stehenden Heere ihm auferlegen.

Art. 8. Wir verlangen eine gerechte Besteuerung.

Jeder trage zu den Lasten des Staates nach Kräften bei. An die Stelle der bisherigen Besteuerung trete eine progressive Einkommensteuer.

Art. 9. Wir verlangen, daß die Bildung durch Unterricht allen gleich zugänglich werde.

Die Mittel dazu hat die Gesammtheit in gerechter Vertheilung aufzubringen.

Art. 10. Wir verlangen Ausgleichung des Mißverhältnisses zwischen Arbeit und Capital.

Die Gesellschaft ist schuldig die Arbeit zu heben und zu schützen.

Art. 11. Wir verlangen Gesetze, welche freier Bürger würdig sind und deren Anwendung durch Geschwornengerichte.

Der Bürger werde von dem Bürger gerichtet. Die Gerechtigkeitspflege sei Sache des Volkes.

Art. 12. Wir verlangen eine volksthümliche Staatsverwaltung.

Das frische Leben eines Volkes bedarf freier Organe. Nicht aus der Schreibstube lassen sich seine Kräfte regeln und bestimmen. An die Stelle der Vielregierung der Beamten trete die Selbstregierung des Volkes.

Art. 13. Wir verlangen Abschaffung aller Vorrechte.

Jedem sei die Achtung freier Mitbürger einziger Vorzug und Lohn.

Offenburg, 12. September 1847.

I/69
The "Offenburg Programme" of 12 September 1847

enthusiasm for the decision to commence completion of Cologne Cathedral in 1842.

In Prussia, King Frederick William IV, seeking to overcome the state's financial difficulties, responded to growing calls for a parliamentary assembly by convening the United Diet, or *Vereinigter Landtag*, in April 1847. However, Members and the Crown argued fiercely about the Diet's competencies, and it was dissolved after just two months.

During the period immediately preceding the 1848/49 Revolution, the opposition finally split into two separate liberal and democrat factions. Both groups agreed on key demands, such as the creation of a nation state. However, in their "Offenburg Programme" of 12 September 1847, the democrats also called for a republic, universal suffrage and effective social policies on behalf of the lower classes. The liberals responded with their Hep-

1. Von der Bundesversammlung, wie sie gegenwärtig besteht, ist für die Förderung der Nationalanliegen nichts Ersprießliches zu erwarten. Sie hat ihre in der Bundesakte vorgezeichnete Aufgabe, soweit sie die Herstellung landständischer Verfassungen, freien Handels und Verkehrs, des freien Gebrauchs der Presse usw. betrifft, nicht gelöst. Dagegen ist die Presse unter Zensurzwang gestellt, sind die Verhandlungen der Bundesversammlung in Dunkel gehüllt, aus welchem von Zeit zu Zeit Beschlüsse zu Tage kommen, die jeder freien Entwicklung Hindernisse in den Weg legen.

2. Das einzige Band gemeinsamer deutscher Interessen, der Zollverein, wurde nicht vom Bunde, sondern außerhalb desselben, durch Verträge zwischen den einzelnen deutschen Staaten geschaffen.

3. Hieran knüpft sich die Frage, ob eine Vertretung der Nation bei der Bundesversammlung Besserung bewirken kann und daher als Ziel der Vaterlandsfreunde aufzustellen ist. Doch die Aussicht auf Verwirklichung dieses Gedankens ist nicht vorhanden: der Bund enthält Glieder, die als zugleich auswärtige Mächte, wie Dänemark und Niederland, sich mit einer deutschen Politik und Stärkung deutscher Macht niemals befreunden werden. Ferner bedingt eine Nationalvertretung auch eine Nationalregierung, ausgerüstet mit den Befugnissen der obersten Staatsgewalt, die bei dem völkerrechtlichen Bunde nicht vorhanden ist.

4. Das Ziel der Einigung Deutschlands zu einer deutschen Politik und gemeinsamen Leitung und Pflege nationaler Interessen, wird wohl eher erreicht, wenn man die öffentliche Meinung für die Ausbildung des Zollvereins zu einem deutschen Vereine gewinnt. Jetzt schon hat der Zollverein die Leitung einer Reihe wichtiger gemeinschaftlicher Interessen in Händen und steht auch in

Vertragsverhältnissen zu auswärtigen Staaten. Durch weitere Ausbildung wird der Zollverein eine unwiderstehliche Anziehungskraft für den Beitritt der übrigen deutschen Länder üben, auch den Anschluß der österreichischen Bundesländer herbeiführen und somit eine wahre deutsche Macht begründen.

5. Unbestritten bleibt, daß die Mitwirkung des Volkes durch gewählte Vertreter hierbei unerläßlich, und unbezweifelt, daß bei dem Entwicklungsgang des Jahrhunderts und Deutschlands die Einigung durch Gewaltherrschaft unmöglich, nur durch die Freiheit und mit derselben zu erringen ist.

6. Anträge, welche in allen deutschen Kammern gleichlautend zu stellen sind:

Einführung der Pressefreiheit
Öffentliches und mündliches Gerichtsverfahren mit Schwurgerichten
Trennung der Verwaltung von der Rechtspflege
Befreiung des Bodens und seiner Bearbeiter von mittelalterlichen Lasten
Selbständigkeit der Gemeinden in der Verwaltung ihrer Angelegenheiten
Minderung des Aufwands für das stehende Heer und Einführung einer Volkswehr.

7. Aus Abgeordneten verschiedener Länder wird eine Kommission gewählt, die im nächsten Jahr über das Steuerwesen und die Zustände der ärmeren Klassen berichten und Anträge formulieren soll, wobei besonders die gerechte Verteilung der öffentlichen Lasten zur Erleichterung des kleinen Mittelstands und der Arbeiter zu berücksichtigen ist.

(Nach dem Bericht der Heidelberger Deutschen Zeitung, Oktober 1847)

I/70
The demands of the Heppenheim meeting on 10 October 1847

penheim Declaration of 10 October 1847, published in their journal, the *Deutsche Zeitung*, which had recently been established in Heidelberg. This programme focussed on constitutional monarchy as the objective of domestic reform and called for the Customs Union to be expanded into a confederation in the cause of national unity. In general, they viewed agreements with the existing authorities as a way to achieve reform.

Growing social tensions in the 1840s led to a further upsurge in political activity. A crisis occurred in June 1844 when Silesian weavers rebelled against the introduction of mechanical looms. In 1847, economic crisis and food shortages led to hunger riots amongst the lower classes in many towns and cities. These fundamental social problems helped to prepare the ground for the revolution which erupted in spring 1848.

The three solutions to the "German Question"

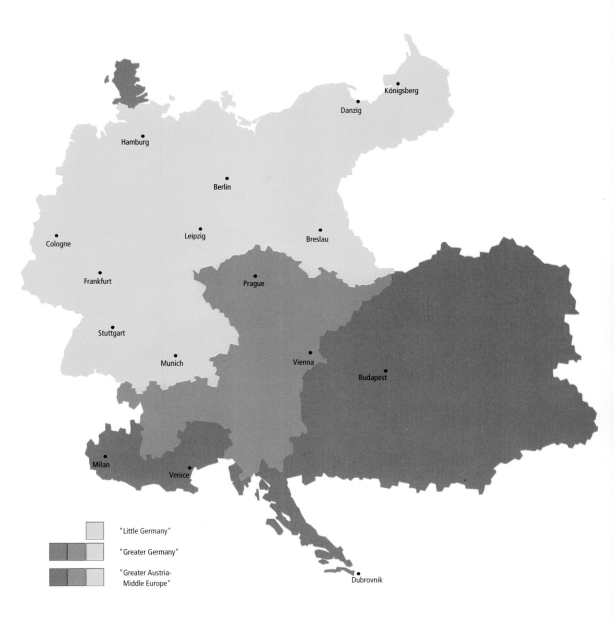

Legend:
- "Little Germany"
- "Greater Germany"
- "Greater Austria-Middle Europe"

The Revolution of 1848/49

II. The Revolution of 1848/49

Towards the middle of the nineteenth century, a strong opposition movement comprising liberal and democratic groups emerged in Germany. One of the groups' shared demands was the unification of Germany into a single nation-state, a demand which, whilst challenging the ruling state powers, raised not only the national issue but also the question of fundamental social change. The national and the social issue were closely intertwined; depending on the political stance of the various movements, their demands saw national unity either as the result of or as the precondition for economic and social reform. Although in some cases the desire for Germany unity was based on an irrational pan-Germanism, initially this was far outweighed by calls for social emancipation. Indeed, the majority of opposition figures clearly distanced themselves from "the conceit and selfishness of Germanomania" (Varnhagen). In the years leading up to 1848, the idea of a German nation-state united a broad spectrum of reformist aspirations. During the debates, negotiations and struggles of the revolutionary years 1848 and 1849, however, it became evident that in practical political terms it was virtually impossible to find common ground amongst the different shades of opinion.

Social and political tensions mounted in late 1847, early 1848 as the economic crisis affecting all European countries since 1946 deepened: popular gatherings, peasants' uprisings and petitions to those in power all increased. The so-called "March demands", drafted initially in southwestern Germany, called primarily for freedom of the press, trial by jury, constitutional government in all the German states and the summoning of a German parliament. The February Revolution in Paris triggered uprisings in Berlin and Vienna. The German princes felt compelled to grant concessions: they endorsed liberal constitutions, appointed liberals to government ministries, promised freedom of the press and freedom of assembly, and pledged the convening of a German parliament.

Frankfurt was the focal point of the Revolution. It was here that the *Vorparlament*, or Pre-Parliament', met. The Pre-Parliament was the first assembly to be convened by the revolutionary movement. Attempts were made by a small group of left-wing republicans to turn it into a kind of permanent revolutionary executive, but they failed. The liberal majority prevailed with their demand for a National Assembly to be elected on the basis of an agreement with the state governments. The elections were held in April, and the National Assembly was officially opened in the Paulskirche on 18 May 1848. There were still no political parties in the modern sense of the term; groupings which resembled parties were only formed in the course of the ensuing debates. The centrist liberal members formed the majority. From the outset, policy-making in the National Assembly was characterized by a notable willingness to seek a compromise with the governments of the German states.

The Assembly had a dual task: to draw up a national constitution and to create a central government. At the beginning of June, proposals for an imperial executive were already under discussion, and the Assembly installed, on its own authority, a provisional imperial government. The composition of this government reflected the difficulty in establishing balanced relations between a unified German state on the one hand and the individual states, especially the most powerful ones, on the other: whilst the election of the Austrian Archduke John as Imperial Administrator was intended to keep the door open to Austria, the newly formed Imperial Ministry was dominated by Prussia. However, the National Assembly, having set up a government for what it now considered a German nation-state, never succeeded in endowing this centralized executive with any genuine power or authority. It had no civil service of its own and no army, and a number of German monarchs refused to allow their troops to swear allegiance to the Imperial Administrator.

The most important and passionately debated issue in parliament between June and September 1848 was the drafting of the "Fundamental Rights of the German People", which were not finally adopted until 27 December 1848. The time taken up by these debates was costly as it gave the traditional powers a chance to regain their strength. But its also showed the importance which the liberals accorded to social and legal reform in the nation-state they aimed to create. The Fundamental Rights were an expression of the desire to abolish the class-based hierarchies of the old social order and, in doing so, to remove the privileges of the nobility and all vestiges of the feudal order. They were to be replaced by a guarantee of equality of opportunity and equality before the law for all citizens, along the lines of the American and French revolutions.

In late summer, as the members set about discussing the Reich constitution, the National Assembly had to face a crisis which, as it highlighted the impotence of the central government, was to prove decisive: the Schleswig-Holstein question. German nationalists in Schleswig, which faced the threat of annexation by Denmark, organized an uprising and were assisted by Prussian troops dispatched at the behest of the German Confederation and the National Assembly. However, Prussia ultimately gave into pressure from Russia and England, and signed an armistice at Malmö, under which the federal troops were withdrawn. Having initially rejected the armistice, the National Assembly was in the end forced to accept it; it was not powerful enough to pursue an independent policy. At the same time, the radical democrats stepped up their campaign; in Lörrach on 21 September a "German Social Republic" was proclaimed by Gustav von Struve. However, this uprising failed, as had Hecker's putsch in April 1848. In Frankfurt, the National Assembly faced the threat of a rebellion by members who opposed the armistice and the policy of compromise pursued by the liberal majority. It was only saved with the help of Austrian and Prussian troops. This military success, and the crushing of other uprisings in Vienna in October and Berlin in November 1848, strengthened the forces of reaction.

In September 1848, the National Assembly began work on a German constitution. Here, too, its willingness to compromise was evident as unitary and federal, democratic and monarchistic elements were combined. The main issue of debate was the territorial limits of the German nation-state. Initially, the majority favoured a "Greater German" solution which would incorporate the German-speaking regions of Austria, thereby separating them constitutionally from the other territories of the Habsburg empire. This solution was thwarted by the Austrian Prime Minister, Prince Felix Schwarzenberg, who, following the suppression of the non-German nationalist movements, introduced a centralized constitution for the Austrian empire as a whole. His action having put an end to hopes for a Greater German solution, the National Assembly decided to offer the hereditary title of Emperor of a "Little German" nation-state to the King of Prussia. However, in 1849 Frederick William IV, in thrall to a romantic notion of a nation-state based on the divine right of kings, refused this offer from a popular assembly set up in the wake of a revolution, and spoke out against the Reich constitution, which had in the meantime been recognized by the governments of 28 German states. In early 1849, fresh uprisings sought to enforce the constitution by exerting pressure from below. However, they were put down in brutal fashion. Following a walk-out by a large number of liberals, the National Assembly was dominated by the republican left. It was finally disbanded by the military forces of Württemberg in Stuttgart, where the "Rump Parliament" was still meeting. The efforts of the National Assembly thus came to nought. The "March Achievements" were repealed in all the German states with the help of the reinstated German Confederation. In 1851 the Fundamental Rights were also repealed almost everywhere.

The German Revolution of 1848/49, which had been an attempt to establish a constitutional state from below by liberal and democratic means as a response to the political and social demands of the times, foundered in its latter stages on the question of German unity. The national question became a power game between a reinvigorated Prussia and Austria. For the time being, the road to social reform was cut off by a resurgence of reactionary forces – only the "New Era" in Prussia was to offer any fresh hope. At the same time, the question of a united German nation-state remained the crux of a Prussian-Austrian dualism which was to dominate politics in the coming decades. As scepticism towards the ideals of preceding years grew, support increased for a policy of realism which sought practicable solutions within the existing framework. In 1852, D.F. Strauß, an erstwhile supporter of the Revolution, wrote: "In comparison with the issue of unity, I consider the question of whether there should be a greater or lesser degree of despotism or constitutionalism, of aristocratic or democratic rule in the German states, to be irrelevant." There was a growing rift between the desire for unity and the desire for social reform.

1. The March Revolution of 1848

In 1847/48 social and political tensions increased against the backdrop of an economic crisis afflicting the whole of Europe. They triggered uprisings against the existing order in all the countries of Europe with the exception of Russia and England: in France against the self-serving rule of the upper middle class; in Italy and Germany against territorial fragmentation, the vestiges of the feudal order and the absolutist constitution; in eastern Europe against foreign domination and social injustice. The conditions which gave rise to these rebellions, and the problems they sought to redress, varied so greatly that there was no uniform revolutionary pattern in Europe.

In Germany, the uprising was supported by a strong national movement which combined demands for national unity with those for social and political reforms. These demands found their expression in the desire shared by all social classes for a national parliament and a constitution valid for the whole of Germany. In March 1848, in the first phase of the Revolution, the movement succeeded in winning concessions from the state governments, first of all in southern Germany. Accompanied by rural uprisings, popular assemblies formed in the large towns and cities put the monarchs under pressure and formulated their so-called "March Demands". In Berlin and Vienna, the

II/72
Street battle
near the Porta Tosa
in Milan on
22 March 1848

monarchs were only willing to grant concessions in the wake of bloody street fighting. Everywhere liberal ministers were now appointed.

The revolution in France

The signal for the uprisings and the overthrow of the old political order throughout Europe was given by the revolution in France. The eco-nomic crisis of 1846/47 had caused a food shortage in France, leading to a radicalization among the new urban proletariat and the rural pop-ulation. The workers and lower middle classes, led by Louis Blanc, demanded secure jobs in state-run factories. Attempts at political re-form by democratic elements of the middle class failed. The result was the February Revolution. Workers, citizens and the national guard fought side-by-side and forced the

II/73
Breaching of
the Mariahilfer Line
in Vienna on
13 March 1848

abdication of the "Citizen King", Louis Philippe. The Republic was proclaimed. However, a conflict soon broke out between the bourgeois majority and the radical socialists over the aims of the Revolution. The bourgeoisie and the military joined forces, and bloodily suppressed the workers' uprising in June 1848.

which united the revolutionary forces although the latters' views on how to put them into practice varied greatly. In most cases, the governments did not dare to quell the uprisings by force, and power fell almost automatically into the hands of the liberal middle class.

In Austria, too, the social uprising was furthered by the economic

II/74
Cavalry attack on demonstrators in front of the royal palace in Berlin on 18 March 1848

The March Revolution in Germany and Central Europe

The events in Paris in February 1848 triggered a chain of revolutions in the individual German states, too. The political unrest among the population was reflected in popular assemblies, demonstrations and petitions – often accompanied by social tumult, especially in rural areas. The first step was taken in southern Germany with the formulation of the so-called "March Demands". Their principal aims were freedom of the press, trial by jury, the arming of civic guards, constitutions in the individual states and the summoning of a German parliament. Constitutionalism and the nation-state in particular were the symbols of what was to be a fundamentally new order: they were the principles

plight of the workers and peasants, rigid suppression of freedom of speech and freedom of the press, and the outbreak of the revolution in Paris, which was enthusiastically welcomed by the masses. As the Czechs, Hungarians and Italians also rose up in rebellion, following a demonstration on 13 March fighting broke out in Vienna between the military on the one hand and students and workers on the other. The chief minister, Chancellor of State Prince Metternich, was ousted and fled to England. The Imperial Government had to allow the civic guard to carry arms and promised to grant a constitution, which was enacted in April.

In Berlin, the politial unrest palpable since the beginning of March turned into open revolt on 18 March. When, in front of the royal palace, the cavalry sought to end a

II/75
Members of the working and middle classes fighting together on the barricades in March 1848

demonstration for a civic guard, freedom of the press and a Prussian parliament, barricades were erected and defended by members of the middle class, workers and students. Finally, the King ordered the withdrawal of his troops and gave into the demands of the revolutionaries. With the words "Prussia will henceforth be part of Germany", the Kings acquiesced in the demand for national unity. A liberal ministry was established, and a Prussian national assembly convened in May. Prussia was to become a constitutional monarchy.

II/76
Barricade in Neue Königstraße in Berlin on 19 March 1848

II/77
Funeral procession
for those killed in
March 1848, paint-
ing by Adolf Men-
zel, 1848

II/78
Waldenburg castle
on fire on 5 April
1848

The social causes of the Revolution

In 1846 and 1847, in the wake of a number of poor harvests, Germany was hit by a serious farming crisis and by famine. As a result of rising food prices and falling real incomes, large sections of the population suffered extreme hardship. This was compounded by a global economic crisis which in 1847 and early 1848 adversely affected industrial production and led to rising unemployment.

The crisis in agriculture and commerce did not last long, however; the situation improved again in the course of 1848.

In southern Germany in particular, but also in Silesia, it was the rural population above all which supported the Revolution. As in the days of the Peasants' War, radical groups marched to local castles and palaces and demanded that they be freed from their remaining feudal obligations. However, these rural revolts did not seriously question the existing order. Once its demands had been met, and the "liberation" of the peasants largely completed, the rural population took no further part in the Revolution.

Besides these rural uprisings, the rapid success of the Revolution was due primarily to the broad support it enjoyed among the urban population: middle-class citizens and workers, master craftsmen and journeymen, and urban middle and lower classes joined forces to fight on the barricades. In the course of the Revolution, however, the social differences between the various

II/79
Food riots in Stettin in 1847

groups became increasingly apparent. The majority of the bourgeoisie soon sought to prevent the lower social classes from pursuing the Revolution any further. The disputes over more radical political and social demands not only destroyed the initial unity of the revolutionary movement, but split the bourgeoisie itself.

II/80
Confrontation between the Mannheim civil guard and protesting supporters of Hecker on 9 April 1848

2. The emergence of the political nation

The road to the Paulskirche

Meetings, demonstrations and street battles had hitherto determined the course of the Revolution. Now, however, in view of its successes the bourgeois-liberal majority, and also many democrats, wanted to pursue a parliamentary road to reform. In their view, a national assembly should be summoned to draw up a pan-German constitution and establish a central authority capable of governing Germany as a whole.

On 5 March 1848 leading liberals and democrats from southern and western Germany met in Heidelberg and announced that the convening of a national assembly could be put off no longer. Although their appeal was addressed to the existing governments, they themselves set up a "Committee of Seven" whose task it was to prepare elections to the national assembly. This committee was the first revolutionary body to be established. It invited all "former or present members of the estates and legislative assemblies in all German states", as well as a number of other public figures, to participate in a *Vorparlament*, or "Pre-Parliament", in Frankfurt. On 30 May more than 500 men met in one of the city's main churches, the Paulskirche.

The strength of representation in this revolutionary assembly varied among the individual German states and political groupings. Only the left-wing democrats, led by Gustav von Struve, had a fixed programme. This minority grouping demanded the setting up of a federal republic, and called upon the *Vorparlament* to immediately assume executive revolutionary powers. The majority of delegates took a very different view: they wanted to establish a new political order by reaching agreement with the princes. By adopting this position, later shared by the National Assem-

II/82
Election meeting of the Berlin Political Club on 20 April 1848

II/81 (opposite)
Members entering the Pre-Parliament in the Paulskirche on 30 March 1848

bly, the *Vorparlament* to all intents and purposes abandoned its revolutionary aspirations and instead sought a compromise with the established powers. When they recognized this, some 40 "radicals", led by Hecker, left the assembly.

Hecker, supported by bands of volunteers, initiated a rebellion in Baden aimed at creating a social republic. He was also supported by German exiles who returned from France and Switzerland. However, he overestimated public support for the republican idea, and after only a few days was defeated by regular troops from Baden and Hesse. Hecker fled to Switzerland and later emigrated to the USA.

The *Vorparlament* laid down the principles for elections to a national assembly and for a German constitution, and appointed a "Committee of Fifty" to prepare the elections. This revolutionary committee worked together with the old Federal Diet and the state governments, which quickly sought to legitimize the election and to enact electoral laws. All "independent" persons were to have the right to vote, a term interpreted in very different ways by the various states. In some cases, workers and domestic servants were not allowed to vote, and direct elections were permitted in only six states; in all the others members were elected indirectly by electoral colleges. At an electoral meeting in Berlin, members of the Political Club called in vain for direct elections to be held in Prussia. There were no political parties as such, and local candidates were nominated either by political clubs, which were being set

II/83
Archduke John of Austria before the National Assembly on the day of his appointment as the Imperial Administrator of Germany on 12 July 1848

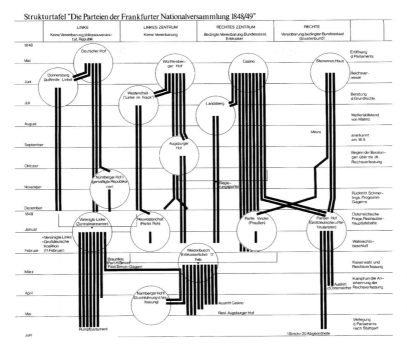

Strukturtafel "Die Parteien der Frankfurter Nationalversammlung 1848/49"

II/84
The political group-
ings in the National
Assembly in
1848/49

up throughout Germany, or by hastily organized election committees. Almost everywhere, middle class liberals were elected.

The National Assembly

On 18 May the National Assembly convened in the Paulskirche for the first time, amid a wave of great enthusiasm and high expectations. In his first speech following his election to the presidency of the Assembly, Heinrich von Gagern referred to the "sovereignty of the nation" and its right to give itself a new constitution. At the same time, he stressed the need for the state governments to be involved.

Including substitutes, a total of 831 members were elected to the National Assembly, of whom initially 330 and later 400–500 on average were present at its sessions. The majority came from the liberal, educated middle class. Civil servants

and academics – above all lawyers – played a prominent role. Trade and industry were represented by only a few members, as were the nobility and the petty bourgeoisie. Peasants and workers had no direct representation in the National Assembly.

On the basis of experience gained in the state parliaments in southern Germany, more stable political groups soon emerged in the National Assembly and endeavoured to organize its work more effectively. Most members belonged to such groupings, which met regularly in the inns of Frankfurt from which they also took their names. These groupings elected executive committees, drew up membership lists and adopted programmes and manifestoes. They soon assumed the task of holding preliminary deliberations to prepare for plenary sessions, and were already referred to as "parties" in some quarters.

The democratic left, which was in a

minority, was the first grouping to organize. Under the leadership of Robert Blum, it met in the Deutscher Hof. However, the most committed republicans soon broke away to form their own grouping, known as the Donnersberg group, and henceforth constituted the far left in the National Assembly. Despite their political differences, on the issue of national unity the majority of left-wing delegates formed a coalition with the right-wing Pariser Hof in favour of a "Greater German" solution when it became apparent that a "Little German" solution excluding Austria would be favoured.

The right wing of the National Assembly was formed by a liberal-conservative group, initially of mainly Austrian and Catholic orientation, which met at the Steinernes Haus and, later, under the leadership of the Prussian Freiherr von Vincke, at the Café Milani. In contrast to the left wing, this group wanted to restrict the task of the Assembly to drafting a constitution, and to base this constitution on an agreement with the ruling princes.

The majority of delegates were moderate liberals who, however, split into two wings: the Württemburger Hof (left Centre) and the Casino Party (right Centre). The Württemberg Hof agreed with the left wing in rejecting the idea of an agreement with the princes. The Casino Party was the strongest group, both numerically and intellectually, and exerted the greatest influence on the course of events in the Assembly. The President of the Assembly, Heinrich von Gagern, was one of its members, as were many professors such as the historians Dahlmann, Droysen, Waitz and Giesebrecht. The majority of its members favoured a constitutional monarchy with restricted suffrage, and later supported a "Little German" solution to the question of German unification.

II/85
The left wing in the
National Assembly

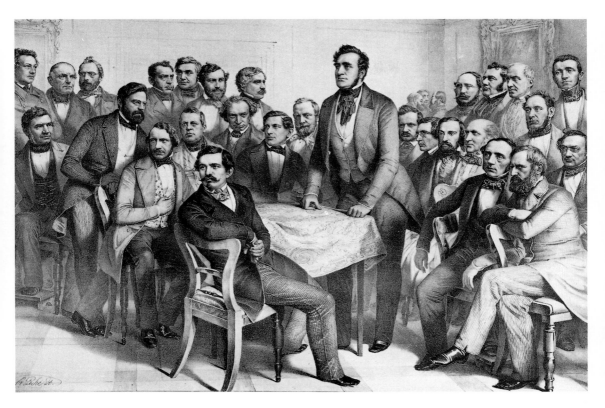

II/86
The members of the
Casino Party in the
National Assembly

The emergence of political parties

Although there had in fact been a number of precursors, especially in the south and west of Germany, the Revolution of 1848/49 saw the birth of political parties in the modern sense of the word. As early as March 1848, following the abolition of censorship and the granting of the freedom of assembly and association, broad sections of the population began to engage in political activity. In many towns and cities, the groups of different political and social persuasions soon became so well organized that it was possible to distinguish between five party-like groupings: the liberals, the democrats, the conservatives, politically active Catholics and a nascent workers' movement. At the same time, people began to articulate a whole range of specific interests and in some cases formed clubs and associations to promote them. German society became more organized politically than ever before.

In parliamentary terms, the bourgeois-liberal centre was the strongest force. It supported the gradual introduction of democratic government accompanied by an extensive liberalization of the economy and society. It perceived the monarchy as a bulwark of the bourgeois order against the threat of social revolution. Outside parliament, the liberals were not nearly as well organized as the democrats; it was often only in response to the activities of the latter that they began to form associations and groups of their own.

The middle-class democrats were the first to set up organizational

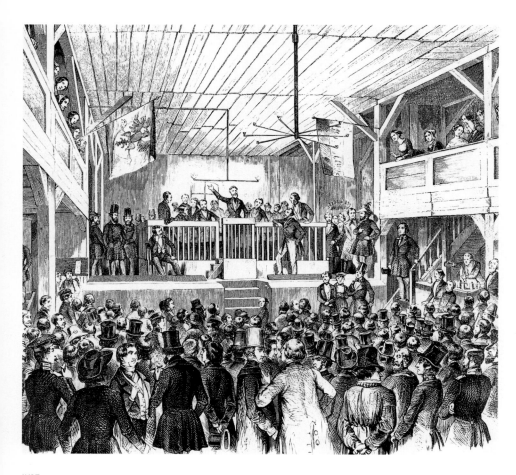

II/87
A meeting of
dem-ocrats in Berlin
in 1848

structures similar to those of a modern political party: an extensive network of groups and associations at regional level supplemented by conferences and central associations at national level. The democrats advocated a republican order based on the principle of popular sovereignty. In their view, this presupposed social reform and an open society in which the lower classes were to be included from the outset.

Having initially adopted a more hesitant and defensive stance, the conservative counterrevolutionary forces also started to exploit the new forms of organization and publicity, especially in Prussia. In Berlin they published the *Neue* *Preußische Zeitung*, also called the *Kreuz-Zeitung*. At the same time, the Prussian landed gentry, the *Junker*, began to organize the defence of the monarchic system in patriotic clubs; they also set up associations to promote their economic interests and to protect their privileges. A network of such clubs and associations soon covered large parts of eastern Prussia.

In spring 1848 the fight for the freedom of the Church gave birth to a broad-based Catholic movement. Through newspapers, assemblies, petitions, associations advocating religious freedom, such as the *Piusvereine für religiöse Freiheit*, and, finally, the first Catholic Church Conference in Mainz in Oc-

III/13

Beschlüsse
des
Arbeiter-Kongresses.

Erster Theil.
Statut für die Organisation der Arbeiter.

I. Die Lokal-Komites für Arbeiter.

§. 1. Es bilden die verschiedenen Gewerke und Arbeitergemein=
schaften im weitesten Sinne des Worts Vereinigungen und wählen,
je nach dem Verhältniß ihrer Zahl, Vertreter zu einem Lokal-Komite
für Arbeiter. Für Gewerke, welche vereinzelt dastehen, dürfte der
Kreis Vereinigungen bieten.

§. 2. Diejenigen Arbeiter, welche noch keine Gemeinschaften
bilden, haben sich ebenfalls zu vereinigen und Vertreter zu wählen,
z. B. die Eisenbahnarbeiter ꝛc.

§. 3. Das Lokal-Komite hat die Verpflichtung, a) regelmä=
ßige Versammlungen der Arbeiter zu veranlassen; b) die Bedürfnisse
und Uebelstände der Arbeiter in ihren Orten oder Kreisen genau zu
erforschen und auf Abhülfe derselben hinzuwirken; c) aus sich einen
Ausschuß zu wählen, der die Geschäfte leitet, bestehend aus 1 Vor=
sitzenden, 1 Beisitzer, 2 Schreibern, 1 Kassirer und 2 Kassenaufsehern.

§. 4. Die Lokal-Komites verschiedener Orte stehen mit einan=
der in Verbindung und zwar a) indem sie sich in kleinere oder grö=
ßere Bezirke ordnen und für alle ein Bezirks-Komite bilden; b) durch
briefliche Mittheilungen, welche sie an das Bezirks-Komite zur Beför=
derung an die einzelnen Lokal-Komites und an das Central-Komite
machen; c) durch Absendung von Abgeordneten zu den Bezirksver=
sammlungen und der vom Central-Komite ausgeschriebenen General=
versammlung für ganz Deutschland.

II. Die Bezirks-Komites

§. 5 haben vorläufig ihren Sitz in folgenden Städten: Danzig,
Königsberg, Stettin, Cöln, Bielefeld, Frankfurt, Hamburg, Stutt-

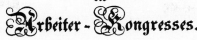

II/88
Resolutions of the
Workers' Congress
held in Berlin from
23 August to 3 Sep-
tember 1848

tober 1848, this movement, hardly represented at all at parliamentary level, fought to achieve its goals. Its membership ranged from supporters of Christian democracy, who shared many of the aims of the March Revolution, to ultramontane and arch-conservative forces, who formed the majority.

In 1848/49 the organization of the workers as an independent political force was only just beginning. In many cases, the workers' associations could not be clearly distinguished from the democratic movement. Moreover, existing social divisions between journeyman, the early urban proletariat and the property-less lower classes continued to impede the establishment of a single organization. Alongside groups advocating a conservative social policy or social reforms, the "League of Communists" led by Marx and Engels pressed for a social revolution.

In the course of 1848 great progress was also made in setting up groups to represent all kinds of economic and social interests. Most sought to express their aspirations, both to the public and especially to the National Assembly, through public addresses, petitions, and assemblies. The Congress of German Crafts and Trades in particular was able to draw on the support of large sections of the population, as was a partly allied movement set up to promote protective tariffs.

3. The work of the National Assembly and the Revolution in crisis

The central government: a head without a body

The election of the Imperial Administrator marked the first major achievement of the National Assembly. It was the result of a compromise between the various appointment of a figure by the princes who would not be accountable to Parliament.

In order to force the Assembly to reach a decision despite these differences of opinion, its President, Heinrich con Gagern, played a "bold stroke": he proposed to the

II/89
Archduke John, the Imperial Administrator, entering Frankfurt on 11 July 1848

groupings on the question of a provisional central authority. The left wing favoured the election of one man to assume executive powers, the right wing a collegiate body; the left wing favoured the election by the National Assembly of one of its members who would then be answerable to it, the right wing the Assembly the election of an Imperial Administrator. Archduke John was chosen, "not because but although he is a prince". He was not accountable to the National Assembly, and was recognized by the princes of the individual states following his election. He thus became the "legitimate" successor of

II/90
(opposite)
Proclamation of the Imperial Administrator after assuming control of the provisional central government

An das deutsche Volk.

Deutsche! Eure in Frankfurt versammelten Vertreter haben mich zum deutschen Reichsverweser erwählt.

Unter dem Zurufe des Vertrauens, unter den Grüßen voll Herzlichkeit, die mich überall empfingen, und die mich rührten, übernahm ich die Leitung der provisorischen Centralgewalt für unser Vaterland.

Deutsche! nach Jahren des Druckes wird Euch die Freiheit voll und unverkürzt. Ihr verdient sie, denn Ihr habt sie muthig und beharrlich erstrebt. Sie wird Euch nimmer entzogen, denn Ihr werdet wissen sie zu wahren.

Eure Vertreter werden das Verfassungswerk für Deutschland vollenden. Erwartet es mit Vertrauen. Der Bau will mit Ernst, mit Besonnenheit, mit ächter Vaterlandsliebe geführt werden. Dann aber wird er dauern, fest wie Eure Berge.

Deutsche! Unser Vaterland hat ernste Prüfungen zu bestehen. Sie werden überwunden werden. Eure Straßen, Eure Ströme werden sich wieder beleben, Euer Fleiß wird Arbeit finden, Euer Wohlstand wird sich heben, wenn Ihr vertrauet Euren Vertreten, wenn Ihr mir vertraut, den Ihr gewählt, um mit Euch Deutschland einig, frei und mächtig zu machen.

Aber vergeßt nicht, daß die Freiheit nur unter dem Schirme der Ordnung und Gesetzlichkeit wurzelt. Wirkt mit mir dahin, daß diese zurückkehren, wo sie gestört wurden. Dem verbrecherischen Treiben und der Zügellosigkeit werde ich mit dem vollen Gewichte der Gesetze entgegentreten. Der deutsche Bürger muß geschützt seyn gegen jede strafbare That.

Deutsche! Laßt mich hoffen, daß sich Deutschland eines ungestörten Friedens erfreuen werde. Ihn zu erhalten ist meine heiligste Pflicht.

Sollte aber die deutsche Ehre, das deutsche Recht gefährdet werden, dann wird das tapfere deutsche Heer für das Vaterland zu kämpfen und zu siegen wissen.

Frankfurt am Main, den 15. Juli 1848.

Der Reichsverweser

Erzherzog Johann.

Die Reichsminister
Schmerling. Peucker. Heckscher.

the Federal Diet, which transferred its powers to him. This compromise with the old powers created additional problems for the National Assembly. At its head there was now a member of the Austrian royal family. This made the decision on whether multi-national Austria should belong to the future German nation-state even more difficult.

Initially, however, great hopes were pinned on the Imperial Administrator. In a declaration "To the German People" he promised, "after years of coercion .... full and unrestricted freedom" and the completion of a constitution for Germany. Democratic associations appealed to the Imperial Administrator to respect the sovereignty of the people and to ensure the accountability of any future head of state.

Soon, however, the weaknesses of the central government became apparent. Following the formation of the Imperial Ministry under Charles Prince of Leiningen, an aristocrat related to the British royal family, it soon became clear that the capacity of the central administration to take effective action was severely restricted by organizational deficiencies and wrangling over powers with the individual states.

Without an army, a police force or a civil service of its own, the central government was dependent in implementing its decisions on political leaders in the states, with whose plenipotentiaries it conducted negotiations in Frankfurt. The question of diplomatic representation proved to be highly contentious. Some states refused to place their armies under a centralized supreme command. On 6 August an appeal was issued to the armies of all the states to swear allegiance to the Imperial Administrator. It was only with reservations that Prussia and Austria agreed to do so.

The debate on fundamental rights

The first objective of the Paulskirche Assembly was to draft a binding catalogue of human and civil rights, taking the American and French revolutions as its model. On 3 July 1848, following the establishment of a provisional central government, the National Assembly declared that it would embark on "the establishment of general rights which the constitution should grant the German people ... The constitution now being drawn up shall lay a lasting foundation for the unity and freedom of Germany and for the wellbeing of the nation." The liberal middle class debated for many months over the actual substance of the newly won freedoms. The debate centred on a new social order and the founding of a German nation-state endowed with a democratic constitution.

The whole of Germany followed the Paulskirche debate closely. Many citizens tried to influence the formulation of the fundamental rights by publishing pamphlets, signing petitions and making suggestions for changes.

The National Assembly's decision to begin by discussing fundamental rights and to leave the remaining constitutional questions until later was a direct result of members' experiences of the police system in the years prior to the March Revolution. They were above all keen to safeguard the rights of the individual vis-à-vis the state: "We want to escape from the situation created by the police state of previous centuries. We wish to establish a constitutional state for Germany ... We must put an end to the system of tutelage and the burden it imposes on Germany from above."

The Fundamental Rights of the German People guaranteed a constitutional state and the rule of law. For

II/91 (opposite)
The Fundamental Rights of the German People, lithography by Adolf Schroedter, Mainz 1848

the first time in Germany, they at the same time established uniform rights for all citizens of the Reich (clause 2). Class privileges were to be removed and replaced by equality before the law for all. "The aristocracy as an estate is hereby abolished .... All Germans are equal before the law" (clause 7).

Legal standardization, uniform civil rights and equality before the law formed the centrepiece of the Fundamental Rights. The Assembly sought in particular to guarantee the rights of the individual vis-à-vis the state. "The freedom of the individual is inviolable" (clause 8). "Every German has the right to express his opinion, be it orally, in writing, in print or visually" (clause 13). The freedom of association and assembly was guaranteed (clauses 29,30), as was that of academic activity and teaching. The Church's independence from the state was the subject of heated debates.

Lastly, they guaranteed the right of all citizens freely to dispose of their property: "Property is inviolable" (clause 32). All remaining privileges of the nobility were abolished. On the one hand, all fuedal dues were declared redeemable and, on the other, property-less dependent workers were granted the freedom to dispose of their own labour: "All subservience and bondage shall cease for ever" (clause 34). The aim of these fundamental rights was, by making property inviolable, to promote the free development of the individual within the framework of legal rules binding on all.

By contrast, none of the social reform measures going beyond the constitutional guarantees for the individual were approved by a majority of members. Although the plight of broad sections of the population had heightened public awareness of the "social question", the Fundamental Rights contained no provision relating to the social obligations of property-owners or people's right to social security. The document was criticized on this point by workers' and artisans' associations and by committed democrats. The conflicts of interest over the social question, which were to prove a major stumbling block for the work of the National Assembly, were already emerging.

The Schleswig-Holstein question

Whilst the Fundamental Rights were still under discussion, a crisis occurred which was to have a decisive impact on the fate of the National Assembly. The duchies of Schleswig and Holstein had joined the German Revolution and had revolted against their ruler, the Danish king, because he wanted to incorporate Schleswig, which unlike Holstein did not belong to the German Confederation, into the Danish nation-state. The duchies' provisional revolutionary government appealed to the Federal Diet for military assistance, which it received under Prussian command.

The German nationalist movement took up the cause of the struggle for Schleswig-Holstein with unparalleled enthusiasm; it became the focal point of aspirations for German unity and a matter of prestige for the National Assembly. The German troops conducted a successful campaign under their Prussian commander. However, in the face of pressure from abroad, notably from England and Russia, Prussia was forced to accept an armistice in the treaty of Malmö, which largely went against the interests of the people of Schleswig-Holstein. During the negotiations on the armistice, the provisional central government in Frankfurt, the legal successor to the Federal Diet,

II/92
Prussian troops
marching into
Schleswig on
23 April 1848

in whose name the war had been fought, was ignored by Prussia. Prussia thus rejected the idea of German unity in favour of its own interests as a European power.

This first foreign policy crisis highlighted the problems facing the National Assembly, problems it had in part created itself. The election of the Imperial Administrator had briefly created the impression that power actually did reside with the new central government. However, in the course of the disputes over the Schleswig-Holstein question, the Assembly had to accept that real power lay elsewhere. The moderate and radical members reacted differently, and the deap-seated differences between the various political groups emerged more clearly than ever before.

The National Assembly had to reach a decision on Prussia's unilateral action; the fate not only of Schleswig-Holstein but of Germany as a whole depended on whether it rejected or accepted the armistice. Acceptance would mean a victory for Prussia over the national movement; the victory of a monarch over the pan-German parliament. Rejection would signal the Assembly's determination to stand up to Prussia and the other European powers, and thus to abandon the path of consensus with the German princes.

On 5 September the National Assembly rejected the armistice, after the most turbulent debate since its inception, by 238 votes to 221. This marked the first victory for the left in the Paulskirche. Many liberals supported the decision, including the spokesman of the Schleswig-Holstein delegation, Dahlmann, who in his speech had said that the Parliament would lose face completely if in the case of Schleswig-

II/93

Stormy debate in the National Assembly in Frankfurt on 5 September 1848

Holstein it bowed to foreign pressure and betrayed the cause of German unity. The Leiningen Ministry resigned after the vote. However, Dahlmann did not succeed in forming a new ministry, nor could he bring himself to support the demand of the left that the struggle now be taken up against Prussia.

The National Assembly remained in a state of powerlessness and passivity. On 16 September it accepted the armistice after all by 257 votes to 236. Many liberals, like Dahlmann, who had originally spoken out strongly against it, now voted in favour. By endorsing Prussian policy, the National Assembly surrendered its authority and finally allowed itself to become dependent on the princes. Cartoonist saw in this decision the funeral of the "seven-month-old child" of German unity.

The inability of the National Assembly to move the Prussian government to reject the armistice was characteristic of its impotence vis-à-vis the ruling powers. For the republicans, this proved the futility of the moderate liberals' idea of persuading the princes, through negotiations, to voluntarily renounce some of their sovereign rights in favour of a German nation-state and a parliamentary system.

Rebellions against the National Assembly

The republicans and the democrats now gained increasing support from the people of Frankfurt. The advocates of the armistice were branded as traitors whereas the republicans were increasingly seen as the vanguard of the national revo-

II/94

(opposite)

Street battle outside the Paulskirche on 18 September 1848

Das merkwürdige Jahr 1848. — Eine neue Bilderzeitung. — 37tes Bild.

Wüthender Angriff der Republikaner auf das in der Paulskirche zu Frankfurt versammelte deutsche National-Parlament, am 18. September 1848.

Was weget und brauset so dumpf heran,
Erfüllt mit Gebrülle die Straßen,
Es ist der Pöbel im tollen Wahn,
Er wüthet über die Maßen.

Warum wogt und braus't es so dumpf heran,
Erfüllt mit Morden die Straßen?
Er will sie werden Mann für Mann,
Die vom Rechte sich nicht abbringen lassen.

Wer hat sie getrieben so toll heran,
Zu erfüllen mit Morden die Straßen?
Die Republikaner im irren Wahn,
Sie können die Ruhe nun hassen.

Die Abgeordneten Preußens für die deutsche National-Versammlung hatten sich ermannt, hatten für den Waffenstillstand mit Dänemark, für Ruhe und Frieden in ihrem Lande und in ganz Deutschland, für Gesetz und Ordnung gesprochen und der Fürst Lichnowsky und General v. Auerswald sich besonders ausgezeichnet; und der größte Theil der Versammlung war auf ihre Seite getreten. Das hatte nun die Republikaner, deren Dichten und Trachten nur darauf geht, durch eine allgemeine Revolution alles von Unterst zu Oberst zu kehren, alles Bestehende zu vernichten und sich selbst zur Herrschaft zu bringen, aufs Höchste erbittert. Sie hetzten das Volk in großen Volksversammlungen auf, machten Verschwörungen und beschlossen endlich durch ihre angeworbenen Haufen die National-Versammlung in der Paulskirche aus einander zu jagen und die, welche für die gute Sache gestimmt hatten, umzubringen. Sie setzten bis am 18. September in's Werk. Tobende Haufen umlagerten die Paulskirche und wollten hineindringen, wurden aber durch das Mili-

tair vertrieben. Nun vertheilten sie sich in die Straßen, bauen Barrikaden und schießen aus den Fenstern der Häuser. Das Militair wird nun kommandirt, die Barrikaden zu nehmen, die Aufrührer zu vertreiben. Und sie rücken vor, die Oesterreicher treu, die Hessendarmstädter muthig und gewandt und die Preußen zuletzt, rasch und ohne Besinnen. Die Barrikaden werden überwältigt, das Feuer aus den Häusern gekämpft. Es war eine Freude, Offiziere und Mannschaft so vieler Stämme wie eine lebendige, muthwolle Mauer für die National-Versammlung des deutschen Reichs in den Tod gehen zu sehen. Das Gesicht entschied sich unausweichlich zu Gunsten der Truppen. Aus der Umgegend waren schon 6 — 7000 Mann versammelt. 12 Geschütze mit Kartätschen und Kavallerieangriffe bereiteten den schrecklichen Kampfe reichen Untergang. Um 8 Uhr war der Sieg entschieden.

Original u. Eigenthum No. 2108.

30 — Neu-Ruppin, zu haben bei Gustav Kühn

II/95
Prussian troops
attacking a barri-
cade in Frankfurt
on 18 September
1848

lutionary movement. At large gatherings of associations of workers
and democrats, at which red flags
were beginning to outnumber the
black-red-gold ones, speakers demanded a walk-out from the
Paulskirche by the entire left wing
or else the dissolution of the National Assembly. The provisional
central government requested the
help of Prussian and Austrian
troops to protect the National Assembly. The crisis escalated. Public
anger was directed above all at the
Prussian troops, who were now being deployed to fight the revolutionaries on the streets. Whilst the

freedom of education was being
debated inside the Paulskirche, outside street battles were raging. Following the murder of two right-
wing deputies, Lichnowsky and
Auerswald, the city was placed under a state of siege. The rebellion
was crushed.

The central government felt in a
stronger position after this military
victory. It became more closely allied with the old ruling powers and
began to introduce counter-revolu-
tionary measures of its own. It
planned to impose punishments for
"press offences" committed by civil
servants and public authorities, and

II/96
Prince Lichnowsky
and General von
Auerswald mur-
dered in Frankfurt
on 18 September
1848

requested the states to submit "exact statistics on existing democratic associations and their branches". Ultimately, however, the main beneficiary of this victory was not the central government but the established powers.

The Republic is proclaimed

The unrest in Frankfurt spread to the states of central and southwestern Germany. Everywhere social revolutionary and republican demands were now voiced which went beyond the aims of the majority in the National Assembly. In Baden, where new financial laws and the trials of those involved in the spring uprisings had caused great unrest amongst the lower classes, Gustav von Struve attempted a putsch. The leaflets he published after the acceptance of the Malmö armistice by the National Assembly reflected the popular mood: "Triumph! The Frankfurt Parliament is exposed! There is no longer a German Parliament – just an enraged population face-to-face with a handful of scoundrels ... The whole of Germany is rebelling against the rule of princes and is fighting for the freedom of the people".

With the slogan "prosperity, education and freedom for all", he proclaimed the "German Social Republic" from Lörrach town hall. To finance it, money was collected from the population against borrowers' notes. The supporters of the monarchy were to be arrested, and the wealth of the state, the Church and the monarchists to be seized and distributed among the local authorities.

The uprising quickly spread to the uplands of Baden, but was defeated on 26 September near Stauffen by superior Baden troops.

II/97
Gustav von Struve proclaiming the German Republic from the town hall in Lörrach

Victory of reactionary forces in Vienna

A new wave of unrest also broke out in the non-German parts of the Habsburg Empire, particularly in Hungary and Italy. The Hungarian Civil Defence Committee under Lojus Kossuth planned a military offensive to achieve independence.

Students belonging to the "Academic League" joined forces with the civic guard and the workers, and prevented the troops from leaving. The ministers and the Emperor fled the city, and Vienna was in the hands of the revolutionaries.

The provisional central government in Frankfurt dispatched the liberal deputy Welcker and Colonel Mosle

II/98
The Vienna library on fire after the capture of the city by troops of Field Marshal Windischgrätz

When, on 5 October, the decision was to taken to incorporate German and Italian troops based in Vienna into Imperial contingents in order to fight the Hungarians, open rebellion broke out in the Austrian capital.

to Austria as "Imperial Commissars" with the task of "taking all the measures necessary to end the civil war and restore peace and law and order". They did not dare to enter Vienna, however, and returned from the imperial headquar-

II/99
Execution by firing squad of Robert Blum in the Brigittengau near Vienna on 9 November 1848

II/100
Austrian Minister of War Latour murdered on 6 October 1848

ters having achieved nothing. Robert Blum, on the other hand, a left-wing member of the National Assembly, fought with the revolutionaries on the barricades.

Field Marshal Prince Windischgrätz, the commander of the imperial troops, imposed a state of siege on Vienna. The city was recaptured after five days. The rebels offered stubborn resistance but in vain. Several thousand dead and immense destruction were the price of the victory over the city by the reactionary monarchist forces. Robert Blum was summarily executed, with no consideration given to his immunity as a parliamentarian.

The National Assembly's protests were muted. Prince Schwarzenberg, a strident supporter of absolutism and the greater Austrian state, was appointed prime minister, the Reichstag was dissolved, and a constitution imposed from above. It became clear that the Revolution in Austria had failed.

Counter-revolution in Berlin

Berlin was another centre of the second wave of revolution. It was triggered by the appointment of Lieutenant General Brandenburg, a relative of the royal family and a reactionary member of the court *camarilla*, as prime minister. His task was to initiate the "counter-revolution". Riots broke out in the city. The liberals were also not prepared to accept this affront, and the he refused even to talk to it. Against its will, the Prussian National Assembly was transferred from Berlin to Brandenburg. The democratic and centre-left members, who refused to accept this transfer, were banned from the inns used by them as meeting places. Ultimately, they were dispersed by armed force.

Although the 40,000 troops which entered Berlin on 10 November under General Wrangel met no resis-

II/101

Disarming of the Berlin civil guard on 11 November 1848

Prussian National Assembly almost unanimously rejected the appointment of a member of the royal family as prime minister.

The Assembly sent a deputation to inform the King of its decision, but tance, a state of siege was imposed on the city two days later. Only then did resistance among democratic groups in the city grow. The civil guard was called up to support the regular troops. This enabled the

II/102
Civil guard firing
on revolutionary
workers on 16 Octo-
ber 1848 in Berlin

II/103
Pamphlet published
by the Democratic
Club in Berlin in No-
vember 1848

monarchy to remain in control of
the situation. It was eventually in a
position to dissolve the Prussian
National Assembly, now in Brandenburg, and to impose a constitution which, by offering a number of
concessions, placated the liberal
middle class.
But even before this, the revolutionary groups which in March had
been so united were beginning to
crumble, the civil guard having
fired on republican workers during
riots in Spandau. In Berlin a leaflet
entitled "Only soldiers can keep the
democrats under control" appeared. The majority of the liberal
middle class abandoned its resistance, and the monarchist counter-
revolution won the day in Prussia
as well.

„Das ist immer das Unglück der Könige
gewesen, daß sie die Wahrheit nicht hören
wollen!"

Der König hat die mit Ueberreichung der bereits bekannten Adresse
von der National-Versammlung beauftragte Deputation empfangen. Nach
Verlesung derselben faltete der König die Adresse zusammen und wandte
sich mit kurzer Verbeugung zum Fortgehen. Als nun der Präsident Un-
ruh das Wort zu ergreifen zauderte, trat der Abgeordnete Jacobi vor
und sprach dem, der Deputation in der Adresse ausdrücklich ertheilten Auf-
trage zufolge, die Worte:
    „Majestät! Wir sind nicht blos hierher gesandt, um eine Adresse
„zu überreichen, sondern auch, um Ew. Majestät mündlich über
„die wahre Lage des Landes Auskunft zu geben. Gestatten Ew.
„Majestät daher —
hier unterbrach der König mit dem Worte:

„Nein!!"

Jacobi entgegnete:
„Das ist immer das Unglück der
„Könige gewesen, daß sie die Wahr=
„heit nicht hören wollen!"

Der König entfernte sich.
Der Abgeordnete Jacobi hat sich hierdurch den Dank des gesamm-
ten Vaterlandes verdient. Möge er und seine Freunde in diesem hoch-
wichtigen Augenblicke nicht nachlassen, die in Wien wie in Berlin be-
drohte Sache des Volkes und der Wahrheit zu vertreten, dann werden
alle ihm mit Gut und Blut zur Seite stehen, um endlich eine von Für-
stenlaune unabhängige Grundlage der Volksfreiheit und des Volksglückes
zu erlangen!

Berlin, den 3. November 1848.

Der democratische Club.

Druck von Ferd. Reichardt u. Co., Neue Friedrichs-Straße 24.

II/104
The dissolution of
the Prussian Nation-
al Assembly by force
on 14 November
1848

4. The failure of the Revolution

The problem of national unity

After the crushing of the "second revolution", the question of German unity became part of a power game between Prussia and Austria, both now reinvigorated. Austria's aim was to strengthen its position as a great power. According to Schwarzenberg's programme, the entire Habsburg empire, together with all the German states, was to form a mid-European confederation, an empire with a population of seventy million. In contrast, the Prussians favoured a "Little German" solution: a federation of German states under Prussian leadership which could be extended at a later date to form a "dual confederation" with Austria.

When the debate on German unity began in the National Assembly in October 1848, the majority favoured the "Greater German" solution, which also formed the basis of the first draft constitution. According to this draft, the territory of the Reich should include all the areas of the German Confederation, the duchy of Schleswig and the East Prussian provinces, but not the non-German speaking regions of the Habsburg empire.

In the debate on the question of the head of state in the new empire in January 1849, the supporters of "Little Germany" advocated a hereditary Prussian emperor. The proponents of "Greater Germany", split between a number of political groups, put forward a number of contradictory proposals ranging from a dynastic imperial directorate to a united democratic republic.

The steps taken by Austria in March 1849, when it rebuffed the National Assembly and adopted a centralized constitution for the whole of the Habsburg empire, destroyed once and for all any hopes for a "Greater Germany". Many of its advocates joined the group led by Heinrich von Gagern, which supported a "Little German" solution. The democratic left was also won over to this solution by the promise of general, equal, secret and direct elections. On 28 March the National Assembly elected the Prussian King "Emperor of the Germans".

The Reich constitution

In October 1848, during a phase of extreme tension, the National Assembly, its room for manoeuvre already significantly curtailed, embarked on the most delicate phase of its work: the institutional part of the constitution. The influence of Prussian and Austrian power politics was particlarly clear in its decisions on the size of the future Reich and on the monarch at its head. Nevertheless, on 27 March 1849, the National Assembly succeeded in adopting the new Reich constitution in what was ostensibly a sovereign act.

The work on the new constitution began in a constitutional committee comprising thirty members, among them the leaders of the liberal movement in the Pre-March period. The draft it submitted was entirely in line with the ideas of the Casino Party, and thus of the bourgeois-liberal majority in the National Assembly. In the winter of 1848/49, during the struggle between supporters of "Little" and "Greater" Germany, the majorities began to shift, which meant that compromises also had to be found with the democratic left.

All in all, the constitution was a balanced compromise which long continued to inspire the development of constitutional law in Germany. It was shaped above all by the concepts and ideas of the bourgeois-liberal majority in the National Assembly: a federal state with a bi-camaral parliament and a hereditary monarch at its head. As a result of concessions to the left, the monarch's powers were restricted and provision made for universal suffrage.

In March 1848, the Prussian King, Frederick William IV, had aroused the hopes of liberals and nationalists with his slogan "Prussia will henceforth be part of Germany". The supporters of a "Little German" solution now believed that the newly adopted constitution would fulfill these hopes. On 28 March 1849, the National Assembly elected the Prussian King "Emperor of the Germans". The National Assembly sent a deputation, headed by its President, Eduard von Simson, to see the Prussian King to in-

II/105
Medallion commemorating the election of Frederick William IV of Prussia as "Emperor of the Germans"

II/106
Frederick William IV
receiving the "Imperial Deputation" of
the National Assembly on 2 April 1849

form him of the result of the election. However, Frederick William IV insisted on the divine right of kings and categorically refused to be made Emperor by the people in a democratic vote: for him, German unity was not to be the product of a popularly elected, sovereign National Assembly, but was to be accomplished solely through "agreements" with the other princes.

In December 1848, the King declared in a letter to Bunsen: "A legitimate king by divine right, indeed the King of Prussia, who may not be blessed with the oldest but with the noblest crown, stolen from noone, is now expected to accept such an imaginary coronet of mud and clay ... Let me tell you bluntly: should the crown of the German nation which, a thousand years old, has rested now for 42 years, ever be conferred again, then it shall be by me and my peers; and woe be-

tide anyone who arrogates to himself a right to which he is not entitled."

The Prussian King's refusal to accept the imperial crown signalled the failure of the constitution adopted by the National Assembly.

The struggle for the imperial constitution

"The hour has come when it will be decided whether Germany shall be free and strong or subservient and scorned. The representatives of the German nation, elected by you and by all the citizens, have adopted the Reich Constitution for the whole of Germany and have proclaimed it inviolable. The entire nation is steadfastly determined to enforce the Reich Constitution ... The major princes and their cabinets refuse to obey the Constitution. They are rebels acting against the law and the will of the nation." With these words, a congress of all the so-called "March associations" held on 6 May 1848 called for the enforcement of the Imperial Constitution, which although accepted by 28 German states had been rejected by the larger ones, notably Prussia, Saxony and Bavaria.

Throughout Germany, workers' and so-called "people's" and "fatherland" associations sought to exert pressure on their governments by organizing petitions, press cam-

force of arms if necessary. Thus, on 8 May, citizens of Heidelberg declared "on our own initiative and of our own free will, solemnly and publicly, that we are ready to protect and defend the Germany Imperial Constitution, drawn up and proclaimed, together with the Fundamental Rights and the electoral law, by the National Assembly in Frankfurt am Main, with our lives and all that belongs to us". In Saxony, the Rhineland, the Palatinate and Baden the unrest turned into open rebellion.

paigns and street meetings. They based their appeals on the "holy right of the revolution". The rejection of the constitution by the monarchist governments called into question all the achievements of the bourgeois-liberal revolution.

The resolutions now being adopted stressed ever more clearly that the Constitution would be defended by

In Dresden the committee of the "Fatherland Association" called for an armed demonstration: "Hurry swiftly with weapons and ammunition! Now is the time!" In the afternoon of 3 May a crowd stormed the armoury. The King fled and a provisional government was installed. For a short time, the sovereignty of the people was a reality.

II/107
The provisional government of Saxony in Dresden town hall in May 1849

Mitbürger!

Der König und die Minister sind entflohen. Das Land ist ohne Regierung, sich selbst überlassen worden. Die Reichsverfassung ist verleugnet.

Mitbürger! Das Vaterland ist in Gefahr! Es ist nothwendig geworden, eine provisorische Regierung zu bilden. Der Sicherheitsausschuß zu Dresden und die Abgeordneten des Volks haben nun unterzeichnete Mitbürger zur provisorischen Regierung ernannt.

Die Stadt Dresden ist dem Vaterlande mit dem rühmlichsten Beispiele vorangegangen und hat geschworen, mit der Reichsverfassung zu leben und zu sterben.

Wir stellen Sachsen unter den Schutz der Regierungen Deutschlands, welche die Reichsverfassung anerkannt haben.

Wir werden Parlamentäre an die Truppen senden und sie auffordern, den Befehlen der provisorischen Regierung gleichfalls Gehorsam zu leisten. Auch sie bindet keine andere Pflicht, als die für die bestehende Regierung, für die Einheit und Freiheit des deutschen Vaterlandes!

Mitbürger, die große Stunde der Entscheidung ist gekommen! Jetzt oder nie! Freiheit oder Sklaverei! Wählt!

Wir stehen zu Euch, steht Ihr zu uns! Dresden, den 4. Mai 1849.

Die provisorische Regierung.
Tzschirner. Heubner. Todt.

II/108
Proclamation of the provisional government of Saxony

II/109
Battle near Waghäusel between rebels and Prussian troops on 22 June 1849

In the old part of the city barricades were erected against the Saxon troops and the Prussian troops sent to reinforce them. The fighting was restricted to Dresden, however, and the call by the provisional government to all the people of Saxony elicited no response. Faced with superior opposing forces, the revolutionary front in the besieged town collapsed. The civil guard withdrew from the barricades and those who continued the fight – amongst them the Russian anarchist Mikhail

Die Landesversammlung in Offenburg

erklärt:

Deutschland befindet sich fortwährend im Zustand voller Revolution, aufs neue hervorgerufen durch die Angriffe der größeren deutschen Fürsten auf die von der deutschen Nationalversammlung endgültig beschlossenen Reichsverfassung und die Freiheit überhaupt. — Die deutschen Fürsten haben sich zur Unterdrückung der Freiheit verschworen und verbunden; der Hochverrath an Volk und Vaterland liegt offen zu Tage; es ist klar, daß sie sogar Rußlands sämmtliche Armeen zur Unterdrückung der Freiheit zu Hülfe rufen. — Die Deutschen befinden sich also im Stande der Nothwehr, sie müssen sich verbinden, um die Freiheit zu retten; sie müssen dem Angriff der fürstlichen Rebellen den bewaffneten Widerstand entgegensetzen.

Die deutschen Stämme haben die Verpflichtung, sich gegenseitig die Freiheit zu gewährleisten, um den Grundsatz der Volkssouveränität vollkommen durchzuführen; sie müssen daher unterstützen überall, wo sie angegriffen werden. — Das badische Volk wird daher die Volksbewegung in der Pfalz mit allen ihm zu Gebote stehenden Mitteln unterstützen.

Die Landesversammlung des badischen Volkes in Offenburg hat nach vorhergegangener Berathung die gestellten Anträge in dem Landeskongresse der Volksvereine, nach ferner stattgefundener öffentlicher Berathung, wobei Abgeordnete aus allen Landestheilen vertreten waren, nach ferner ausführlicher Diskussion in der Versammlung des Volkes

beschlossen:

1) Die Regierung muß die Reichsverfassung, wie sie nun nach der durch die Ereignisse beseitigten Oberhauptsfrage feststeht, unbedingt anerkennen und von den ganzen bewaffneten Macht, deren Durchführung in andern deutschen Staaten zunächst in der baierischen Pfalz unterstützen.

2) Das gegenwärtige Ministerium ist sofort zu entlassen, und Bürger Brentano, Obergerichtsadvokat zu Mannheim, und Bürger Peter, Reichstagsabgeordneter von Konstanz mit der Bildung eines neuen Ministeriums zu beauftragen.

3) Es muß alsbald unter sofortiger Auflösung der jetzigen Ständekammern eine verfassunggebende Landesversammlung berufen werden, welche in sich die gesammte Rechts- und Machtvollkommenheit des badischen Volkes vereinigt; — diese Landesversammlung soll gewählt werden von und aus den sämmtlichen volljährigen Staatsbürgern des Landes und zwar unter Beibehaltung der für die bisherige II. Kammer beanstandeten Wahlbezirke.

4) Es muß ohne allen Verzug die Volksbewaffnung auf Staatskosten in's Leben gerufen werden, und es sind alle ledigen Männer von 18—30 Jahren als erstes Aufgebot sofort mobil zu machen. — Alle diejenigen Gemeindebehörden, welche nicht alsbald die Bewaffnung ihrer Bürger anordnen, sind augenblicklich abzusetzen.

5) Die politischen Flüchtlinge sind sofort zurück zu rufen, die politischen Militär- und Civilgefangenen zu entlassen und alle politischen Prozeße nieder zu schlagen; — namentlich verlangen wir aber auch die Entlassung derjenigen Militärgefangenen, welche in Folge der politischen Bewegungen wegen sogenannter Disciplinar- und Insubordinationsvergehen bestraft wurden.

6) Die Standgerichtsbarkeit muß aufgehoben werden. —

7) Bei dem Heere soll eine freie Wahl der Offiziere stattfinden.

8) Wir verlangen alsbaldige Verschmelzung des stehenden Heeres mit der Volkswehr.

9) Es müssen sämmtliche Grundlasten unentgeltlich aufgehoben werden.

10) Es müssen die Gemeinden unbedingt selbstständig erklärt werden, sowohl was die Verwaltung des Gemeindevermögens, als die Wahl der Gemeindevertreter betrifft; es müssen alsbald im ganzen Lande neue Wahlen für die Gemeindevertretung stattfinden.

11) Es werden sämmtliche von den s. g. Kammern in Karlsruhe seit dem 17. Januar d. J. gefaßten Beschlüsse für null und nichtig erklärt und darunter namentlich das s. g. Wahlgesetz vom 10. v. M., welches einen förmlichen Angriff auf die Reichsgesetzen gegebenen Bestimmungen enthält.

12) Die Geschwornengerichte sind augenblicklich einzuführen und kein einziger Criminal-Prozeß darf mehr von Staatsrichtern entschieden werden.

13) Die alte Verwaltungsbüreaukratie muß abgeschafft werden und an ihre Stelle die freie Verwaltung der Gemeinden oder andern Körperschaften treten.

14) Errichtung einer Nationalbank für Gewerbe, Handel und Ackerbau zum Schutze gegen das Uebergewicht der großen Kapitalisten.

15) Abschaffung des alten Steuerwesens, hierfür Einführung einer progressiven Einkommensteuer nebst Beibehaltung der Zölle.

16) Errichtung eines großen Landespensionsfonds, aus dem jeder arbeitunfähig gewordene Bürger unterstützt werden kann. — Hierdurch fällt der besondere Pensionsfond für die Staatsdiener von selbst weg. Der Landesausschuß der Volksvereine besteht aus folgenden Mitgliedern:

L. Brentano von Mannheim.
J. Fickler von Konstanz.
A. Goeg von Mannheim.
Peter von Konstanz.
Werner von Oberkirch.
Rehmann von Offenburg.
Stay von Heidelberg.
Willmann von Pforzen.
L. Steinmetz von Durlach.
Bernwag von Kenzingen.
Richter von Achern.
Bögen von Mannheim.
A. Ritter von Karlsruhe. } Soldaten aus der Garnison
J. Stark von Lottstetten. } in Rastatt.

Als Ersatzmänner wurden gewählt:
H. Hoff von Mannheim.
Torrent von Freiburg.
A. Rotteck von Freiburg.
Happel von Mannheim.
Junghanns von Roßbach.
Kiefer von Emmendingen.

Ersatzmänner der Soldaten:
Aurelius Cordel aus Philippsburg.
Sebastian Bannwarth aus Bleichheim, Amts Kenzingen.

Derselbe wird beauftragt, die nöthigen Anordnungen zur Durchführung dieser Beschlüsse mit allen ihm zu Gebote stehenden Mittel zu treffen, und von dem Ergebniß die heutigen Volksversammlung dem Landesausschuß in Rheinbaiern, sowie den Landesausschüssen der übrigen Nachbarstaaten sofort Nachricht zu geben.

Offenburg, den 13. Mai 1849.
Im Namen der Landes-Volksversammlung.
Goegg.

* Der Landes-Ausschuß hat sich in zahlreicher Begleitung von Offenburg nach der Festung Rastatt begeben, wo er vorerst inmitten der Bürgerschaft und der braven 6000 Mann starken Besatzung in Permanenz berathet. Heute (14. Mai) Nacht 3 Uhr trafen die befreiten Bürger Struve, Blind, Bornstedt nebst den gleichfalls vom Volke aus den Bruchsaler Kerkern befreiten Soldaten in Rastatt ein.

Bakunin and Richard Wagner – surrendered to troops brought in from Prussia after a six-day struggle.

Despite the defeat in Saxony, revolts also broke in the Bavarian Palatinate and in Baden. The people of the Palatinate were also fighting for the independence from Bavaria. Democratic and republic ideas played a prominent role in this people's war. On 17 May the Palatinate broke away from Bavaria.

In Baden, a popular assembly in Offenburg on 13 May, attended by 35,000 people from throughout the state, declared: "The German monarchs are determined to repress freedom and have joined forces in pursuit of this objective; their betrayal of the people and of the Fatherland is clear for all to see ... The people of Baden will therefore support the popular movement in the Palatinate with all the resources at its disposal". The Baden government had in fact accepted the Constitution, but the republicans wanted more: instead of a constitutional monarchy, they demanded the setting up of a republic, democratic and social reforms, the free election of army officers, the removal without compensation of all feudal dues, protection against the dominance of capitalists, and state unemployment benefits.

Between 10 and 12 May the Baden army rebelled in the main garrisons throughout the state. The soldiers' rebellion against their officers encouraged the popular democratic

II/110
Proclamation of the Offenburg state assembly on 13 May 1849

movement to organize an open revolt. Conditions were favourable for a successful revolution; it was the last hope of democrats throughout Germany.

Companies of riflemen, members of the nationalist gymnasts' movement set up by Friedrich Ludwig Jahn, workers' battalions, and Polish and Hungarian legions moved into Baden to offer their support. The Prussian army and troops of

al government in Baden, led by Lorenz Brentano, itself prevented more vigorous military action: it first failed to provide real military support for the poorly equipped Palatinate rebels; it then outlawed the radical democratic opposition, which had joined forces in the "Club of resolute progress"; and, in particular, it sought to prevent the armed struggle from spreading to other states.

II/111
The outbreak of the Rastatt rebellion on 13 May 1848

the Imperial Administrator under the command of the Prince of Prussia, who was some years later to become Emperor William I, intervened. The uprising in Baden and the Palatinate was defeated after an armed struggle lasting almost two months.

The endurance, tenacity and courage of the popular army could not compensate for its growing military disorganization. The provision-

The left wing in the Frankfurt Parliament was unable to assume leadership of the movement, even after the liberals and conservatives had walked out of the National Assembly leaving the enforcement of the Imperial Constitution "in the hands of the nation itself".

Rastatt, the last remaining stronghold of the revolutionaries and the town where the uprising had begun, fell on 23 July 1849. The

II/112
"Granted mercy by powder and lead"

Prussian military courts sat in Baden until the end of October 1849, meting out summary executions under martial law, prison sentences and terms of hard labour. Some 80,000 people persecuted on political grounds – about 6 per cent of the population of Baden – emigrated. By autumn 1849, the liberal and democratic movement in France, Italy, Hungary and Germany had been defeated.

The forces of reaction in the 1850s

The Revolution failed. It foundered on the opposition of the old dynasties, the armies loyal to the monarchy, and the bureaucracy. However, it also foundered on the growing rifts in its own camp. The middle-class liberals recoiled before the radical political demands of the republicans and committed democ-

II/113
The victory of the forces of reaction in Europe in 1849, cartoon by F. Schroeder in the *Düsseldorfer Monatsblatt*

rats. This was compounded by a conflict between the propertied and unproperties classes, which intensified continuously against the backdrop of the early years of the industrial revolution.

With the onset of a reactionary backlash in all the German states, liberal ministers were replaced by conservatives. Many parliaments were dissolved, and the constitutions revised. Once again, the mon-

II/114
Trial by jury of Johann Jacoby in December 1850

archs ruled without any real control by the people. In Prussia, the government introduced the three-class voting system, under which voters were divided into three categories according to the amount of tax they paid: the first category, the minority of high wage earners (just 4% of the population), was able to elect just as many electoral college members and members of parliament as the largest category, that of low wage earners (80% of the population).

Freedom of opinion and freedom of the press were restricted by censorship and police surveillance. In 1851, the German Confederation, reinstated by Prussia and Austria as an instrument of oppression, repealed the Fundamental Rights of the German People. The last na-tional uprisings in multinational Austria were quashed, and reactionary forces triumphed everywhere under the German Confederation's leadership. Liberals, democrats and social revolutionaries were arrested and sentenced to long terms of imprisonment. All "suspicious" political associations were banned.

This persecution triggered mass emigration to Switzerland, England and above all the United States. The attempt by the German people to create a democratic nation-state had failed.

II/115
Emigrants' ship
in 1850

The German Confederation after 1815

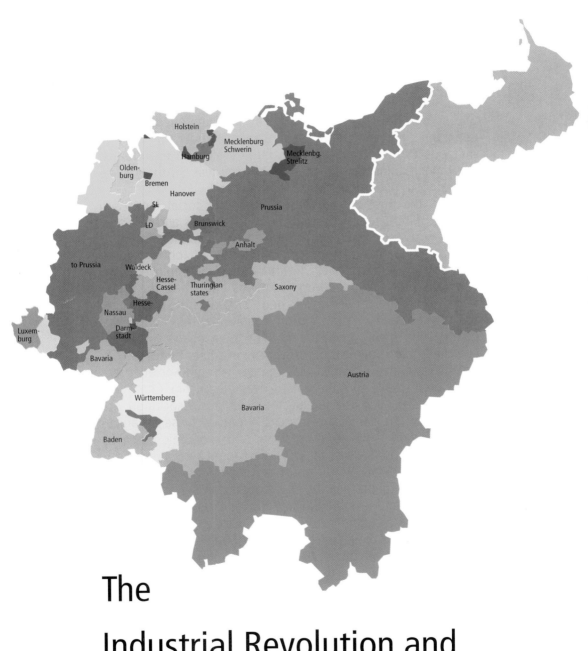

Holstein

Mecklenburg
Schwerin

Mecklenbg.
Strelitz

Hamburg

Olden-
burg

Bremen

Hanover

SL

Prussia

LD

Brunswick

Anhalt

to Prussia

Waldeck

Hesse-
Cassel

Thuringian
states

Saxony

Nassau

Hesse-

Luxem-
burg

Darm-
stadt

Bavaria

Austria

Württemberg

Bavaria

Baden

The
Industrial Revolution and
the Founding of the Empire

III. The industrial revolution and the founding of the Empire

In the 1850s, as a period of political reaction set in, economic developments gave rise to an entirely new political and social situation as, in Germany too, the industrial revolution gathered pace. Heavy industry grew dramatically, and industrial conurbations emerged in the Ruhr, the Saarland and in Upper Silesia in particular. New methods of financing via joint stock companies and merchant banks allowed modern production methods to be introduced on a large scale and encouraged the rapid expansion of markets. Germany was on the way to becoming a modern industrialized country.

With the onset of industrialization, the social landscape changed fundamentally. Alongside a prosperous and self-confident industrial middle class, there emerged an industrial proletariat whose ranks swelled continuously as formerly independent artisans lost their livelihoods and unemployed agricultural workers flooded into the towns and cities. The situation of these industrial workers deteriorated as the level of real incomes sank. Their housing conditions were often appalling, and their wages barely kept them above the bread line. Self-help organizations such as consumer cooperatives, health insurance schemes and mutual lending societies endeavoured to alleviate the most extreme hardship. Charitable organizations, such as Kolping's journeymen's association, operated with the same aim in mind. None of these organizations questioned the existing social and economic order. By contrast, the proponents of socialism sought radical solutions and called for the overthrow of the capitalist system by the workers. They found their leading theoretician in Karl Marx.

The heartland of industrialization was Prussia which, since it was also the leading power in the Customs Union, acquired increasing economic weight within Germany. This also strengthened its political position vis-à-vis Austria. Moreover, the fact that, even in the 1850s, Prussia's economic policy benefitted broad sections of the middle class was to have a great bearing on future political developments.

From 1858 onwards, it again appeared that the Prussian state might be willing to accommodate the political aspirations of the liberal middle class. Many people saw in the accession to power of William, the Prince Regent, who formed a liberal-conservative ministry and announced far-reaching reforms in a programmatic speech to the Ministry of State, the beginning of a "New Era" in Prussia. This was a major boost for political liberalism throughout Germany. There was hope that the promised reforms would be implemented and, moreover, that the nation would be unified under the leadership of a liberal Prussia.

Encouraged by developments in Prussia, and spurred on by Italian unification, liberals and democrats formed the National Association. It took up the idea of a "Little Germany", that is of German unification on a parliamentary basis under Prussian leadership, which had failed in 1849. 1861 saw the creation of the German Progressive Party, which then formed the "Executive of the National Association in Prussia", a party alliance made up of committed liberals and democrats whose leading figures belonged to the National Association. The Progressive Party pursued the same aims in Prussia as the National Association in Germany as a whole. The Prussian government, however, unlike other state governments, did not seek to cooperate with the liberals, and it soon came to a confrontation over the question of army reform which increasingly acquired the character of a constitutional conflict. The Progressive Party saw this as a decisive trial of strength with the conservative-monarchist state and the absolutist leanings of the *Junker*. It was a trial it was unable to win, however. In September 1862 Bismarck, the great opponent of the liberal movement, entered the political stage following his appointment as Prussian prime minister. As early as 1848 he had become renowned as an ultraconservative *Junker*, and he now steered a tough antiparliamentary course and practically governed outside the framework of the constitution using a budget adopted without consulting Parliament. Ultimately, the Progressive Party was powerless against him. The conservative attitude of the population and the shared interests of the property-owning middle classes and the Prussian state forced the Progressive Party to shy away from any revolutionary action. It therefore opted to oppose government policy "where the propertied classes are not yet against us".

This stance was one of the reasons why the workers turned away from the Progressive Party. Following the founding of the General Association of German Workers by Lassalle in 1863, the Progressive Party, which had originally seen itself as a rallying point for all liberal and democratic forces, now only had the middle class to fall back on as a reservoir of electoral support. From this juncture on, the middle and working classes went separate ways in striving for democracy.

Whilst opposition to his domestic policies crumbled, Bismarck scored a series of foreign policy successes. In the conflict over Schleswig-Holstein, in which all nationally minded forces, whether proponents of a "Little" or a "Greater" Germany, were passionately involved, Prussia took the lead and forced Austria on to its side. Following the military victory over Denmark, the duchies were placed under the administrative control of Prussia and Austria. Prussia, however, pressed for annexation of the two duchies, and the resulting conflict with Austria eventually escalated into war. With Prussia's victory over Austria, the struggle for supremacy in Germany finally swung in its favour. The German Confederation was dissolved and the way was open for a "Little German" solution of the question of national unity under the leadership of a conservative Prussia.

For Bismarck this foreign policy victory abroad brought with it a victory on the domestic front. Henceforth, a section of the liberals opted to support his power politics; although it ran counter to all liberal traditions, it gave them hope of achieving a German nation-state. Whilst the left wing of the Progressive Party stood firmly by its views on freedom, and thus rejected Prussian claims to national leadership "as long as Prussia has not achieved internal freedom" (Waldeck), other liberals believed that conditions in Prussia could only be changed in line with liberal ideals following the unification of Germany. "Without a reshaping of Germany .... there is also absolutely no long-term possibility of achieving a decent and free constitution in Prussia" (Forckenbeck).

The North German Confederation, set up following Prussia's victory over Austria, was the first step on the road to German unification and extended Prussia's sphere of influence as far as the river Main. Although elections to the Reichstag, the Confederation's parliament, were general, secret, equal and direct, the powers of the parliament were limited. As Chancellor, Bismarck was accountable only to the King of Prussia, who was also the president of the Confederation, but not to parliament.

The constitution of the North German Confederation was already tailored to the possible accession of the south German states. Moreover, the south German states were linked to the North German Confederation by military alliances. A further bond between them was established by the newly created parliament of the Customs Union whose members were elected from all the German states. For reasons of foreign policy, however, Bismarck initially did not yield to the national liberals' demands to press ahead with the process of political unification. Above all he feared an intervention by France, which since Prussia's victory over Austria had felt that its supremacy in Europe was under threat. The growing tension between Prussia and France, exacerbated by the embroilment over the candidacy of a Hohenzollern prince for the Spanish crown, eventually led to a declaration of war by France. This sparked a wave of national outrage in Germany. The military pacts between the German states came into effect and were supplemented, following negotiations conducted during the war, by treaties with a binding force akin to that of international law between the German monarchs and governments. Following the military defeat of France, and the abdication of the French Emperor, a ceremony held in the Hall of Mirrors in Versailles on 18 January 1871, and attended by high-ranking members of the German military and nobility, marked the founding of the German Reich, an act accomplished from above by Prussia and the German princes.

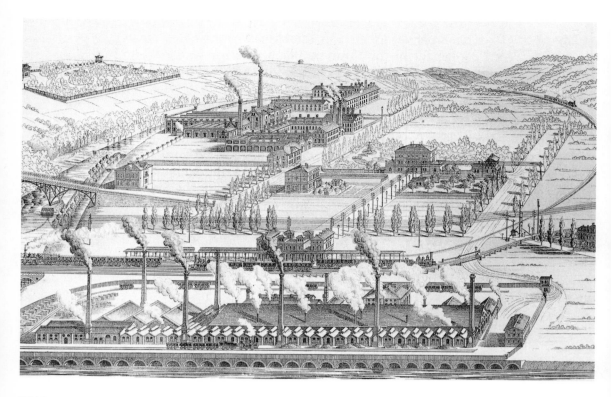

III/116

View of an iron-rolling works in Hagen around 1860

1. The industrial revolution

In Germany, the industrial revolution began in earnest in the early 1850s against the backdrop of a worldwide economic upturn. Railway construction and heavy industry were its driving forces. Of the two, railway construction had the most decisive impact: the rail network expanded rapidly from 3,280 km in 1845 to 11,633 km in 1860 and 19,575 km in 1870. During the economic boom of the 1860s, the railway companies paid out dividends of between 10 and 20%.

At the same time, the production of steam engines and machine tools was also increasing. Cheap labour, recruited from the declining artisanal sector and, above all, the agricultural proletariat of eastern Germany, flooded into the new industrial centres. The necessary capital was provided by joint stock companies and large banks. The industrial revolution was accompanied by the emergence of a new and self-confident upper middle class which, whilst wielding great economic power, often took no great interest in politics.

The founding of the Reich in 1871 spurred on the economic upswing. However, the boom of the first few *Gründerjahre*, or founding years, was followed in 1873 by a major economic crisis which ushered in a prolonged period of economic uncertainty.

Railway construction and the expansion of heavy industry and, later, of the machine-tool sector, required a supply of labour on a scale hitherto unknown. It came predominantly from the agrarian regions of eastern Germany where, following the "liberation" of the peasants and the capitalization of the rural economy, a rural proletariat made up of impoverished seasonal labourers emerged and formed a kind of "reserve army" for the process of industrialization. During the 1860s, these workers migrated in large number from east to west, where they settled in Berlin, the new industrial regions of the Ruhr and other industrial cities. The second precondition for the growth in the economy was the large-scale availability of capital. Joint stock companies and banks were set up for the sole purpose of financing industrial enterprises. Whereas in the period from 1818 to 1849, only 18 joint stock companies had been set up in Germany, this figure rose to 251 between 1850 and 1859 alone.

New commercial and financial methods also accelerated the development of innovative manufacturing techniques, thereby facilitat-

ing a sharp increase in productivity: whilst a conventional puddling furnace took 24 hours to convert three tons of pig iron into steel, the new Bessemer converter needed only 20 minutes. However, the highly phospherous German iron ore prevent the large-scale application of the Bessemer technique in Germany. Ores with a low phospherous content had to be imported and were therefore expensive. Only with the development of the Siemens-Martin furnace and the Thomas converter, a refined version of the Bessemer converter, did the smelting of ore from Lorraine become economically viable, thereby facilitating the mass production of steel in Germany. New branches of industry emerged, such as chemical and electrical engineering. BASF (*Badische Anilin- und Sodafabrik*) was set up in 1863, and in 1866 Werner von Siemens developed the dynamo. The World Exhibitions became the

III/117
Machine hall at the Hartmann Machine Tool Factory in Chemnitz

III/118
Interior view of an
iron-rolling factory
in Königshütte (Up-
per Silesia), painting
by Adolf Menzel

III/119
The Great Hall of
the Berlin Stock
Exchange

places where competing industrial nations presented their products. Of the World Exhibition in Paris in 1867, a German contemporary self-confidently reported: "Our steel was unbeatable, our glass and paper was of the highest quality, and our chemical products were better than those of the English and the French. Our mechanical weaving looms, our machine tools and our locomotives were at least as good as those from England and America – and we have achieved all this in a relatively short space of time". On the crest of a tremendous economic upsurge, Germany was transformed into an industrialized country within but a few decades.

Agricultural production also increased substantially by virtue of new and more efficient farming

III/120
The Reichsbank
building in Berlin

III/121
Steel-making
using the Bessemer
process

methods; to the east of the Elbe in particular, mechanization was facilitated by large-scale cereal farming. Moreover, mineral fertilizers, the pioneering discovery of Justus von Liebig, permitted a more intensive use of farm land. A large number of agricultural associations, which propagated the new farming techniques and provided the necessary machines, soon sprang up.

The market for agricultural products was also more favourable than ever before. During this period, the concept of free trade united the generally conservative large landowners on the one hand and the liberal middle class on the other. Not until the 1870s, as the threat of cheap of grain imports from Russia and America loomed, was there a fundamental change of course.

III/122
The giant Krupp
canon at the World
Exhibition in Paris in
1867

The founding of the Reich in 1871 and the huge sums paid as war reparations by the French fuelled an economic boom in the so-called *Gründerjahre*, or "founding years". In a phase of frenetic economic activity, a multitude of new companies sprang up. Often, this wave of industrial expansion led to a process of chaotic urban growth

There was a wave of bankruptcies, as companies set up without a solid financial basis and more "with an eye to the future" proved incapable of weathering the crisis. In response, companies merged to form groups and trusts, their aim being to achieve a dominant market position and to provide security against fluctuations in economic activity.

III/123
Mechanization of agriculture: a steam-driven threshing machine

whose social repercussions frequently proved irreparable.

In 1873 the "epidemic of untrammelled greed for money" (S. v. Waltershausen) ran out of steam. The collapse of the stock exchange, first in Vienna and then in Berlin, led to a massive slump in share prices and to an economic crisis which, for the first time, was triggered by industrial overproduction.

The economic downturn in 1873, and the resulting slowdown in economic growth, shattered the self-confidence of the middle class. A well-known lawyer, Rudolf von Gneist, summed up the *Zeitgeist* when he referred to the years after 1873 as a "period of general dissatisfaction ... in which a pessimistic outlook on life dominates the spirit of the age".

2. New social structures and political theories

A further consequence of the years of rapid economic growth between 1850 and 1870 was the transformation of the agricultural and artisanal working class of the Pre-March period into an industrial proletariat. This period also witnessed the beginning of urbanization. Journeymen who could no longer hope to find a secure livelihood in their trades; master-craftsmen who could no longer cope with increasing industrial competition; and day-labourers increasingly sought jobs in the factories. The social misery of the working class was unspeakable. Charity organizations were set up to alleviate the most extreme social hardship. At the same time, new socialist theories propagating the destruction of capitalism as the only way to liberate the working class began to gain ground.

In the 1850s and 1860s, the growing industrial towns and cities drew in labour from the immediately surrounding regions. At the same time, a massive wave of migration from east to west set in. Agricultural workers from east of the river Elbe increasingly became a reservoir of labour for industry in the Rhineland and Westphalia. The German population grew from 35 million in 1850 to 42 million in 1871. In 1860, some 2.6 million people lived in cities with more than 100,000 inhabitants. Factory buildings altered the face of towns and cities, and the Ruhr region in particular developed an industrial landscape. Nevertheless, in 1873, two thirds of the German population still lived on the land. The favourable economic climate did nothing to ameliorate the plight of the industrial working class.

III/124
First and last pages of a set of labour regulations from the time of the industrial revolution

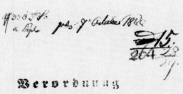

III/125
A week-day market
on Alexanderplatz
in Berlin around
1860

These workers, who were now pouring into the town and cities, lived in appaling housing conditions. On the outskirts of Berlin shanty towns grew up, and increasing numbers of tenement blocks were built where, in 1867, on average 6–7 people lived in one room. An 18-hour working day, breadline wages and child labour compounded the misery of the industrial working class.

The social groups threatened by the process of industrialization set up

III/126
A shanty town on
the outskirts of
Berlin around 1875

self-help organizations: Raiffeisen founded rural loan societies; Schulze-Delitzsch set up credit associations for small businesses; and consumer associations, as well as the first trade unions, came into being. The Protestant and Catholic churches both ran charitable institutions for tradesmen and workers. Kolping and Ketteler, Wichern and Bodelschwingh all sought to find in Christianity a remedy for the social ills of the time. All these attempts to alleviate the social consequences of industrialization and capitalist economics for certain sections of the population were limited to improving the existing order.

By contrast, Marx and Engels did not view the workers as objects in need of assistance. They were not concerned with reformist improvements but insisted that the system of capitalist exploitation itself must be destroyed in an act of self-liberation by the working class, who were its victims. Marx and Engels had published the Manifesto of the Communist Party in 1848, but only now did it acquire any genuine significance. The Manifesto ended with the words: "Workers have

III/127
A public kitchen in Berlin

III/128, 129, 130
Karl Marx and
Friedrich Engels, the
authors of the Communist Manifesto

nothing to lose but their chains. They have a world to gain. Workers of the world unite." In the 1850s and 1860s Marx began to research the laws and trends underlying the capitalist mode of production in an effort to prove that the revolution of the proletariat was not merely a subjective goal but an objective historical necessity. He published these fundamental studies in his uncompleted work *Das Kapital*, the first volume of which appeared in 1867.

Manifest

der

Kommunistischen Partei.

Ein Gespenst geht um in Europa—das Gespenst des Kommunismus. Alle Mächte des alten Europa haben sich zu einer heiligen Hetzjagd gegen dies Gespenst verbündet, der Papst und der Czar, Metternich und Guizot, französische Radikale und deutsche Polizisten.

Wo ist die Oppositionspartei, die nicht von ihren regierenden Gegnern als kommunistisch verschrieen worden wäre, wo die Oppositionspartei, die den fortgeschritteneren Oppositionsleuten sowohl, wie ihren reaktionären Gegnern den brandmarkenden Vorwurf des Kommunismus nicht zurückgeschleudert hätte?

Zweierlei geht aus dieser Thatsache hervor.

Der Kommunismus wird bereits von allen europäischen Mächten als eine Macht anerkannt.

Es ist hohe Zeit daß die Kommunisten ihre Anschauungsweise, ihre Zwecke, ihre Tendenzen vor der ganzen Welt offen darlegen, und den Mährchen vom Gespenst des Kommunismus ein Manifest der Partei selbst entgegenstellen.

Zu diesem Zweck haben sich Kommunisten der verschiedensten Nationalität in London versammelt und das folgende Manifest entworfen, das in englischer, französischer, deutscher, italienischer, flämmischer und dänischer Sprache veröffentlicht wird.

3. Parties and associations

By transforming the face of society, the industrial revolution also radically altered the political landscape. Existing political groupings sought to adapt to the new conditions and to develop programmes which, each proceeding from its specific political viewpoint, offered solutions to the problems of a nascent industrial society. As social, religious and national tensions grew, new parties also emerged. They competed with the existing parties and groupings, and shaped the political system in subsequent decades. Despite the many mergers, rifts and name changes, especially in the liberal camp, the party system which evolved in the decade before the founding of the Empire remained largely intact until the Empire's collapse in 1918.

The origins of social democracy

The industrial proletariat, whose ranks swelled as industrialization progressed, soon began to form independent organizations and to articulate its political interests. The first workers' associations, formed in the wake of the Revolution of 1848, were suppressed during the reactionary backlash. Nevertheless, the founding of trade unions and parties continued. In 1863, Ferdinand Lassalle founded the General German Workers' Association. He called for universal suffrage and the setting up of state-assisted production cooperatives. In 1869, a more strongly marxist-oriented workers' party, the Social Democratic Workers' Party (SDAP), was set up by August Bebel and Wilhelm Liebknecht. These two parties merged in Gotha in 1875 to form a unified German workers' party. At first glance, it appeared that the more radical "Marxists" had

III/131, 132
Ferdinand Lassalle and the statute of the General German Workers' Association of 1863

Statut

des

Allgemeinen Deutschen Arbeitervereins.

———

§. 1.

Unter dem Namen

„Allgemeiner Deutscher Arbeiterverein"

begründen die Unterzeichneten für die Deutschen Bundesstaaten einen Verein, welcher, von der Ueberzeugung ausgehend, daß nur durch das allgemeine gleiche und direkte Wahlrecht eine genügende Vertretung der sozialen Interessen des Deutschen Arbeiterstandes und eine wahrhafte Beseitigung der Klassengegensätze in der Gesellschaft herbeigeführt werden kann, den Zweck verfolgt,

auf friedlichem und legalem Wege, insbesondere durch das Gewinnen der öffentlichen Ueberzeugung, für die Herstellung des allgemeinen gleichen und direkten Wahlrechts zu wirken.

§. 2.

Jeder Deutsche Arbeiter wird durch einfache Beitrittserklärung Mitglied des Vereins mit vollem gleichen Stimmrecht und kann jeder Zeit austreten.

III/133
(opposite)
Scroll commemorat-
ing the "Unification
Party Congress" in
1875

gained the upper hand in the party. However, its "Gotha Programme" revealed that a whole range of "Lassallean" ideas had remained intact. The programme was there-fore sharply criticized by Marx.

The conservatives

The conservatives fought against the social impact of the industrial revolution from a very different an-gle. They feared the dissolution of the existing political and social or-der and therefore aimed to estab-lish a political system which was both patriarchal and welfarist and based on a hierarchy of social groups. The conservatives fought against "progress" which they viewed as an attack on the natural God-given order of human life. Their struggle against liberalism was at the same time a struggle for the preservation of the old order, which they saw threatened by the burgeoning power of the industrial middle class. It was precisely those groups whose political and eco-nomic privileges were guaranteed by the allegedly God-given order who fought hardest to defend it: aristocratic large landowners and supporters of the Crown. They fought against universal suffrage and the removal of class barriers, and for the restoration of the rights of estate owners and the nobility. Contemporary cartoons lampoon-

III/134
Declaration of the
House of Hohen-
zollern for the
Prussian people

ing the "knights" of the "*Kreuz-Zeitung* Party" showed the leader of the conservatives, Ludwig von Gerlach, as Don Quixote mounted on a donkey and accompanied by "Jesuit father" Friedrich Julius Stahl, the theoretician of conservatism, and Bismarck in the protective shell of backwardness.

Liberalism

The political, economic and social demands of the liberals – a constitutional state based on the rule of law, parliamentary control of the executive and unrestricted liberty in economic and social relations – aimed to create a society of free and independent citizens. But the economic and social preconditions for achieving this liberal ideal were still largely absent. Despite this, only a few liberals recognized the resultant need, especially in view of their own political objectives, for a policy of state-assisted social welfare.

In 1858 Crown Prince William, later Emperor William I, became regent on behalf of the mentally ill King Frederick William IV of Prussia. This ushered in a "New Era" in Prussia: the reactionary ministry was dismissed and the Prussian lower house dissolved. Elections were held, this time not controlled by the government, and the liberals gained an overwhelming majority. Prince William appointed a liberal-conservative cabinet, and his statement on government policy aroused great expectations among liberals not only in Prussia but in Germany as a whole.

In 1859, liberal and democratic supporters of "Little Germany" formed the National Association whose aim was to promote the unification of Germany under Prussian leadership. The National Association took up the ideas of 1848; it called for the instalment of a central government and the summoning of a national assembly. It was prepared to cooperate with the princes. Only a few of the latter, including the Grand Duke of Baden, took up this offer, however.

In response to the widespread disappointment over the Prussian government's antiparliamentarian stance in the conflict over army reform, in 1862 conservatives joined forces with liberal and democratic

III/138, 139, 140
Leading members of
the German Pro-
gressive Party:
Theodor Mommsen,
Rudolf Virchow,
Hermann Schulze-
Delitzsch

supporters of "Greater Germany" to form the Reform Association in Frankfurt. Its aim was to achieve national unification through a re-form of the German Confederation under Austrian leadership. Austria sought to exploit the anti-Prussian sentiment manifest in this aim, but its attempts to reform the German Confederation foundered on Prussia's refusal even to attend the conference of princes in Frankfurt in 1863.

In Prussia itself, there was increasing confrontation between the crown and parliament over the question of army reform. Opposition left-wing liberals and democ-

III/141
"... it's often diffi-
cult getting to the
top", cartoon lam-
pooning the difficul-
ties facing the Na-
tional Association

III/142
The conference of princes in Frankfurt in 1863

rats set up the German Progressive Party, which advocated a resolute struggle for a parliamentary constitutional state and a new social order. For the first time, a Prussian party also included a call for national unity in its programme.

A drift to the left among the Prussian middle class became evident at the elections to the lower house of parliament in 1861: while the conservative grouping gained only 14 seats, the Progressive Party won 109.

Following the refusal by this liberal majority in the lower house to approve the funds needed for the reorganization of the Prussian army, the conflict over military reform became a conflict over the constitution as the government and the monarch refused to alter their stance: they wanted the practical dissolution of the *Landwehr*, a reserve militia set up as part of the army reform introduced by the Prussian war minister von Boyen and very popular with the liberals, and a mandatory three-year period of military service followed by four or five years of service in the reserve. In line with the Prussian state's absolutist tradition, their ultimate aim was transform the army into an instrument unconditionally obedient to the Crown.

Bismark's hour came in the course of this conflict: at the time Prussia's envoy to Paris, he was appointed prime minister, and, as a staunch defender of the monarchist government, used his superior political skills to counter the demands of the Progressive Party.

Before the lower house he declared: "The Prussian Kingdom has not yet completed its mission. It is not yet ready to become a mere ornament for your constitutional structure, nor is it yet ready to become a simple cog in your parliamentary machine."

4. The founding of the Empire

Bismarck, who in the domestic field had come to be known as the "conflict minister" and appeared hopelessly isolated, used his immense diplomatic skill to achieve a series of impressive successes in the foreign policy sphere. As they could also be seen as steps on the road to a solution of the national question, these successes led to a gradual swing in public opinion. In the conflict over Schleswig-Holstein, in which nationalists of all hues – "Little German" and "Greater German" – were passionately involved, Prussia took the lead and forced Austria onto its side. Following the victory over Denmark, the duchies were placed under the administrative control of Prussia and Austria. Ultimately, however, Prussia pressed for the annexation of the duchies, thereby unleashing a conflict with Austria which culminated in war. Prussia's victory marked its final triumph in the struggle for supremacy in Germany. The German Confederation was dissolved, and the way was clear for a "Little German" solution to the national question under the leadership of a conservative Prussia.

The newly established North German Confederation, to which all the German states north of the river Main belonged, was clearly only a transitional solution. Its constitution was already tailored to the possible accession of the south German states. France, under Napoleon III, felt its supremacy in Europe threatened by the success of Prussia's expansionist *Machtpolitik*. The constant rise in tension between the two countries, com-

III/143
The battlefield
at Königgrätz on
3 July 1866

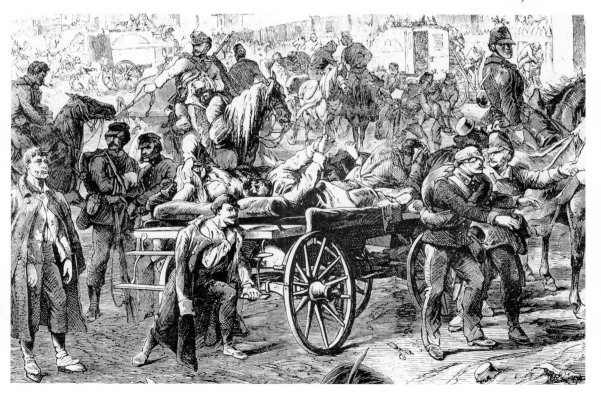

pounded by the embroilment over the candidacy of a Hohenzollern prince for the Spanish crown, finally led to war. The south German states immediately sided with Prussia, and on 18 January, in a defeated France, William I was proclaimed German Emperor – the Kaiser of the new German Reich.

The German-Danish war

In 1864, Bismarck, the Prussian prime minister, played what turned out to be a master stroke in the field of German and European affairs: he ensured that Prussia assumed the leadership in the fight against Denmark. Prussia forced Austria onto its side, thereby separating it from its former allies in

Germany, the small and medium-sized states.

Following the victory over Denmark, under the terms of the Treaty of Gastein Schleswig was initially placed under the administrative control of Prussia, and Holstein under that of Austria. However, Austria's weakened position enabled Prussia to make increasingly open demands for the annexation of the two duchies. At the same time, Prussia finally foiled Austrian plans for a mid-European economic customs union.

The decisive year: 1866

In 1866, Austro-Prussian dualism in the struggle for political and economic supremacy in Germany esca-

III/144
Ceremonial welcome for the victorious Prussian army in Berlin on 21 September 1866

lated and led to war. With the Prussian victory at Königgrätz, Bismarck's concept of "national unification from above", forged by diplomacy and war, had won the day.

Bismark sought to capitalize on this victory in the field of domestic politics as well. By tabling a so-called "indemnity bill", he now requested the Prussian lower house retroactively to sanction his unconstitutional action over the question of army reform. Impressed by Bismark's successes, the majority of members acquiesced.

The events of 1866 split the liberals: the majority abandoned their opposition to Bismarck's power politics. They placed their hopes for achieving national unity in a "revolution from above", thereby giving their national aspirations precedence over their liberal convictions. "Freedom through unity" became a slogan they used to set their minds at rest. In autumn 1866, a national liberal grouping was formed in the Prussian lower house, and for more than a decade Bismarck was able to rely on its support for his policies.

The North German Confederation

With the annexation of Schleswig-Holstein, Kurhessen, Nassau and Frankfurt, the militaristic and authoritarian Prussian state came to dominate the territory of Germany as far south as the river Main. Austria, cut off from this "Little Ger-

Deutschlands Zukunft.

Kommt es unter einen Hut? Ich glaube,
s kommt eher unter eine Pickelhaube!

III/145
"Germany's future", cartoon on the possible consequences of Prussia's supremacy in Germany

many", was spared in the Treaty of Prague signed in 1866 but had, in return, to give its consent to Prussia's annexations, renounce the goal of restoring the German Confederation, and approve the founding of the North German Confederation.

The constitution of the North German Confederation, which came into being on 16 April 1867, was essentially Bismarck's own work. It guaranteed Prussian hegemony,

tion of general, direct and secret elections was of little significance as the Reichstag was given only limited powers and had practically no influence on the formation of the government.

The main beneficiaries of the united economic area created by the North German Confederation were the national liberal members of the middle class, who were also its most outspoken supporters. The Confederation was opposed by left-

III/146
First regular sitting of the North German Reichstag on 24 February 1867

and in large part formed the basis of the Reich Constitution of 1871. The King of Prussia became the hereditary president of the Confederation. The Chancellor was responsible solely to him and not to parliament, the elected Reichstag. Prussia also had a dominant position in the Federal Council, or Bundesrat. Given the monarchical bias of this constitution, the introduc-

wing liberals, socialists, traditional conservatives and the political Catholic movement. Many people in the annexed German states remained anti-Prussian, especially in Guelphic Hanover and the old free imperial city of Frankfurt. The south German states aligned themselves with the North German Confederation by signing defensive-offensive alliances with Prussia.

III/147
(opposite)
The seating arrangements in the North German Reichstag

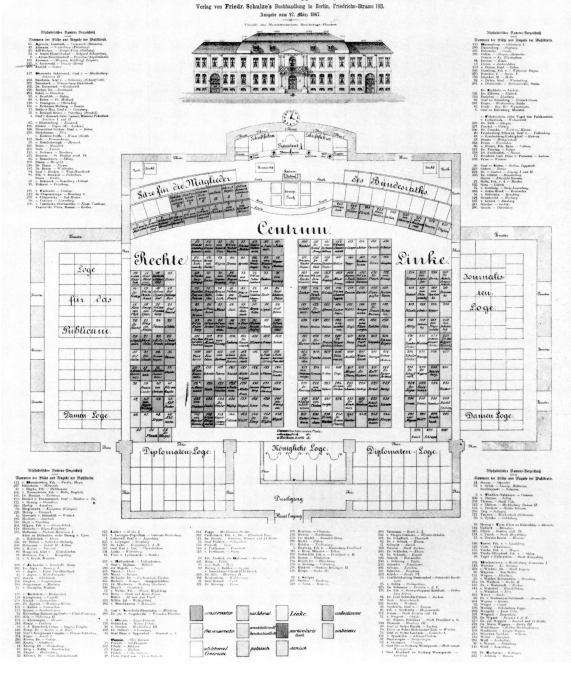

III/148
William I and
the French envoy
Benedetti in Bad
Ems

III/149
Bismarck's draft of
the "Ems Telegram"

The Franco-Prussian war

Following Prussia's victory over Austria, France feared that its dominant position in Europe was under threat. The issue of the candidacy of a Hohenzollern prince for the Spanish throne ultimately triggered a war between the two countries as neither was prepared to suffer a diplomatic defeat.

A wave of outrage swept the whole of Germany in response to the declaration of war by France. The south German states rushed to the aid of Prussia, and placed their armies under Prussian command. With the help of the new railway network, the deployment of forces along the border with France was completed with unexpected speed. At the battle of Sedan, Prussia gained a decisive victory over the French imperial forces. The prisoners taken included Napoleon III. This victory was marked by jubilant celebrations throughout Germany. The brotherhood in arms between Prussia and the other German

III/150
A crowd celebrating
the declaration of
war on 19 July 1870
in Paris

39ste Depesche
vom
Kriegs-Schauplatz.

Der Königin Augusta in Berlin.

Vor Sedan, den 2. September, ½2 Uhr Nachm.

Die Capitulation, wodurch die ganze Armee in
Sedan kriegsgefangen, ist soeben mit dem General
Wimpfen geschlossen, der an Stelle des verwundeten
Marschalls Mac-Mahon das Commando führte.
Der Kaiser hat nur sich selbst Mir ergeben, da er das
Commando nicht führt und Alles der Regentschaft in
Paris überläßt.   Seinen Aufenthaltsort werde Ich
bestimmen, nachdem Ich ihn gesprochen habe in einem
Rendezvous, das sofort stattfindet.
    Welch' eine Wendung durch Gottes Führung!

Wilhelm.

Berlin, den 3. September 1870.

Königliches Polizei-Präsidium.
von Wurmb.

III/151
Dispatch from the
front with news of
the victory at Sedan

III/152
William I on the battlefield at Sedan on 2 September 1870

states at the battle of Sedan ushered in a new chapter of German history: in a spirit of unbridled self-conceit, the victory over the French was interpreted as a portent that Germany was destined for greatness and unity. The war now entered a new phase, with the proclaiming of the republic in Paris; Léon Gambetta, the minister of war, set about organizing a people's army to break the encirclement of Paris.

Although an acceptable peace settlement was still in reach, military success encouraged a German war aims policy which, no longer satisfied merely with defending Germany, sought to make financial and territorial gains. Following the victories of August 1870, most political groups in Germany vociferously demanded the incorporation of Alsace and Lorraine into the emerging nation-state. For reasons of power politics, Bismarck also favoured such a move. Only a small minority, pointing out that the people of Alsace and Lorraine did not want to become part of Germany, rejected annexation. It included the *Frankfurter Zeitung*, a liberal-democratic newspaper, and many representatives of the political workers' movement; they condemned the separation of Alsace and Lorraine from France as a flagrant violation of the right to self-determination to which Germans had so often laid claim for their own nation. "The military *camarilla*, the professors, the middle class and the bar-room politicians allege that this (the annexation) is the way to safeguard

Germany for ever against war with France ... It is the most effective way to change the forthcoming peace into a mere ceasefire which will last until France is again strong enough to demand the return of the lost territories. It is the most effective way to push Germany and France into ruinous self-laceration" (manifesto of the Social Democratic Workers' Party, adopted on 5 September 1870). The annexation of Alsace and Lorraine would indeed poison relations between France and Germany for decades to come, thereby constraining Germany's room for maneouvre in the field of foreign policy.

gotiations and the military power of Prussia secured the founding of the Reich "from above". Hence, the German Reich was the product not of decisions taken by a German national assembly, but of treaties, similar to agreements under international law, between the German monarchs and governments which were subsequently ratified by the Reichstag of the North German Confederation and the parliaments of the south German states.

The proclamation of the Empire took place before the German princes on 18 January 1871 in the Hall of Mirrors in Versailles. The ceremony was a act of self-glorifi-

In the wake of the military victories in the first months of the war, the deposition of the French Emperor, and the encirclement of Paris, the way was open for completing German unity by merging the south German states with the North German Confederation. Diplomatic ne-

cation by the Prussian military and the German nobility. However, the national fervour which gripped the German people following the founding of the new Reich could not fully conceal the deep rifts in the alliance between Bismarck and the liberal and national movement.

III/153
Victorious troops entering Berlin on 16 June 1871

III/154
Proclamation of
the German Empire
at Versailles on
18 January 1871,
painting by Anton
von Werner

The German Confederation after 1850

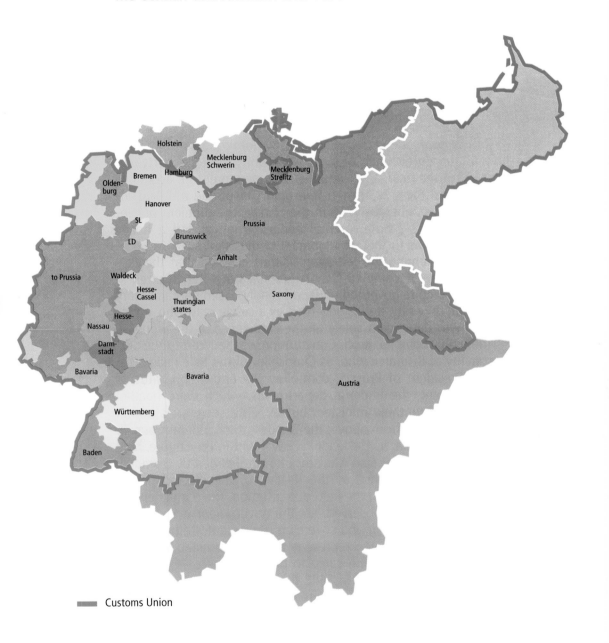

Holstein

Mecklenburg
Schwerin

Bremen Hamburg

Mecklenburg
Strelitz

Olden-
burg

Hanover

SL

Prussia

LD

Brunswick

Anhalt

to Prussia

Waldeck

Hesse-
Cassel

Thuringian
states

Saxony

Hesse-
Nassau

Darm-
stadt

Bavaria

Bavaria

Austria

Württemberg

Baden

Customs Union

Imperial Germany

IV. Imperial Germany

The German Empire of 1871 was based on a unequal alliance between the national and liberal movement on the one hand and the conservative Prussian leadership on the other. It was the product of numerous compromises, and was already criticized by contemporaries as being "incomplete". The founding of the Empire was greeted with enthusiam by the great majority. However, measured against the lofty goals of the 1848 revolution, which had been to create unity through liberty and to place the new state on an equally new political, economic and social basis, it at the same time constituted a defeat for middle-class liberalism. From the outset, the problem of "incompleteness", both internal and external, placed a heavy burden on the further development of the Empire.

Critics among the left-wing liberals claimed that the Empire was an "incomplete" constitutional state. They wanted to see the Empire governed under a broadly based parliamentary system. In reality, it was governed by a single man who, moreover, was dependent solely on the confidence of the Emperor. The highly complex Reich Constitution was tailored to the personality of Bismarck who, as Chancellor of the Reich and Minister-President of Prussia, controlled the entire apparatus of government: the imperial departments, which were headed not by accountable ministers but by state secretaries bound by instructions from above; the Bundesrat, or Federal Council, in which Prussia, as the leading power within the Empire, held sway; and the Prussian Ministry of State headed by Bismarck himself. The influence of the Reichstag, the elected parliament, was limited to the field of legislation. The parliamentary principle was not observed, i.e. the government was not dependent on a strong and sovereign parliament. Rather, it acted "above" the parties represented in the Reichstag, a system which even at the time came to be known as a "Chancellor dictatorship". Whereas in 1848 the goal had been to create a democratic constitutional state based on the sovereignty of the people, the Empire founded in 1871 was an authoritarian state based on a national monarchy.

The Empire also remained "incomplete" with respect to the aspirations of the middle-class movement for social reform and emancipation. This movement called for the new state to be adapted to the new industrial society and for the nation, as the sum of all social forces, to be given a decisive say in the political process. Its demands were ignored, however. Instead of embracing change, the Empire sought to preserve the traditional order of Prussian society, characterized by the dominant position of the aristocratic landowners, the *Junker*. The opposition parties – the left-liberal Progressive Party, the Social Democrats, and the Catholic Centre party – were denounced as "enemies of the Reich". The first decade following the founding of the Empire was marked by heightened social and party-political tensions.

This period also witnessed the *Kulturkampf*, a great struggle between Church and State in which the autonomy of politics and the state vis-à-vis the denominational interests of the Catholic Centre party was stubbornly defended. Because of its links with the papacy, the Centre was seen as "ultramontane" and internationalist. Moreover, Bismarck feared an alliance between the Catholics and other opposition groups in the Empire, in particular the Catholic Polish minority in Prussia's eastern provinces. In 1871, immediately after the founding of the Empire, he unleashed an internal "preventive war" in an effort to establish his control over these forces. At the same time, an ideological clash between liberalism and Catholicism led to a hardening of the party-political fronts. The laws enacted to fight the Catholic church during the *Kulturkampf* destroyed the belief that the creation of a national community would lead to mutual toleration and a peaceful balancing of interests. By giving its approval to the ban on the Jesuit order and the expulsion of individual Jesuits, the National Liberal party abandoned its own constitutional principles.

The internal structure of the Empire was shaken even more violently by the battle against social democracy. Bismarck's anti-socialist law of 1878 prevented the integration of the working class into the nation-state. A political party was made subject to a special body of criminal law solely on the basis of its convictions – a flagrant violation of liberal legal thinking. Bismarck nevertheless won the approval of the middle classes which had long feared the threat of "red anarchy". Two attempts on the life of Emperor William I in the spring of 1878 were taken as a pretext to dissolve the Reichstag and hold new elections, although no link could be established between the Social Democrats and the would-be assassins. Following these elections Bismarck was able to draw on the support of a compliant parliamentary majority – even the National Liberals, concerned over the wave of public outrage and the fear of revolution amongst its voters, gave their approval to the anti-socialist law. Only with great difficulty did the party prevent a break-away by its left wing. Even at the time, critics alleged that Bismarck had also used the anti-socialist law as a tool to create an internal rift among the National Liberals. In the following years, the liberals found no answer to the social question. They rejected Bismarck's policy of state welfare provision – the positive counterpart of his anti-socialist legislation. One of the aims of Bismarck's social policy was to reconcile the working class to the existing social and political order by raising its material wellbeing. Its success in precisely this respect was limited, however, even though the system of social insurance was further expanded during the Wilhelmine period. Rather, the workers' organizations and the large industrial and agricultural interest groups formed during the period of economic crisis after 1873 continued to face one another across an unbridgeable divide. The nation-state became increasingly divided along class lines.

The new Empire's situation in the foreign policy field was no less precarious. Since the new "Little German" Empire did not unite all Germans within its borders, fears were expressed in many quarters that it would now embark upon a policy of national conquest. This was compounded by strains caused by the national minorities within the Empire, which right up until the Empire's demise in 1918 were never really integrated and continued to create serious internal problems. Only through an extremely complex alliance system, and repeated declarations that Germany was a "satiated state", did Bismarck succeed in gaining a place for the Empire in continental Europe's traditional balance of power. His diplomatic efforts reached a climax at the Berlin Congress of 1878. However, the international crises of the 1880s showed that the danger of a war on two fronts had not yet been banished. The new alliances – the Triple Alliance between Germany, Austria-Hungary and Italy, and Germany's Reinsurance Treaty with Russia – only temporarily restored the equilibrium among Europe's leading powers, especially since the German Empire now embarked on a colonial policy which, as it marked a break with the affirmation that it was territorially "satiated", put it on a collision course with England.

Thus the Empire remained an "incomplete national state", under threat from within and without. In attempting to master all these difficulties, Bismarck always resorted to he same method: he sought to strengthen the conservative state and to cement the status quo. This ultimately led to the rupture of his alliance with the National Liberals, an alliance which had come about solely as a result of Bismarck's foreign policy successes in 1864 and 1866 and whose inception was marked by a compromise on domestic policy: the approval of the so-called "indemnity bill" which put an end to the constitutional conflict of the 1860s by retroactively sanctioning his reactionary and antiparliamentary policy. The turnaround in domestic politics in 1878/79, which deprived the Liberals of all influence on the further course of events, was the equivalent of a second founding of the Empire along conservative lines. The change of course in economic policy, which saw a shift from free trade to tariffs intended to protect the interests of large industrialists and landowners, caused a split within the National Liberals. Whilst favouring the so-called "productive classes", the new protective tariffs and the rise in indirect taxation placed a heavy burden on the economically weak sections of the population and lent political impetus to the social democratic movement. Middle-class liberalism was eroded by the conflict of interest between agriculture and industry on the one hand and the workers on the other. At the same time, the alliance of economic convenience between industrialists and large landowners reinforced the influence of Prussia's traditional ruling elite which in turn supported the conservative course charted by the government. A campaign of ideological propaganda was unleashed in favour of protective tariffs and anti-socialist legislation, with the conservative landowners resorting to extreme slogans such as: "The constitutional state has had its day. We shall have to return to the patrimonial and patriachal order". The liberal era came to an end in 1878/79: liberals in the civil service were largely replaced by conservatives, and the liberal ministers in Prussia resigned. The reorganization of the imperial departments and the reform of the Reich's financial system strengthened the power of the Reich government and thus also of the Chancellor. In last few years of the Bismarckian period, the aristocratic landowners east of the river Elbe (the *Junker*), the large industrialists and the conservative state leadership joined forces in pursuit of their common interests.

Bismarck's dismissal in 1890 precipitated a crisis of government in the Empire. The young Emperor William II wanted to be "his own chancellor". However, his attempt to set up a system of "personal rule" in which ministers would be no more than obedient instruments of his will failed. The Emperor was unable to set a clear course in the field of domestic and foreign policy: he had neither the requisite specialist knowledge nor the ability to coordinate the many parallel institutions – the imperial offices, the Federal Council, the Prussian Ministry of State, the Reichstag and the Prussian Parliament – let alone, as Bismarck had done, to play them off against one another. A "New Course" was proclaimed nonetheless: the anti-socialist law was repealed and, in the so-called February Decrees of 1890, a comprehensive package of social security legislation announced. But this attempt to reconcile the working class to a more "social" Empire did not succeed. The Social Democrats were able to increase their share of the vote from 763,000 in 1887 to 1.4 million in 1890.

The shift to a policy of imperialism, or *Weltpolitik*, marked the final attempt to mask tensions at home – this time by successes abroad. However, the hopes of liberal imperialists such as Max Weber and Friedrich Naumann, who expected a dynamic foreign policy to create more internal dynamism as well, were not fulfilled. The new *Weltpolitik* in fact did more to strengthen the conservatives' claim to power: their calls on all national forces to "rally round" the Emperor and, in particular, their propaganda campaigns in favour of a powerful navy, won them broad support. William II's claim that the German Empire had become a "world empire" was rapturously received. In reality, the successes were meagre and their price high: rather than enhancing the Empire's prestige, the new *Weltpolitik* resulted in Germany's self-inflicted isolation and an alliance between her international rivals France, England and Russia. Its failure utlimately prompted a blind push forward – into the catastrophe of the first world war.

Neither the "truce" between the political parties (even the Social Democrats voted for the war credits) nor the wave of popular enthusiam which greeted the outbreak of war in August 1914 lasted for long. The war aggravated the rifts on domestic policy, and they became entwined with differences on Germany's war aims: some parties called for a negotiated peace, others for a peace based on military victory and annexation.The radicalization of left and right was reflected in the founding of the Spartacus League on the one hand and the German Fatherland Party on the other. However, the military collapse of the German Empire provided an opportunity for a new beginning and for a return to the liberal and democratic ideals which had underpinned the national idea in the early part of the 19th century.

IV/155
Prince Otto
von Bismarck,
portrait by Franz
von Lenbach

1. The "Little German" nation-state: institutions, parties, internal problems

The founding of the German Empire in 1871 marked the achievement, long desired, of German unity. But it had been imposed "from above": sovereignty lay not with the people but with the 22 princes and the three free cities which came together to form a federal state. Prussia's dominance was overwhelming, and many of the aspirations of the liberal and democratic movement remained unfulfilled. The Chancellor was politically accountable to the Emperor, not to parliament. The rights of the democratically elected Reichstag were largely restricted to participation in the passing of legislation. The struggle to extend the Reichtag's role and to parliamentarize the Empire's system of government remained a fundamental aspect of domestic politics. However, the Empire was "incomplete" not only as a constitutional state but also as a nation-state: large sections of the German-speaking population remained outside its borders. Conversely, large national minorities within the Empire created serious problems of integration.

The Reich Constitution and the Empire's internal structures

Elections to the Reichstag were general, equal, direct and secret. Next to the Emperor, the Reichstag was, in constitutional terms, the most important institution. However, its political influence was largely restricted to the sphere of legislation. It had very little say in the formation of governments and government policy. The Empire was characterized by a form of "government above the parties"; on the decisive political questions of the day, parliament's role was reduced to that of merely expressing an opinion. Contemperories coined the term "Chancellor dictatorship" to describe this system.

The Constitution of 1871, largely the work of Bismarck, guaranteed the Chancellor a wealth of powers which the parties were unable either to control or restrict. The Chancellor was accountable not to parliament but only to the Emperor. A relationship of loyalty and confidence between Chancellor and Emperor was therefore essential. The Chancellor determined the guidelines of policy. He had the power to propose the appointment or dismissal of the state secretaries who headed the Reich Offices, and he chaired the meetings of the Bundesrat, or Federal Council, which was the Empire's supreme governing body. For almost the entire duration of the Empire, he was by custom head of the Prussian Ministry of State.

In the same way as the Chancellor was responsible for directing the Empire's civilian policy, the generals were in charge of all matters relating to military command. They were in turn responsible to the Emperor as the supreme commander of the armed forces. The Constitution did not prescribe the primacy of civilian authorities over the military. Subsequently, therefore, especially in the years preceding the first world war, generals and admirals came to exert a fateful influence on policymaking as a whole.

The German Empire was a federal state in which Prussian supremacy was overwhelming. More than half of the population lived within Prussia's borders, and almost two thirds of the imperial territory was Prussian. In the Bundesrat, or Federal

Council, which was the legislative body of the Empire's constituent states, Prussia had a blocking vote. However, the decisive issue of German federalism was the dependence of the Empire on financial transfers, so-called matricular contributions, from the constituent states. The reform of the Empire's financial system thus developed into yet another fundamental constitutional problem.

The German Empire of 1871 contained sizeable national minorities within its borders. The steps taken to integrate them were not political but purely bureaucratic in nature. In 1872/73 German was made the only language used in schools in the Polish-speaking areas, and in 1876 it was made the sole language of commerce. From 1878 onwards, German became the only language permitted in schools in North Schleswig too. Even the people of Alsace and Lorraine, a majority of whom were German-speaking, posed a problem for the Empire. They were aware of the advantages of the French constitution and were not prepared to be treated as "second-class" citizens by the imperial administration.

The founding of the Empire created a unified economic and customs area. Combined with the existing technical potential for industrial production, this prompted a phase of rapid economic growth. Progress towards greater harmonization was also made in the fields of transport, the postal systems, coinage, weights and measures and the legal system: a uniform penal code was introduced in 1872 and a civil code in 1900. Both are still in use today, having been only partly amended or extended.

IV/156
A sitting of the Reichstag, 1908

The parties in the Reichstag

As a consequence in particular of universal suffrage, the loose groupings and electoral associations which had existed hitherto were replaced by broadly based and well-organized mass parties, each with its own political programme. However, the Imperial Constitution of 1871only gave them the choice between two alternatives: loyalty to the Chancellor or opposition. They were given no genuine share in power. Soon, therefore, a highly problematical distinction was made between mere party-political interests and the supposedly overriding interests of the state, which were the exclusive domain of the government.

The National Liberal Party was supported above all by the Protestant educated middle class and the industrial upper middle class. Its aim was to establish a powerful nation-state which would at the same time be based on a liberal constitution. In practice, however, it placed more emphasis on consolidating the power of the state, and until 1878 was Bismarck's most important parliamentary ally.

The left-wing liberals, who drew their support from the crafts and liberal professions, favoured a parliamentary monarchy and the rigorous extension of the constitutional state. Until 1910, they remained divided between the German Progressive Party and the German People's Party. Only with the merger of these two parties to form the Progressive People's Party did the left-wing liberals establish a common organizational base. Heavily influence by Leopold Sonnenman, the south German liberals adopted the idea of welfare provision by the state. In the long term, this laid the foundation for cooperation with the Social Democrats. Friedrich Naumann and Theodor Barth championed the opening of German liberalism to the left.

The conservatives, attached as they were to the importance of tradition and the legitimate rule of kings, were staunch supporters of the individual state dynasties. Their attitude to unification and to the concept of a "German" policy was sceptical. Not until 1876 did the majority of the Prussian Conservative Party finally accept the founding of the Empire. "Old" conservative opponents of Bismarck joined forces with "new" conservatives to form the German Conservative Party. Its political profile was shaped by the agrarian interests of large landowners, and the rural population of eastern Germany was its main source of electoral support.

Conservative industrialists and landowners who supported Bismarck, the so-called "Free Conservatives", set up the Reich Party. They accepted Bismarck's constitution and it unitarian elements but rejected any steps to "parliamentarize" the Empire.

The political Catholic movement viewed the founding of the Empire as a threat. The predominance of Protestants in the new "Little German" nation-state and the influence of liberal ideas forced it into opposition. During the so-called "cultural struggle", Bismarck denounced the Catholic church as an enemy of the Empire in an attempt to curb its influence on the state. However, political Catholicism in southern Germany and the Rhineland was not geared exclusively to promoting denominational interests: its support for social reform made it a non-socialist rallying point for the lower classes.

In 1875, the "Lassallian" General German Workers' Party, set up in 1863, and the Social Democratic Workers' Party, established in 1869 and influenced by Karl Marx, joined forces in Gotha to form the Social Workers' Party of Germany (SAPD). It adopted the so-called Erfurt Programme in 1891 and was henceforth called the Social Democratic Party of Germany (SPD). Calls for worker-run producers' cooperatives, trade union demands and radical democratic goals were the central elements of the programme adopted by the SAPD in Gotha. Its overall aim was to alter the internal structures of the German nation-state through a process of reform. Marx sharply criticized the Gotha Programme and its reformist tendencies. He himself propagated a radical and revolutionary transformation of the German nation-state.

IV/161
Members of parliament in the lobby of the Reichstag building in Leipziger Strasse

IV/162
A sitting of the
Reichstag in 1905,
painting by Georg
Waltenberger

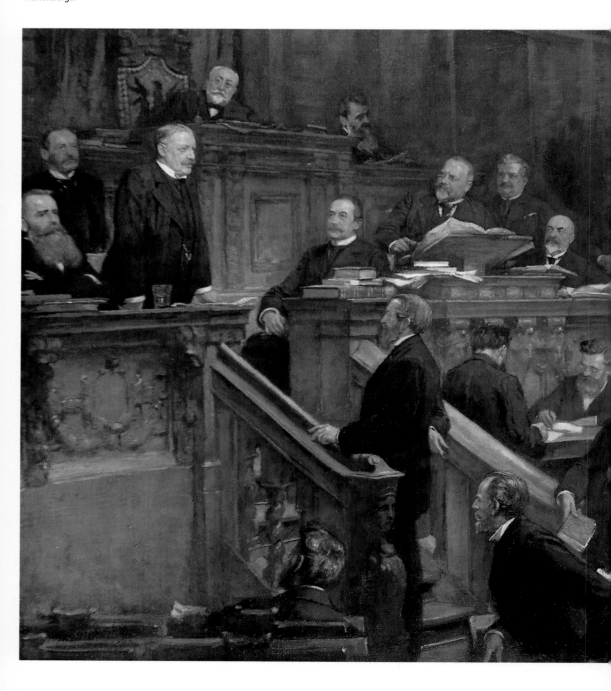

Reichs-Gesetzblatt.

№ 34.

Inhalt: Gesetz gegen die gemeingefährlichen Bestrebungen der Sozialdemokratie. S. 351.

(Nr. 1271.) Gesetz gegen die gemeingefährlichen Bestrebungen der Sozialdemokratie. Vom 21. Oktober 1878.

Wir Wilhelm, von Gottes Gnaden Deutscher Kaiser, König von Preußen rc.

verordnen im Namen des Reichs, nach erfolgter Zustimmung des Bundesraths und des Reichstags, was folgt:

§. 1.

Vereine, welche durch sozialdemokratische, sozialistische oder kommunistische Bestrebungen den Umsturz der bestehenden Staats- oder Gesellschaftsordnung bezwecken, sind zu verbieten.

Dasselbe gilt von Vereinen, in welchen sozialdemokratische, sozialistische oder kommunistische auf den Umsturz der bestehenden Staats- oder Gesellschaftsordnung gerichtete Bestrebungen in einer den öffentlichen Frieden, insbesondere die Eintracht der Bevölkerungsklassen gefährdenden Weise zu Tage treten.

Den Vereinen stehen gleich Verbindungen jeder Art.

§. 2.

Auf eingetragene Genossenschaften findet im Falle des §. 1 Abs. 2 der §. 35 des Gesetzes vom 4. Juli 1868, betreffend die privatrechtliche Stellung der Erwerbs- und Wirthschaftsgenossenschaften, (Bundes-Gesetzbl. S. 415 ff.) Anwendung.

Auf eingeschriebene Hülfskassen findet im gleichen Falle der §. 29 des Gesetzes über die eingeschriebenen Hülfskassen vom 7. April 1876 (Reichs-Gesetzbl. S. 125 ff.) Anwendung.

§. 3.

Selbständige Kassenvereine (nicht eingeschriebene), welche nach ihren Statuten die gegenseitige Unterstützung ihrer Mitglieder bezwecken, sind im Falle des

Reichs-Gesetzbl. 1878.

Ausgegeben zu Berlin den 22. Oktober 1878.

IV/165
The Anti-Socialist
Law passed by the
Reichstag in 1878

IV/166
Police breaking up
a workers' meeting

following new elections, a compliant parliamentary majority agreed to his anti-socialist law. Even the National Liberals voted in favour, thereby betraying the principles of a constitutional state. All socialist and communist associations were forcibly disbanded and their publications outlawed. Socialist "agitators" were arrested by the police and expelled from Germany. However, the workers stood by their leaders. The failure of this policy of repression was not conceded until 1890, when the government decided not to extend the anti-socialist law. But, for a long time, the Social Democrats continued to feel the effects of being denounced as "enemies of the Empire".

IV/167
Searching the house
of a political suspect

Die deutsche Sozialversicherung steht in der ganzen Welt vorbildlich und unerreicht da.

IV/168

Contemporary depiction of Bismarck's social insurance legislation

As a counterpart to his anti-socialist law, Bismarck expanded the provision of social welfare by the state. With the help of a system of social security, the workers were to be won over to the authoritarian rule of the monarchy.

The legislation passed in the field of health, invalidity and pension insurance constituted a form of "state socialism" which, although undoubtedly a major and exemplary social advance, was not intended by Bismarck as a programme of social reform geared to protecting the workers and humanizing the world of work in an industrial society.

Rather, his declared aim was to "generate in the great mass of unpropertied people the conservative frame of mind engendered by the certainty of a secure pension." In commenting on his policy of "taming" the working class, Bismarck once remarked that "people who have the prospect of a secure pension are far more satisfied and easier to handle than those who do not." However, his attempt to use welfare provision as a means of alienating the working class from social democracy failed.

In the period of economic instability following the crisis of 1873, the workers' movement became more radical. At the same time, the first large federations representing the interests of industrialists and landowners came into being. They demanded an end to free trade and the introduction of a system of protective tariffs. By keeping out cheap imports, they wanted to maintain excessively high domestic prices which would in turn enable them to keep the prices of their exports especially low.

The Central Association of German Industrialists was set up in 1876 as an umbrella organization for these interest groups.

The agrarian crisis of the 1870s also prompted the large landowners east of the river Elbe to turn their backs on the principle of free trade. They set up the Association of Fiscal and Economic Reformers in 1876 to promote their interests and to press for the enforcement of protective tariffs. The German Conservative Party, which was formed in the same year, adopted their demands. Thus, in their call for protective tariffs, heavy industry and agriculture had found common ground in their fight against economic liberalism.

However, Bismarck's plans went far beyond a mere change of course in tariff policy. By clearly distancing himself from the liberals, his erstwhile allies during the "cultural struggle", he wanted to pave the way for an alliance of convenience with the conservative parties.

According to Bismarck, the *Junker* had "the advantage of being patient and conservatively minded people loyal to the state"; they provided the state with most of its tax revenue and were a reliable source of support on which the state could draw in every kind of internal and external crisis.

Bismarck also planned a fiscal and financial reform designed to consolidate the authority of the imperial government. By increasing revenue from tariffs and indirect taxes (on tobacco, brandy, coffee), this reform would have ended the Empire's dependence on the matricular contributions of its constituent states. However, his plans foundered, more than anything on the opposition of the federally minded Centre party.

The National Liberal grouping in the Reichstag split over the tariff bill. Only a minority continued to support Bismarck. This was a great success for the Empire's conserva-

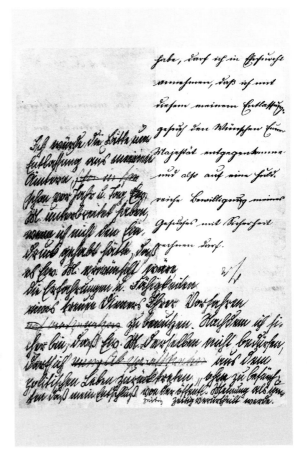

tive elite. All hope of enhancing the powers of parliament, and giving the Reichstag genuine powers of control over the government, had been dashed. In many respects, the Empire acquired the features of a class-based state. This turning point in domestic policy has rightly been called a "second founding" of the Empire.

IV/169
Last page of Bismarck's letter of resignation of 18 March 1890

IV/170
"Dropping the pilot", cartoon by Sir John Teniel published in "Punch" in March 1890

3. Wilhelmine Germany

The struggle against social democracy, the tough line taken on national minorities, the three-class electoral system in Prussia and the setbacks in making the government accountable to parliament – these were the main sources of conflict in the "Wilhelmine era", which lasted from 1890 to 1918. Only Germany's dynamic economic growth, which transformed it into Europe's most powerful industrialized country, kept the lid on the smouldering tensions in society and prevented them from erupting into the open. Public life became increasingly bureaucratized and militarized. Coupled with an emotionally charged imperialistic foreign policy, this created a strong bond in Germany between nationalism and militarism on the one hand and the authoritarian monarchist state on the other.

Emperor William II was intent on curbing Bismarck's political influence and establishing a "personal regime". A "new course" was to be steered: in the domestic sphere there was to be a reconciliation with the Social Democrats, and in the foreign policy field Germany

IV/171
An automobile
in 1897

was to strive for world power status. This led to a conflict with Bismarck, who saw this course as a threat both to his policy of containing socialism and nationalism, and to his concept for maintaining peace in Europe. In 1890 Bismarck offered his resignation, which was accepted by the Emperor.

The policies pursued by his successors, whether it was Caprivi's, and then Hohenlohe's, attempt to "govern above the parties", or Bülow's efforts to base his government on a "block" of conservative and bourgeois parties in the Reichstag,

came to nothing. Even the cautious attempt by Bethmann-Hollweg to overcome the Empire's political ossification by working together with the left-liberal Progressive People's Party and the Social Democrats failed. Conservative forces within the civil service and the officer corps continued to determine the thrust of domestic policy.

1895 witnessed the beginning of a fresh phase of strong economic growth and rapid technical development. Expansion in the fields of chemical and electrical engineering in particular triggered a second

IV/172
Landing of the first
Parseval-class air-
ship in Munich on
14 October 1908

IV/173
Front page of the Social Democrat's newspaper, published in London, announcing the SPD's success at the Reichstag election of 1890

wave of industrialization. Powerful companies such as Krupp and Siemens came to dominate the markets. But as Germany was transformed into Europe's most powerful industrial country, internal tensions once again began to rise.

The repeal of the anti-socialist law and the passing of social welfare legislation in 1890/91 had been intended to reconcile the Social Democrats to the Empire. But under August Bebel the SPD maintained its opposition. Disappointed, the Emperor turned away from what he called "these rogues without a fatherland". However, Caprivi, the new Chancellor, refused to resort again to a policy of repression against the SPD, whose membership was now steadily growing. By contrast, his successor, Prince Ho-

henlohe-Schillingsfürst, took a tougher line and proposed stiffer penalties for political "subversion" and trade-union activity. However, the two bills he introduced (1894 and 1899) with this aim in mind were rejected by the Reichstag.

The question of revolution or reform was hotly contested within the SPD. Full employment and rising real incomes cast doubt on Marx's theory of impoverishment and revolution. The leading advocates of reform were Georg von Vollmar and Eduard Bernstein. They opposed the Marxist line of the party "centre" led by Karl Kautsky. The reformers received their strongest support from the trade unions.

The first trade unions had been set up in the 1860s as organizations representing the economic and social interests of the workers. They were unable to develop into mass organizations until the repeal of the anti-socialist law. The Free Trade Unions, organized in associations for each branch of industry, had 50,000 members in 1890, 680,000 in 1900 and more than 2.5 million in 1913. Under Carl Legien the "General Commission", which directed the Free Trade Unions, became Europe's largest labour organization. In comparison, the liberal Hirsch-Dunker labour association and the Christian trade unions played a less important role.

The employers also set up large and influential organizations. In response to a major textile workers' strike in Crimmitschau in 1904, the employers' associations came together under two umbrella organizations: the Central Office of German Employers' Associations and the Federation of German Employers' Associations. Both had close links with the Central League of German Industrialists, a conservative organization which supported protective tariffs. A group broke away from the Central League to form the Federation of Industrialists, which represented the interests of the emerging chemical industry and of export-oriented small and medium-sized companies. Politically, it lent its support to the National Liberals. The Agrarian League was set up in 1893, primarily to oppose any reduction of the grain tariffs. One of its "weapons" was strongly antisemitic agitation.

The liberal middle class, which saw its position being gradually eroded by the clash of interests between industrialists and landowners on the one hand and the workers on the other, was called upon by Johannes Miquel, the new leader of the National Liberals, to "rally around" the monarchy to prevent any further strengthening of the social democratic movement. On the defensive on domestic issues, it supported all the more fervently an aggressive and imperialist foreign policy. The "Pan-German League", the "Navy League" and the "colonial associations" endeavoured to spread nationalistic but also antisemitic ideas. Interest groups not only dominated the extraparliamentary sphere; owing to the weakness of the Reichstag, they also came to exert a dangerous, direct influence on policymaking.

Leading left-wing liberals such as Max Weber and Friedrich Naumann hoped not only that a dynamic foreign policy would loosen up the ossified internal structures of the Empire, but also that social reforms would reconcile the working class to the state. However, Naumann's plans, and those of the National Social Association he set up, foundered on the interests of the dominant conservative elite.

But in other areas too all attempts at reform were quickly stifled by the Emperor's strengthening hold on power, by the fragmentation of the political parties which, moreover, as a result of the electoral system in Prussia and the Empire did not fully reflect the balance of forces in German society as a whole, and by the overwhelming influence of the interest groups.

In October 1908 an interview given by the Emperor was published in the British newspaper "Daily Telegraph". His unauthorized comments did a great deal of harm to Germany's external relations. All the parties were outraged by the Emperor's high-handedness in giving the interview without any prior consultation. Chancellor von Bülow refused before parliament to accept responsibility. William II backed down in the face of the unanimous criticism. He issued a public statement pledging that henceforth he would only perform the duties imposed on him by his "constitutional

IV/174
The Krupp steel-
casting plant, 1912
(detail)

IV/175
The Strike, painting
by Robert Koehler
1886

responsibility". Although this affair strengthened the position of the Reichstag, the opportunity to further parliamentarize the system of government was not seized. Only the Social Democrats, the Centre and the left-wing liberals called for an amendment of the constitution. The Social Democrats and the liberals also fought in vain for a change in the three-class electoral system in Prussia, which divided the citizens entitled to vote into three categories depending on the amount of tax they paid. But elections to the Reichstag also were unfair. In 1871, the Empire was divided into constituencies in each of which a member of parliament was elected by around 100,000 inhabitants. However, the process of urbanization in the main industrial centres created many distortions which worked against the SPD in particular. Despite this, at the Reichstag elections of 1912, the SPD succeeded in becoming the strongest party in parliament.

In the east, an expropriation law passed in 1908 made possible the confiscation of Polish property as part of a policy of Germanization. Germans were then settled on this land. The "Eastern Marches Association" publicly propagated a "struggle against the Poles". In Alsace-Lorraine, tension came to a head in 1913 in the small town of Zabern when Prussian troops broke up a public meeting and arrested 28 demonstrators. In ordering their detention, the officer in charge had assumed powers which were vested exclusively in the courts. He was nevertheless acquitted by a military court. The Reichstag tried in vain to intervene.

During these crises, and in subsequent parliamentary debates in the years leading up to the first world war, it became clear that the Reichstag was in no position to risk a serious trial of strength with the pillars of the state: the Emperor's court, landowners, industrialists, the civil service and the army.

4. German foreign policy
1871–1914

The founding of the German Empire in 1871 marked the emergence in central Europe of an economic and military power which the other major countries viewed as a potential threat to the balance of power in Europe. The enmity of France, resulting from the annexation of Alsace-Lorraine, was a great burden on the Empire. Only by establishing a complex system of alliances and repeatedly declaring that Germany was "satiated", did Bismarck succeed in incorporating the Empire into continental Europe's traditional balance of power and thus in guaranteeing its security. William II charted a very different course. His so-called "world policy" aimed to assure Germany a "place in the sun". This made the Empire's foreign policy unpredictable. Following the break with Russia, Germany's efforts to build up its navy and its constant great-power posturing also led to a worsening of its relations with Great Britain. The result was the Empire's self-inflicted isolation.

Bismarck had set down the basic principles of his foreign policy in the so-called "Kissingen Memorandum". The aim was for Germany to use its "free hand" as a neutral

IV/176
Extract from the "Kissingen Memorandum" of 16 June 1877, in the handwriting of Herbert von Bismarck

IV/177
Bismarck at the
Congress of Berlin,
woodcut from a
painting by Anton
von Werner

mediatator to steer the antago-
nisms between the imperialist great
powers over colonial policy and to
divert them from the centre of Europe to its periphery. His ideal was
"an overall political situation in
which all powers except France
need us and, wherever possible,
are dissuaded by their relations
with one another from forming
coalitions against us."

Bismarck's underlying motive in
drafting his foreign policy was to
avoid the nightmare of an all-pow-
erful coalition among the other
great powers of Europe against
Germany ("*cauchemar des coalitions*"). This fear was fuelled by the
diplomatic intervention of Russia
and Great Britain in support of
France when, in 1875, the German
press and general staff discussed
plans for a preventive war in re-

sponse to a reorganization of the
French army. "Is war in sight?",
asked the conservative paper *Die
Post* on 8 April 1875. Bismarck denied that this was the case.

The concept underpinning Bismarck's foreign policy, namely the
voluntary limitation by Germany of
its claim to leadership within the
European balance of power, was
put into practice at the Congress of
Berlin in 1878. Bismarck offered
Germany's assistance as a mediator
in settling the dispute between
England, Austria-Hungary and Russia over the delimitation of their respective spheres of influence in the
Balkans. Bismarck became the
"honest broker" of European interests, the German Empire the guar-
antor of stability in Europe.

German colonial policy was subordinated by Bismarck to the goal of

diverting tensions from the heart of Europe to its periphery. Only reluctantly, and for reasons of maintaining the balance of power with Europe, did he give in to pressure from the "Colonial Association" and the "Association for German Colonization" led by Carl Peters. In 1884/85 parts of Southwest Africa, Cameroon, Togo, a region of East Africa and a number of Pacific islands became German colonies.

Following Bismarck's dismissal, William II charted a "new course": "our task is to pursue a world policy; our aim to become a world power; our means a strong navy." Building up the German navy was a

IV/178
William II in 1890, painting by Max Koner

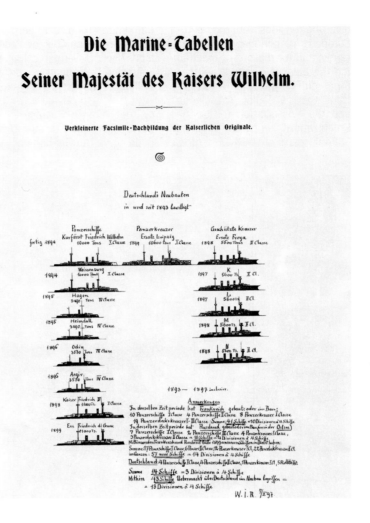

IV/179
A naval table
drawn by Emperor
William II

matter of prestige for the Emperor and his entourage although they were aware that it would set Germany on a collision course with Great Britain. The "line to St. Petersburg" established by Bismarck was also severed: the Reinsurance Treaty of 1887 was not renewed in 1890. The result was a rapprochement between France and Russia. The German Empire overestimated its own strength.

As the imperial powers rushed to divide up the world between them, William II demanded a "place in the sun" for the German Empire. Germany's attempts to enlarge its colonial empire were of limited success, however: the only colonies added between 1897 and 1899 were Kiao-Chow, the Carolines, the Peleus and the Marianne Islands and part of the Samoan groups of islands. The Emperor's grandiloquent speeches and the brutality of the German "expeditionary corps" and "protective forces" in crushing rebellions in the colonies damaged Germany's standing in the world.

Nor did Germany seize the chance of a rapprochement with Great Britain when Franco-British rivalry over the Sudan reached a peak in the Faschoda crisis of 1898. The

IV/180
"The boiling caul-
dron", a cartoon
on the Balkan crisis
published in
"Punch" in 1908

building of the German navy and the Berlin-Baghdad railway threatened British interests. In 1904, Britain and France finally settled their differences over colonial policy and signed the Entente Cordiale. Their joint resistance foiled Germany's attempts to gain greater influence over Morocco. Finally, in 1907 Russia and England concluded an agreement on their spheres of interest in Asia. The Empire began to feel "encircled".

The desire among the Balkan peoples to achieve national unity and independence at the expense of the Austro-Hungarian Empire by divid-

ing up the territories formerly occupied by Turkey, which they had defeated together in 1912, ran counter to the economic and alliance-based interests of Europe's great powers. The political and military embroilments over the Balkans threatened to light the fuse of the European "powder-keg".

On 28 June 1914, Archduke Franz Ferdinand, the heir to the Austrian throne, was assassinated, together with his wife, by a Serbian nationalist in Sarajevo. Austria resolved to settle the Serbian question once and for all, and in its own way. To do so, it needed the backing of its

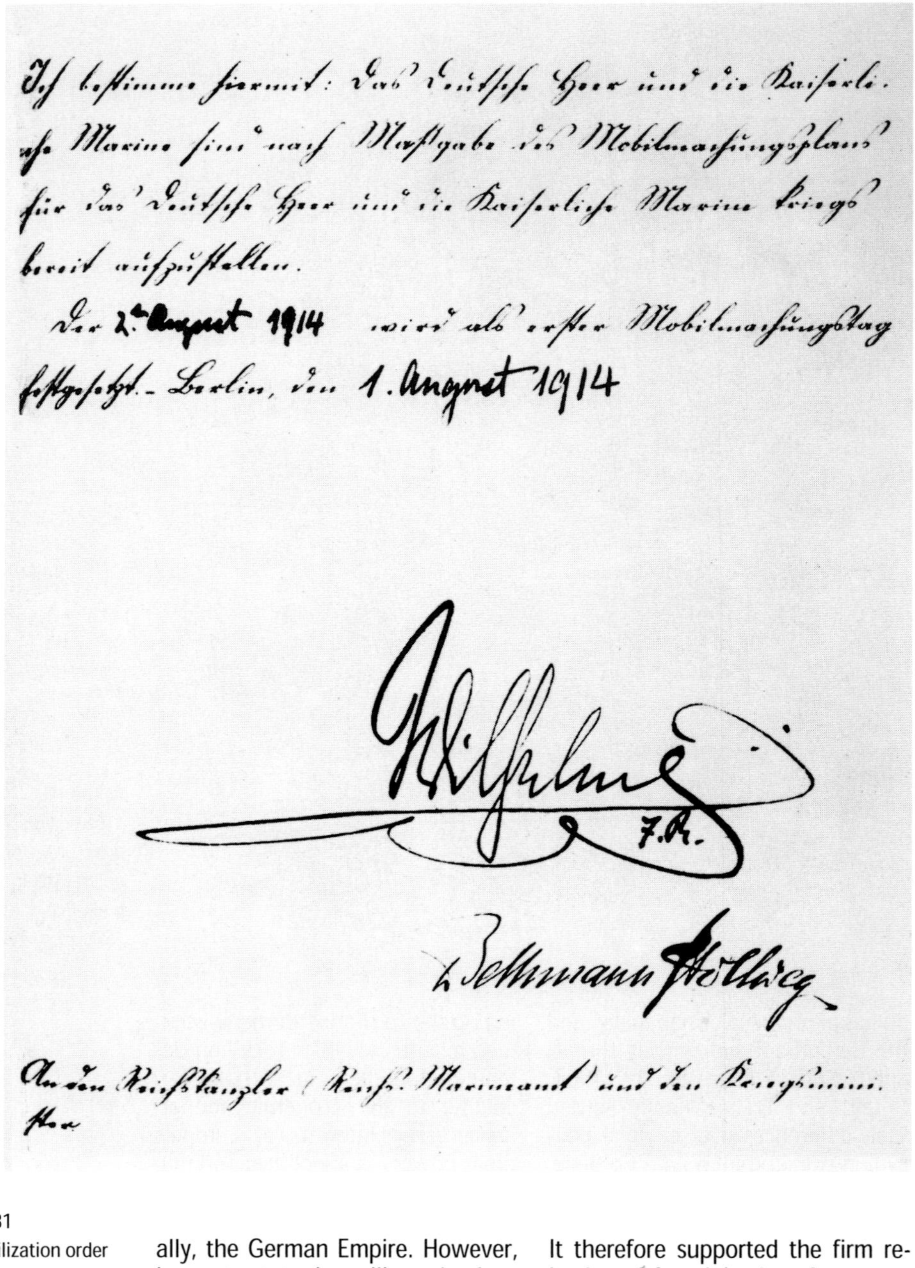

Ich bestimme hiermit: Das Deutsche Heer und die Kaiserliche Marine sind nach Maßgabe des Mobilmachungsplans
für das Deutsche Heer und die Kaiserliche Marine kriegs-
bereit aufzustellen.
Der 2. August 1914 wird als erster Mobilmachungstag
festgesetzt. – Berlin, den 1. August 1914

Wilhelm
I.R.

v. Bethmann Hollweg

An den Reichskanzler (Reichs-Marineamt) und den Kriegsminis-
ter

IV/181
Mobilization order of 1 August 1914

ally, the German Empire. However, in contrast to its military leaders, the Empire's diplomats wanted to avoid war if at all possible. England also wanted to seek a negotiated settlement. France, on the other hand, was tied to Russia under the Poincarè agreement of 1912 in the case of any conflict in the Balkans. It therefore supported the firm rejection of Austria's plans for annexation. When on 31 July 1914 Russia ordered a general mobilization, in Berlin the die was cast in favour of a military solution. The automatic sequence of mobilization by the great powers destroyed any hope of a political settlement.

IV/182
General rejoicing at
the outbreak of war,
early August 1914,
Berlin

5. The First World War

The First World War was caused just as much by Germany's arms race with France and its naval rivalry with England as it was by Russia's aggressive Balkans policy and the German Empire's close ties with the uncertain fate of the multinational Austrian state. It was not least the blind trust in one's own own military superiority which prompted the headlong rush into war. The USA entered the war in 1917. In the same year, the Bolshevist revolution succeeded in Russia. These two events marked the end of the era of bourgeois self-confidence and European world domination. The defeat of the German Empire was at the same time the defeat of its conservative ruling elite. The struggle to restructure Germany along social democratic lines was burdened from the outset by the onerous terms of the Treaty of Versailles.

The declaration of war in 1914 was greeted with enthusiasm in every quarter. Only a few warned against it. The parties agreed a political "truce". Ostensibly, the nation was united in its support for a just war of self-defence. Even the Social Democrats approved the war credits.

The war began with Germany's invasion of Belgium. However, the rapid German advance was halted in the autumn at the battle of the Marne. The ensuing years of bloody trench warfare at Verdun, in northern France and in Flanders cost the lives of millions of soldiers.

The German army suffered its "black day" on 8 August 1918, when allied tanks broke through its defences at Amiens. Its retreat to the defensive positions along the so-called "Siegfried line" began. Hopes of victory in the west had long been replaced by fears of a complete military collapse.

In the east, the German army was initially on the defensive. In August 1914, East Prussia was threatened by the "Russian steamroller". This threat was averted, however, by German victories, under General von Hindenburg, at the battles of Tannenberg and the Masurian Lakes. After initial successes, the Russian offensive in the Carpathians also ground to a halt, the Russian army having suffered huge losses. A German-Austrian counter-offensive led by General von Makkensen brought the Russian Empire to the brink of collapse. The agitation of communist revolutionaries fell on fertile soil among the ranks of the Russian army. In 1917, the German supreme command allowed Lenin, the leader of the Bolsheviks, to travel through Germany by train on his way to Russia. Following their successful October revolution, in March 1918 the Bolsheviks were forced to bow to the harsh terms of the Treaty of Brest-Litovsk. Russia lost its western provinces; the Ukraine gained independence. Although troops were urgently needed in the west, further military action was taken, the so-called "railway advance", to force Russia to pay reparations. By pushing through their "great eastern solution", the supreme commanders of the German army, Hindenburg and Ludendorff, won a victory of doubtful value over the political leadership.

In December 1916 the German Empire for the first time announced its willingness to enter into peace negotiations. But its offer was rejected by the allies. Their rejection was a boost for those in Germany who wanted victory at any price and at the same time had set themselves the goal of preventing any democratic "softening" of the internal structure of the Empire. Chancellor Bethmann-Hollweg, was dismissed. His successor, Georg Michaelis, was fully under the influence of the

IV/183
German reservists on their way to the western front, August 1914

supreme command of the army. Hindenburg and Ludendorff were now not only Germany's military leaders but also de facto its political leaders.

In 1917 the SPD, the Centre and the Progressive People's Party formed the "Cross-party Group", whose aim was to introduce a parliamentary monarchy and a negotiated peace without victors or vanquished. Its programme formed the basis of the so-called "peace resolution" adopted by the Reichstag in July 1917.

For a number of SPD members of parliament, the cross-party group's proposals did not go far enough. Resolutely opposed to any continuation of the war, they refused to approve further war credits. In the spring of 1917 they broke away from the SPD to form the Independent Social Democratic Party (USPD). Formally, they linked up with the "International Group" which under its leaders Karl Lieb-knecht and Rosa Luxemburg had, since 1915, been actively fighting against the war aims of the Reichstag majority using slogans such as "Down with the war!" As the "Spartacus Group", the International Group formed the nucleus of the later Communist Party of Germany (KPD).

The extreme military and political tensions of 1917 prompted William II to offer the prospect of a reform of Prussia's three-class electoral system. However, only once the military situation had become completely hopeless, were the Empire's leaders, under the influence of the supreme army command, willing to make any genuine concessions: by proposing a number of substantial reforms in October 1918, the new Chancellor, Prince Max von Baden, took a decisive step towards the creation of a truly parliamentary system of government – too late, however, as it was soon to turn out.

V/184
Battlefield at Verdun

The German Reich after 1918

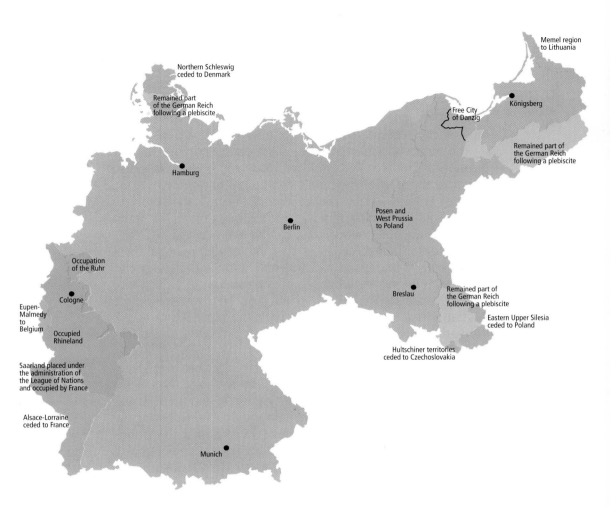

Memel region
to Lithuania

Northern Schleswig
ceded to Denmark

Remained part
of the German Reich
following a plebiscite

Free City
of Danzig

Königsberg

Hamburg

Remained part of
the German Reich
following a plebiscite

Posen and
West Prussia
to Poland

Berlin

Occupation
of the Ruhr

Cologne

Breslau

Remained part of
the German Reich
following a plebiscite

Eupen-
Malmedy
to
Belgium

Occupied
Rhineland

Eastern Upper Silesia
ceded to Poland

Hultschiner territories
ceded to Czechoslovakia

Saarland placed under
the administration of
the League of Nations
and occupied by France

Alsace-Lorraine
ceded to France

Munich

The Weimar Republic

V. The Weimar Republic

In the autumn of 1918, after four years of war, the national fervour which in August 1914 had appeared to unite the German people across all the traditional barriers had given way to complete disillusionment and exhaustion. The certainty of imminent military defeat caused old conflicts to resurface, culminating in spontaneous revolutionary uprisings at the beginning of November in many parts of the Reich.

The authoritarian monarchist state collapsed with the abdication of Emperor William II on 9 November 1918. This also signalled the start of the public debate on the form which the German Empire, established following the military victory of 1871, should assume in the wake of military defeat. The traditional military and political elite having been largely discredited, the Social Democrats were now the leading political force in Germany. They aimed to carry out fundamental economic and social reforms but at the same time sought to prevent under any circumstances a radicalization of the revolution on the Russian model. They cooperated with the old military establishment and the imperial administration to ward off attacks from the radical revolutionary camp.

In the midst of revolutionary unrest, elections were held for a constituent National Assembly. The result confirmed social democracy as the leading political force, and a Social Democrat, Friedrich Ebert, also became the first President of the Reich. The constitution of 11 August 1919 ended the transitional period of almost one year following the abdication of William II and laid the foundations of the Weimar Republic. It satisfied the old liberal demand for parliamentary democracy, thereby guaranteeing direct popular influence on the political decision-making process. Before the constitution was adopted, however, important decisions had already been taken which were to have a lasting effect on developments in Germany and increasingly poisoned the political atmosphere. In the Treaty of Versailles the victors dictated that Germany should cede certain territories, and this considerably weakened the economic power of the Reich. Reparation demands were a financial burden, made all the heavier by the fact that the German currency had lost much of its value as a result of the war debt. The war-guilt clause, however, was the main reason why the Treaty of Versailles was rejected by all Germans. Nevertheless, the political leaders had no choice but to sign the Treaty. The nationalist Right, who had found the defeat and the revolution impossible to accept, now spread the "stab-in-the-back" legend, accusing the parties which had advocated a negotiated peace in 1917, the parties that were now jointly governing the country, of betraying an "undefeated" army. The right-wing extremist agitation escalated into putsches and assassinations, as well as provoking a counter-reaction from the extreme left. The Reichstag elections of 1920 reflected the strength of anti-republican feeling, which was further intensified by economic developments. The government passed on the cost of the lost war to those whose loans had helped finance the war, and in so doing it lost the support of broad sections of the middle class, who saw the basis of their existence threatened by the depreciation of their savings. Reparations and the occupation of the Ruhr pushed inflation to a peak in 1923. By the time the revaluation of the mark (the *Rentenmark*) initiated the stabilization of the economy, a redistribution of national wealth had taken place which seriously disrupted the social structure of the Reich.

The victorious powers recognized that Germany was not economically in a position to meet the Allied reparation demands. This gave rise to a series of conferences and plans aimed at trying to solve the reparations problem, which dominated German domestic and foreign policy for years. Heavy though the remaining financial burden was, foreign investment loans permitted the modernization of German production facilities and, from 1924, led to economic recovery in Germany, which had a favourable influence on social and economic developments. Real wages as well as production and export figures reached or exceeded their pre-war levels around 1926. This relative prosperity made people feel that they had had a narrow escape and even look with some optimism, albeit momentary, to the future; in retrospect, these feelings combined to form in people's minds the vivid but illusory image of the "golden twenties".

The successes in foreign policy which Gustav Stresemann, during his six years in office, pursued with a consistency that was unique in the conditions prevalent in the Weimar Republic, strengthened the position of the Reich, mitigated the consequences of the lost war and allowed Germany to break out of its postwar isolation. International agreements, the withdrawal of foreign troops from occupied areas, further reductions in reparation demands and progress towards Germany's acceptance as an equal partner were all steps on the way to a revision of the Treaty of Versailles. At home, the dispute between the Reich and the former territorial princes, the attitude of the judiciary and the conflict with the army and navy were all reminders that the forces of authoritarianism had not been broken. The figurehead of these forces, which tended to be anti-republican, was Field Marshal Paul von Hindenburg, who had remained loyal to the Emperor and in 1925, after the death of Friedrich Ebert, was elected by a majority of the German people to become the second Reich President – an office endowed by the republican constitution with considerable power.

The world economic crisis, which began in 1929, caused a profound transformation of the German political scene. It brought to an end the phase of consolidation and led to an increasing radicalization and polarization of politics, which gradually crippled the democratic institutions. Foreign capital, which had mostly taken the form of short-term loans, was withdrawn. Industry tried to reduce wages in order to remain competitive. In view of increasing unemployment, the traditional weapon of the unions – strike action – was blunted. The extremist parties of the Left and Right, which had always rejected the parliamentary system, suddenly found that they were able to prevent the formation of stable democratic majorities, since the middle-class democratic parties were becoming fragmented and were steadily losing support. The crisis of the parties developed into a parliamentary crisis and thus a crisis of the Weimar Republic as such. From March 1930 onwards a parliamentary majority supporting the republic no longer existed. The Chancellor governed by virtue of a series of emergency decrees, which made him independent of Parliament. In this situation the Reich President increasingly became a key political figure. The extensive rights he enjoyed under the constitution gave him a dominating position vis-à-vis Parliament, which was no longer able to take majority decisions. Political decision-making shifted from Parliament to the President's office. In view of Parliament's weakness and the Chancellor's dependence on the confidence of the President alone, the Weimar system came to resemble the pre-republican system of government under the Emperor. With Parliament having been virtually eclipsed, the achievements of the 1918/19 Revolution lost their political base. Although democratic elections still took place, their results increasingly strengthened those parties which opposed democracy, thereby further undermining the parliamentary system. Large – and important – sections of the population turned their backs in disillusionment on the parliamentary system and relied on an authoritarian solution to the political and social conflicts. While Socialists and Social Democrats waged a bitter battle with each other and the Republic also faced increased pressure from the extreme Left, political expediency brought about an alliance of the Right, aimed at persuading the President to "form a truly national government". After Hindenburg had been re-elected Reich President in the spring of 1932 it became possible to seek such a solution to the crisis, now also favoured by the majority of the German people. Two years' experience of an anti-parliamentary presidential cabinet did not offer the prospect of a return to a form of government consistent with the "spirit of the constitution". On the contrary, after two more attempts to govern by means of presidential cabinets had failed, the President was more prepared to "place his trust" in the man who had for years been making a name for himself as the most radical anti-republican and anti-parliamentarian and who, moreover, enjoyed mass support: Adolf Hitler, the leader of the National Socialist German Workers' Party (NSDAP).

V/185
Mutiny of the fleet in Wilhelmshaven in early November 1918

1. The Revolution of 1918/19 and the creation of the Republic

Even the Revolution of 1918/19 did not bring about a truly democratic political and social order in Germany. Although the previous system of constitutional monarchy, with its pronounced authoritarian features, was replaced by parliamentary democracy, success in realizing the more ambitious goal of a thorough transformation of the state, the economy and society was very limited. In the spring of 1919, the historian Friedrich Meineke concluded that so far "no complete revolution of the political and social order has taken place in our country".

The hopes of victory that had been raised one last time by the German offensive of March 1918 were de-

V/186
Demonstration in Berlin on 9 November 1918

2. Extraausgabe   Sonnabend, den 9. November 1918.

Vorwärts

Berliner Volksblatt.
Zentralorgan der sozialdemokratischen Partei Deutschlands.

Der Kaiser hat abgedankt!

Der Reichskanzler hat folgenden Erlaß herausgegeben:

Seine Majestät der Kaiser und König haben sich entschlossen, dem Throne zu entsagen.

Der Reichskanzler bleibt noch so lange im Amte, bis die mit der Abdankung Seiner Majestät, dem Thronverzichte Seiner Kaiserlichen und Königlichen Hoheit des Kronprinzen des Deutschen Reichs und von Preußen und der Einsetzung der Regentschaft verbundenen Fragen geregelt sind. Er beabsichtigt, dem Regenten die Ernennung des Abgeordneten Ebert zum Reichskanzler und die Vorlage eines Gesetzentwurfs wegen der Ausschreibung allgemeiner Wahlen für eine verfassunggebende deutsche Nationalversammlung vorzuschlagen, der es obliegen würde, die künftige Staatsform des deutschen Volk, einschließlich der Volksteile, die ihren Eintritt in die Reichsgrenzen wünschen sollten, endgültig festzustellen.

Berlin, den 9. November 1918. **Der Reichskanzler.**

Prinz Max von Baden.

Es wird nicht geschossen!

Der Reichskanzler hat angeordnet, daß seitens des Militärs von der Waffe kein Gebrauch gemacht werde.

Parteigenossen! Arbeiter! Soldaten!

Soeben sind das Alexanderregiment und die vierten Jäger geschlossen zum Volke übergegangen. Der sozialdemokratische Reichstagsabgeordnete Wels u. a. haben zu den Truppen gesprochen. Offiziere haben sich den Soldaten angeschlossen.

Der sozialdemokratische Arbeiter- und Soldatenrat.

V/187
Front page of the Social Democrat newspaper *Vorwärts* annoucing the abdication of the Emperor on 9 November 1918

stroyed by the Allied counter-offensive. At the end of September 1918 the German Military High Command had to admit that the war which was to have brought Germany supremacy in Europe was now lost and that only an immediate end to the hostilities could prevent a complete military collapse. Politically, the German request for an armistice was accompanied by a reform of the Reich Constitution and of the electoral system. At the beginning of October 1918 the new Reich Chancellor, Prince Max of Baden, formed his cabinet in close consultation with the majority parties in the Reichstag. These parties' efforts over the years to make the executive answerable to Parliament were thus at long last successful.

However, William II and the military command were not at all prepared to submit to the new government of the Reich supported by Parliament. And so within a few days the internal crisis escalated dramatically. Beginning in the seaports, the revolutionary movement spread across the whole of Germany. In many towns and cities, spontaneously formed Workers' and Soldiers' Councils assumed political and military command. The call for the Emperor's abdication grew ever louder.

On 9 November 1918, the revolutionary unrest reached Berlin. Reich

Die Gründung der deutschen Republik.

V/188

The first Council of
People's Represen-
tatives and the
proclamation of
the Republic

Chancellor Max von Baden persuaded William II to abdicate and
he handed over his own post to the
Social Democrat Friedrich Ebert.
But the pace of events was quick-
ening. From a window of the Reichstag building, Ebert's party col-
league Philipp Scheidemann proclaimed the "German Republic".
Shortly afterwards, in front of the
royal palace, Karl Liebknecht, leader of the Spartacus League, proclaimed the "Free Socialist Republic". Thus began the dispute about
the shape of the new republic. The
Berlin Workers' and Soldiers' Councils entrusted governmental authority to a "Council of People's Representatives", consisting of equal
numbers of Majority Social Democrats and Independent Social Democrats. The Social Democrats accepted this "mandate of the revolution" in order to consolidate their
position as the leading political
force in Germany. At the same
time, Ebert and the other SPD leaders considered their main task to
consist in "saving the German peo-

ple from civil war and famine".
They believed that the only way to
cope with the consequences of the
lost war was to work with the imperial bureaucracy and the military
establishment. This cooperation
and agreements reached with the
Land governments largely predetermined the political order of the Republic. An equally significant decision was the Stinnes-Legien Agreement of 15 November in the economic sector. Industry, represented
by the Ruhr industrialist Hugo Stin-
nes, recognized the trade unions as
negotiating partners; in return, the
chairman of the Association of Free
Trade Unions, Carl Legien, re-
nounced on behalf of his organization most of the demands for nationalization.
The Left wanted far-reaching economic and social reforms to safeguard the revolutionary socialist
achievements. Only then should
elections take place for a national
assembly; radical forces were even
contemplating a republic governed
in all spheres by Workers' and Sol-

V/189
Demonstration
against the elec-
tions to the Nation-
al Assembly

diers' Councils. By contrast, the Social Democrats were stalwart supporters of parliamentary democracy. Establishing the new political
and social order was to be the exclusive responsibility of an elected
national assembly, for which the
SDP managed to secure a clear majority at the National Congress of

Workers' and Soldiers' Councils in
mid-December 1918.
On 28 December 1918, fundamental differences, especially on military policy, forced the Independent
Social Democrats to resign from the
Council of People's Representatives. The radical leftist forces of
the Spartacus League staged an up-

V/190
Poster for the elec-
tions to the Nation-
al Assembly on
19 January 1919

V/191
Government troops
on guard duty dur-
ing the Spartacist
uprising in January
1919

rising in Berlin in January 1919, which the Government, using free corps, brought to a bloody end. However, the troops with which the SPD leaders sought to protect the republic were themselves anti-democratic. The murder of Rosa Luxemburg and Karl Liebknecht by free corps on 15 January 1919 was the first in a long series of assassi-

V/192
Spartacists fighting
in the newspaper
district

nations for which the extreme Right was responsible.

When the National Assembly was elected on 19 January 1919, with women being entitled to vote and stand for election for the first time, the Social Democrats emerged as the strongest party but did not obtain an overall majority. In the constituent assembly, which convened

V/193
Friedrich Ebert's
inaugural address
to the National As-
sembly in Weimar
in February 1919

in Weimar because of the distur-
bances in Berlin, they were obliged
to cooperate with the democratic
middle-class parties. Together with
the Centre party and the German
Democratic Party, the SPD formed
the so-called Weimar Coalition,
which held a three-quarters majority. Friedrich Ebert became the first
President of the new Republic.

The Constitution

The constitution of the Weimar Republic, drafted by the left-wing liberal Hugo Preuss, the new State
Secretary at the Ministry of the Interior, was strongly influenced by
the liberal and democratic tradition
of 1848. The central political organ
was now the Reichstag – the gov-

V/194
The first women
parliamentarians

V/195
Friedrich Ebert,
portrait by Lovis
Corinth, 1924

ernment depended on its confidence, and its legislative decisions were now subject to hardly any restriction by the Reichsrat, the body representing the constituent states, or *Länder*. However, the Reich President was given considerable powers to enable him to act as a counterweight to Parliament: he appointed the government and could dissolve the Reichstag; in particular, Article 48 gave him extensive powers during a state of emergency. The system of proportional representation encouraged the fragmentation of parties. Contrary to the provisions drafted by Preuss, the federal constitution and the strong position of Prussia remained intact. However, through Erzberger's financial reform in particular, the central government was given additional weight. Even after the defeat, German unity in the form established in 1871 was not questioned by any significant section of the German population.

The constitution of the Weimar Republic pointed the way towards a democratic social order, and incorporated Social Democratic ideas on the welfare state. But the disparities between the constitution and a social reality that lagged far behind its aims placed a heavy burden on the young Republic.

The Treaty of Versailles and its implications for domestic politics

In the Treaty of Versailles the victors dictated that Germany should cede certain territories and be largely disarmed. The assertion that Germany bore sole responsibility for the war, which the German side vehemently disputed, was used to justify reparation demands. However, the unity of Germany remained intact, although for security reasons the Germans in Austria were not permitted to join the Reich and to that extent were denied the right to self-determination.

In Germany the Treaty of Versailles encountered unanimous disapproval. The democratic politicians, who with great reluctance had been forced by circumstances to sign the Treaty, were subjected to vicious slander.

It was from this very agitation against the Treaty of Versailles, against the politicians in favour of fulfilling the conditions of the Treaty of Versailles and the "November criminals", that the extreme Right derived its political strength. On 13 March 1920 rightwing radicals staged the Kapp Putsch in Berlin. The insurgents wanted to eradicate the parliamentary democratic state and to restore the monarchic system. The armed forces, the *Reichswehr*, refused to quell the revolt by force of arms. The Government and the Reichstag had to flee to Dresden and Stuttgart. The SPD and the unions called a general strike, whereupon the putsch collapsed after only a few days. Its failure, however, was not seized upon as an opportunity for thorough stabilization of the democratic order.

The radicalization of domestic politics, the serious economic and social problems resulting from the war, and Germany's hopeless situation in the field of foreign affairs were reflected in the Reichstag elections of 6 June 1920. The parties of the far Right and Left were able to increase their vote consider-

V/196
The German delegation before leaving for Versailles in 1919

Die deutsche Friedensdelegation

Prof. Schücking   Giesberts   Landsberg   Brockdorff-Rantzau   Leinert   Dr. Melch

6612

Phot. August

V/197
Demonstration in
Berlin against the
Versailles Treaty

ably. The Weimar Coalition lost almost 40 per cent of its seats and
thus the majority, which it was unable to regain before the demise of
the Weimar Republic in 1933. Thus
began the years of political instability, with minority cabinets replacing
each other in rapid succession.

V/198
Soldiers with the
imperial naval en-
sign participating
in the Kapp Putsch
in Berlin in March
1920

2. The parties of the Weimar Republic

The Revolution of 1918/19 and the adoption of the Weimar constitution placed the parties at the centre of political power. However, even though a new start was made in some respects, the parties, which continued to be marked in every way by the political system of the Empire, failed to adjust to the requirements of the new parliamentary democratic order. Even after 1918, the parties still primarily regarded themselves as representing more or less clearly defined social groups and constituencies. They were reluctant to assume governmental responsibility and, in view of their voters' interests, were often unable to reach compromises and form stable majorities. Thus the initially large majority enjoyed by the "Weimar Coalition", which consist-

ed of Social Democrats, the Centre and left-wing Liberals, was already lost in the third Reichstag election of June 1920. Thereafter, the country was mainly governed by politically unstable minority cabinets formed by the middle-class parties. Long before the profound crisis of the early thirties, political influence began to shift away from the parties and Parliament to the executive and to the Reich President in particular. The inability of the parties to form democratic majorities created a vacuum which the authoritarian and anti-democratic forces were ultimately able to fill.

V/201
SPD poster, 1932

V/202
Poster of the Centre party, 1932

the SPD, the left wing tended to support the radical socialist programme of the Spartacus League. After cooperation with the SPD had failed, the USPD became increasingly radical and eventually broke up in 1920. Only then did the Communist Party of Germany (KPD), which had developed from the Spartacus League, become a mass party representing the workers. Even after giving up their putsch tactics in 1923, the Communists steered an uncompromising course of opposition and obstruction against the Weimar Republic and helped swell the ranks of the anti-democratic majority, which became ever larger after 1929.

With the Revolution of 1918/19, the former opposition, the Social Democrats, were called upon to assume political leadership. The SPD, deliberately forming an alliance with the middle-class parties, used its position to establish a parlia-

The Independent Social Democratic Party (USPD), a left-wing party formed in 1917, was already divided at the beginning of the Weimar Republic. While the majority of the party favoured a programme of socialist reform in cooperation with

mentary republic. Until 1932 the party also remained the strongest political grouping, but its leaders failed in their efforts to extend the party's appeal beyond its traditional social constituency, with its strong working-class links, and to transform the SPD into a left-wing party enjoying mass support. In fact, the Social Democrats became increasingly embroiled in a conflict between loyalty to ideological principles and the requirements of government. This struggle, which was also waged within the party, often forced the SPD on to the defensive and not infrequently prevented it – despite its important role in the formulation of decisions on domestic and foreign affairs – from actively influencing the Republic's political course.

In 1918/19, after initially trying to become an interdenominational party, the Centre again developed into a party reflecting Catholic beliefs and principles. Its supporters ranged from aristocratic landowners to Christian trade unionists. Whereas the majority of the Bavarian People's Party favoured restoration of the monarchy, the majority of the Centre upheld the parliamen-

V/204
DDP poster, 1920

V/203
DVP poster, 1930

tary democratic Republic, though often with some reservations. From 1919 to 1932 the Centre participated in every Reich government, playing an important mediating role and providing several chancellors. However, under the party chairman, Ludwig Kaas, elected in 1928, and particularly during Heinrich Brüning's chancellorship, the Centre too became increasingly conservative and thus ever less able and willing to cooperate with the Social Democrats.

the constitutional field – helped set up the Republic and actively supported it, was clearly stronger. But as early as 1920 the DDP lost a large proportion of its voters to the nationalist-liberal German People's Party (DVP), which was only gradually persuaded by Gustav Stresemann to support the Weimar constitution and assume governmental responsibility. However, in the longer term neither liberal party was able to retain the support of large sections of the middle-class electorate. The deep-rooted crisis of liberalism manifested itself during the Weimar period in the increasingly rapid decline of the DDP and DVP vote until, especially after 1930, they were no more than mere splinter parties.

In December 1918 the German National People's Party (DNVP) was formed as the successor to the two conservative parties of the Empire. It was a monarchist party and primarily represented the interests of agriculture and heavy industry. For a long time DNVP policy vacillated between consistent opposition to the Weimar system and a readiness to cooperate to some extent. The

V/205
DNVP poster, 1920s

In 1918/19 the Liberals again split into two parties. Initially, the left-wing liberal German Democratic Party (DDP) which – particularly in

V/206
Campaign hoardings on Potsdamer Platz in the run-up to the presidential election in 1932

participation of the DNVP in the governments formed in 1925 and 1927 was a major bone of contention within the party. The party's right wing under Alfred Hugenberg finally asserted itself in 1928; under his leadership, the DNVP was put back on an implacably anti-republican course, culminating in cooperation with the National Socialists.

1921 and 1922; one of these was Adolf Hitler's National Socialist German Workers' Party (NSDAP). The extreme Right was responsible for numerous assassinations, acts of violence and attempted coups. However, apart from occasional partial successes, for a long time the far right had only limited political appeal. Not until the onset of the economic, social and political crisis in 1929 did the NSDAP, which had been efficiently reorganized in 1925, become a great rallying point for all opponents of the democratic system and all victims of the economic crisis.

Following in the footsteps of earlier antisemitic nationalist organizations and of the free corps of the revolutionary period, militant right-wing extremists formed a multitude of secret societies and parties in

V/207
Constitution day ceremony in the plenary chamber of the Reichstag on 11 August 1924

3. 1923, the year of crisis

The history of the year 1923 encapsulates almost all the foreign and domestic political problems, as well as the economic and social difficulties, which were such obstacles to the establishment and stabilization of a democratic order in Germany after 1918.

The year began with French and Belgian troops marching into the Ruhr, the industrial heart of the German Reich. The occupation forces were sent to enforce the French reparation demands, particularly for coal from the Ruhr, and to secure the Ruhr as a political pawn. In Germany the occupation of the Ruhr aroused a wave of national outrage. The Reich Government called for passive resistance to the occupation forces. But the enormous cost of the acts of resistance and the production losses plunged the German economy into a financial crisis. Inflation, already galloping as a result of war debts and reparation liabilities, now degenerated into hyperinflation. Within a few months the German currency lost virtually all of its value.

The critical political situation, the increasing violence on both sides in the Ruhr dispute, the economic and social distress in the wake of inflation – these also served as an ideal breeding ground for extremist groups of various complexions. Supported by the French occupation forces, separatist circles tried to induce the Rhineland to break away from Germany. In central Germany and in Hamburg the Communists redoubled their efforts to

V/209
French soldiers in
the Ruhr in 1923

foment revolution. At the other end of the political spectrum, Bavaria in particular became a hotbed of reactionary conservative and right-wing extremist activity. At times a military dictatorship even seemed to be imminent in the Reich.

Not until August, when it was impossible to go on financing the Ruhr struggle, was there a reorientation of national policy. Under the DVP politician Gustav Stresemann a Grand Coalition comprising the SPD, the DDP, the Centre and the DVP was formed, whose vigorous action succeeded in overcoming the acute crisis. On 26 September 1923, initially in the face of strong opposition, not least from his own party, Stresemann gained approval for the unconditional cessation of the struggle in the Ruhr. Ten days later, he defended himself in the Reichstag against accusations of treachery from the nationalist Right with these words: "The courage to

V/210
Acts of sabotage in
the Ruhr during the
French occupation

V/211
Company wages
being transported
in Berlin as inflation
hits its peak

assume responsibility for giving up passive resistance is perhaps more nationalist than the slogans with which the decision was opposed." At the same time, radical measures were taken to rehabilitate the German currency. *Reichswehr* units marched into Saxony, and its Popular Front government was removed from office. Although less vigorous action was taken against the anti-republican tendencies of the Right in Bavaria, the situation became more stable there too in the months that followed the abortive Hitler Putsch of 9 November 1923.

V/212
Bread shortages
in 1923, the year
of inflation

Almost miraculously, the Republic came through its ordeal in the autumn of 1923. The immediate danger of right and left-wlng coups was averted and a period of stabilization began.

Yet the anti-democratic reservations about the Republic remained strong among many sections of the population as well as in the bureaucracy, judiciary and armed forces. But above all the traumatic experience of inflation caused large sections of the middle classes to lose faith in the republican and democratic system.

V/213
The *Reichswehr* marching into Dresden at the end of October 1923

V/214
National Socialist combat patrol during the Hitler putsch in Munich on 9 November 1923

4. Rapallo and Locarno

During the twenties, Gustav Stresemann had a decisive influence on German foreign policy. From 1923 to 1929, he headed the German Foreign Office in seven different cabinets. The aim of his foreign policy was to regain German primacy in Central Europe in the context of the new situation created by the war. The key to this policy was a rapprochement with the Western powers, particularly France, coupled with efforts to revise the territorial provisions of the Treaty of Versailles regarding the east.

reparations. By means of a policy of strict "fulfilment" of the allied reparation demands, the Reich Government tried to prove the impossibility of fulfilling them and to ensure their revision. However, the absence of any German efforts to rehabilitate the mark tended to deepen the victors' suspicions. France in particular tried to insist on more stringent demands. The Western powers' unease about German foreign policy was increased by the contacts which Germany had been maintaining since 1920 with

V/215
Chancellor Joseph Wirth and the Soviet delegation in Rapallo on 16 April 1922

The Treaty of Versailles and the problem of reparations were the framework within which the foreign policy of the Weimar Republic was conducted. In 1921, following threatening ultimatums from the Allies, Germany had to agree to pay 132,000 million marks in war

the young Soviet Union. These contacts led to the signing on 16 April 1922 of the Treaty of Rapallo, in which the two sides waived each other's financial liabilities, established diplomatic relations and agreed on closer economic cooperation. With this treaty, Germany

V/216
President Hinden-
burg greeting Soviet
officers

broke out of its international isolation and kept open the option of a
revision of its eastern border with
Poland. This policy was reaffirmed
by the German-Soviet Friendship
Treaty, which was signed in Berlin
on 24 April 1926.

After the occupation of the Ruhr,
Gustav Stresemann also initiated a
reorientation of the German Government's policy towards the West.
Through compromise, and above all
through reconciliation with France,
he wanted Germany to regain

V/217
The final meeting in
Locarno in October
1925

V/218
Ceremony marking
French withdrawal
from the first
Rhineland zone,
with President von
Hindenburg and
Konrad Adenauer,
mayor of Cologne

V/219
Meeting of the International Reparations Commission
in London in 1924

equal rights within the international community. This policy of rapprochement culminated in October 1925 in the treaties concluded at Locarno, in which the German Reich recognized the status quo in the west which Versailles had cre- ated. Improved relations with the Western powers also meant that steps could be taken towards a fresh start on reparations policy. Under strong American influence, the 1924 Dawes Plan and the 1929 Young Plan established consider-

V/220
Foreign ministers
Stresemann, Chamberlain and Briand,
and state secretary
Schubert, in Geneva
in September 1926

ably more favourable conditions for the settlement of German obligations. Germany's return to the fold of the leading European nations was underlined by its accession to the League of Nations in September 1926. In recognition of their contribution to the cause of European peace, Stresemann and the French Foreign Minister, Aristide Briand, were awarded the Nobel Peace Price in the same year. Stresemann's death in October 1929 was a severe loss to the Republic.

V/221
Gustav Stresemann
addressing the
League of Nations
in Geneva on
10 September 1926

V/222
The funeral of
Foreign Minister
Gustav Stresemann
on 3 October 1929;
the cortège in front
of the Reichstag
Building

V/223
Free corps soldiers
in Munich in 1919

5. Parties and movements

V/224
Members of the
youth organization
Wandervogel on an
outing in the 1920s

With the 1918/19 Revolution, responsibility for governing Germany passed into the hands of the political parties. The Weimar Republic was a modern-style party democracy, yet at the same time it was a "party state against its will". Both the ruling classes and the population at large undoubtedly had serious reservations about the parties. This was reflected not least in the position of the Reich President and

in the political hopes placed after 1925 in Field Marshal von Hindenburg as a sort of "substitute Emperor".

These negative feelings partly stemmed from a traditional rejection of party politics, a legacy of authoritarian rule. But they also owed much to the material and psychological uprooting of large sections of the younger generation as a result of the world war. Even where experience of the front did not lead to membership of free corps or of authoritarian and conservative ex-servicemen's organizations, such as the *Stahlhelm*, it often resulted in a profound aversion to the alleged incompetence of the parties, to their political squabbling and seeming paralysis.

The desire for a new beginning, the urge for change and movement, as well as for a firm sense of purpose which far transcended politics in the narrow sense of the word, rekindled many of the ideas which had been reflected since the turn of the century in what was known as the Youth Movement. The youth associations that were part of this movement, above all the *Wandervogel* organization founded in 1901, experienced a renaissance in the twenties. The forms of leisure activity and organization developed

V/225
Rally of the Red Front in Berlin in 1926

V/226
Hitler's personal
bodyguard, the
nucleus of the SS,
in 1925

V/227
Parade of the
Reichsbanner
Schwarz-Rot-Gold
in Berlin in 1928

by them also spread to the youth organizations of the democratic parties.

The new principle of forming a movement, based on militant political organizations was taken up with particular zeal by the radical Left and Right. The National Socialists in particular succeeded at a very early stage in winning over large groups of young people and students and organizing them rigorously in the various NSDAP associations. In sharp contrast to the

V/228
Social Democrats
canvassing for votes
in the Reichstag
elections of Decem-
ber 1924

parties, which depended on a traditional following, the Nazi movement managed to appeal to and integrate highly diverse social groups. The youth associations' desire to feel closely integrated in a community was now harnessed as a political force by the National Socialists to promote their ideology of the *Volksgemeinschaft* or "national community".

formed was the *Reichsbanner Schwarz-Rot-Gold*. Uniforms became increasingly conspicuous at the meetings and rallies of every political party.

Meanwhile, political life in general was becoming increasingly militarized. Fighting and bloodshed in the streets and meeting places, especially between Communists and National Socialists, became almost

V/229

Police after a beer-hall brawl in Berlin in 1932

In the light of the increasing appeal of the NSDAP and KPD towards the end of the Weimar Republic, the democratic parties also adopted these organizational principles. The main republican militia to be

everyday occurrences after 1930. In the end, in 1933 it was the political party which most clearly embodied the notion of a "movement" and the new concept of party-political organization which won the day.

V/230
A Berlin street scene
in the late 1920s

6. Controversial modern trends

In the twenties Germany experienced a great upsurge in intellectual and artistic life. The roots of this cultural revival and the modern ideas and creations which furthered it mostly originated around the turn of the century. But it was now that these developments achieved their widest impact, especially since in many respects the new democratic constitution offered them much greater scope. At the same time, cultural activities became, to an unprecedented degree, the subject of intellectual discussion and political argument.

In literature and drama, in painting and in architecture, expressionism and other related styles initially remained predominant. From about 1923, new art forms appeared, for which the term "New Objektivity" was soon coined. The most enduring legacy, both in Germany and internationally, came from the architecture of the twenties, particularly from the creative ideas of the "Bauhaus" school. In addition, a new type of mass culture began to develop. It was promoted both by new and often highly agitational approaches to literature and drama and by the extraordinary rise of the mass media, to which the press contributed just as much as the new media of film and radio.

V/232
The Bauhaus in
Dessau, set up by
Walter Gropius

V/233
Setting trends in
publicly assisted
housing: the
"horseshoe estate"
in Berlin-Britz, de-
signed by Bruno
Taut and Martin
Wagner and built
between 1925 and
1927

Altogether, many different changes in outlook and behaviour could be observed during the 1920s. In the sports and bathing boom, in sexuality and in other spheres, such as fashion, a more liberal attitude towards the body manifested itself. Many other traditions and standards became less of a constraint. This was reflected not least in the changing role of women, who – partly as a result of the transforma-

V/231 (opposite)
"Bauhaus stair-
case", painting by
Oskar Schlemmer,
1932

V/234
A scene from the film "The Blue Angel" with Hans Albers and Marlene Dietrich

tion that took place during the First World War – were increasingly going out to work and appearing in public with growing self-confidence.

In the economic sphere the progressive industrialization of Germany now extended to almost every sector and region. During the twenties this process was accompanied by a strong tendency towards rationalization. The introduction of the conveyor belt in production and of the typewriter and the open-plan office in the administrative sector not only had a lasting impact on the working environment but also created considerable social problems. This applied even more to agriculture, the crafts and the increasingly concentrated commercial sector, which regarded themselves as the main losers in the process of industrialization and modernization.

Social distress and fear of social decline gave rise to fundamental opposition to all things modern. This

V/235
Meeting of the
writers' section of
the Academy of Arts
in Berlin in 1929:
(from the left) Al-
fred Döblin, Thomas
Mann, Ricarda
Huch, Bernhard
Kellermann, Her-
mann Steht, Alfred
Mombert, Eduard
Stucken

opposition went hand-in-hand with a pronounced rejection of the new lifestyles and behavioural patterns and an often fanatical crusade against all modern cultural and artistic trends. During the years of the Weimar Republic, all modern phenomena were the subject of sharp controversy – a fundamental divergence of views which added considerably to the already serious political differences.

V/236
The 1926 Motor
Show in Berlin

V/238
The New York
Stock Exchange
in Wall Street on
"Black Friday",
1929

7. The Great Depression

All moves towards a more comprehensive and lasting stabilization in Germany were brought to an abrupt end by the Great Depression. The Wall Street Crash of 25 October 1929 suddenly made the public aware of the symptoms of crisis, which were by no means new. Declining investment, the closing down of production facilities, cuts in income, mass unemployment and protectionism in turn influenced and accelerated the international economic slump.

In Germany, the crisis hit an economy which had obvious structural weaknesses. For years farmers had complained of falling incomes and were heavily indebted. The modernization of industry, the building boom in cities, towns and villages, indeed the entire economic up-

V/239
Insolvent bank
in 1931

swing of the twenties was largely financed by short-term investments of foreign capital. In view of the universal shortage of capital, these funds were now gradually being recalled. Furthermore, political events in Germany, and particularly the National Socialists' electoral successes, had a disastrous effect on the confidence of foreign investors.

The Brüning Government steered a rigorous deflationary course: government spending was drastically restricted, taxes were raised, public officials' salaries were cut, and a general wave of wage and income reductions began. Besides the fact that the economic crisis was erroneously taken to be a temporary decline in economic activity, the

V/239
Insolvent bank
in 1931

V/240
Queue of unemployed people in Berlin during the Great Depression

Rauchen nicht g... ...ler

Arbeitsvermittlung von 8½ – 2 Uhr
Sonnabends bis 12 Uhr.

Die Abstempe...
nach

ür die einzelnen Be...
ittlung.

1   2

3
Kontroll...

4
Kontrolle

V/241
Labour exchange
in Berlin in 1930

spectre of inflation played just as important a role in this context as the Brüning Government's fixation on solving the reparations problem. At any rate, the economic collapse was further aggravated by the Government's economic and financial policies. Industrial production fell by 1932 to almost half its 1928 level, and shares lost two thirds of

V/242
Members of a
voluntary labour
brigade in 1932

their value. In the middle of 1931 the crisis worsened again as a number of banks went bankrupt, sucking some well-known industrial concerns into the maelstrom.

The central problem of the Great Depression, however, was mass unemployment. The unemployment figures, which had been high even during the years of relative prosper-

V/243
Passers-by looking at an NSDAP poster for the 1932 presidential election

V/244
Uniformed NSDAP deputies in the Reichstag after the elections of October 1930

ity, soared at the end of 1929. One year later, four million people were already registered as unemployed, and at the beginning of 1932 the six-million mark was exceeded, as against only twelve million people in employment. The provision of social security, particularly for the longer-term unemployed, was totally inadequate. Although the government and local authorities gradually developed a whole range of job-creation measures, this had no dramatic effect to begin with. Thus

8. The dissolution of the Republic

During the final years of the Weimar Republic ways of overcoming the economic crisis and the political radicalization it caused were increasingly sought outside the parliamentary democratic order. The difficulties of forming a democratic majority furthered a growing shift in the balance of political power away from the parties and Parliament to the Reich President and his

V/245
Meeting of Heinrich Brüning's cabinet in the Chancellery garden in August 1930

the Great Depression resulted in the impoverishment of large sections of the population and in a general radicalization of politics, which the democratic order of the Weimar Republic, built as it was on weak foundations, proved unable to handle.

conservative advisers. The efforts to transform the Republic into a more authoritarian state seriously weakened the forces and institutions of democracy. And so, on 30 January 1933, political power finally fell into the hands of the National Socialists.

V/246
Chancellor Heinrich
Brüning and the
French Foreign Min-
ister Aristide Briand
on their way to Lon-
don in July 1931

When the Grand Coalition under Chancellor Hermann Müller (SPD) broke up at the end of March 1930, no attempt was made to form a parliamentary government. The Reich President and his advisers favoured a presidential cabinet led by the Centre politician Heinrich Brüning; though not commanding a parliamentary majority, the cabinet was to govern with the aid of the emergency decrees provided for in

V/247
Hitler and Hugen-
berg in Bad Harz-
burg on 11 October
1931

V/248
Franz von Papen's
new cabinet in front
of the presidential
residence on 1 June
1932

V/249
A polling station
in Berlin during
the elections to the
Prussian State As-
sembly on 24 April
1932

Article 48 of the constitution and the right to dissolve the Reichstag. When the Reichstag overwhelmingly rejected the Government's stringent austerity programme on 16 July 1930, a general election was called, which led on 14 September 1930 to the NSDAP's first landslide victory. Chancellor Brüning saw his primary political task as the final elimination of the reparations burden. Economic measures were subordinated to this goal. The Government deliberately used the Depression as leverage to resolve the reparations question and was prepared to accept their consequences. And in fact the reparations pay-

V/250
Chancellor von
Schleicher outlining
his government's
policies in a radio
broadcast on 15 De-
cember 1932

ments were suspended for a year under the Hoover Moratorium of 1931, and in July 1932 they were completely terminated by the Lausanne Conference. However, this foreign-policy success came too late for Brüning himself to reap its benefits. The steadily worsening economic crisis led to the rapid growth of extreme right-wing forces in particular. In October 1931 the National Socialists, the German National People's Party, and the *Stahlhelm* joined ranks in the "Harzburg Front" to fight the Brüning Government and the Republic. Through skilful manoeuvring between these groups, Hitler ultimately succeeded in becoming its key political figure. Although in the presidential election of 1932 Hitler lost to Hindenburg, who was supported by all the democratic parties, the NSDAP finally emerged as the strongest party in July 1932.

The fall of Brüning at the end of May 1932 heralded the final phase of the dissolution of the Weimar Republic. General von Schleicher and the new Chancellor, Franz von Papen, the chief advisers to the President, tried to harness the dynamism of the National Socialist movement for their own political ends. The ban on the SA was lifted, the Reichstag dissolved and the SPD-led Prussian State Government removed from office. But the Government still failed to secure its toleration by the NSDAP parliamentary group; Hitler umcompromisingly demanded full political power. By the end of 1932 the conservatives' political strategy had failed once and for all. Not even Schleicher's surprising political switch to support of the unions and to Gregor Strasser's wing of the NSDAP could now prevent Hitler from becoming Chancellor.

The German Reich in 1939

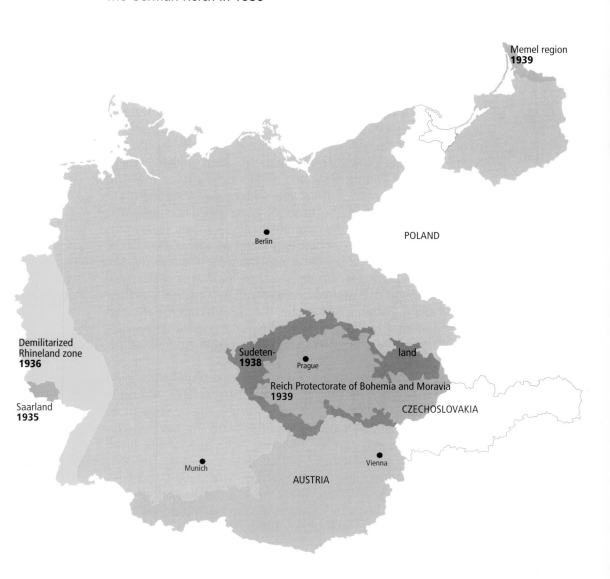

Memel region
1939

POLAND

Berlin

Demilitarized
Rhineland zone
1936

Sudeten-
1938

Prague

land

Reich Protectorate of Bohemia and Moravia
1939

CZECHOSLOVAKIA

Saarland
1935

Munich

Vienna

AUSTRIA

The Third Reich

VI. The Third Reich

In many ways, the 30th January 1933 marked the culmination of attempts to find an authoritarian answer to the economic, social and political crisis afflicting the Weimar Republic since 1929. At the same time, however, it marked the beginning of a development which, going well beyond previous attempts, was within a short space of time to remove all vestiges of the parliamentary and democratic system. To begin with, the National Socialists took advantage of an idea enjoying widespread support in right-wing and middle-class circles: that of a conservative renewal of state and society led by a strong national government on the basis of mass popular support. It was this idea which had ultimately removed any misgivings Hindenburg had about appointing Hitler as Chancellor. But it soon became clear who was using whom for their own ends. Although the National Socialists were initially in a minority in the government of "national concentration" headed by Hitler as Chancellor, within a few weeks the illusion that Hitler could be instrumentalized at will as a "drummer" to elicit the support of the masses, and then simply discarded, had evaporated.

The last elections which, with certain reservations, could still be viewed as free took place on 5 March 1933. Although the National Socialists did not win outright, they were able to form a parliamentary majority together with the German Nationals. The passing of the "Enabling Act" freed Hitler of all constitutional restraints and parliamentary control. The KPD already having been eliminated, the SPD was the only party to vote against the new law. The Centre and the middle-class parties voted in favour. The next step was a ban on all other parties, or the latters' self-dissolution. The Third Reich became a one-party state under the tutelage of the NSDAP. The Reichstag's role was reduced to that of acclamation for Hitler's policies. The system of parliamentary democracy had been destroyed. From this point on, the NSDAP and its organizations controlled all aspects of political, economic and cultural life in Germany. The SA, the SS and the police, now also controlled by the NSDAP, were the tools used by the National Socialists to establish their totalitarian system and to consolidate their rule. The first concentration camps were set up as early as February 1933. In June 1934 Hitler destroyed the power of the SA, which had increasingly laid claim to a leading role alongside the party. Henceforth the SS, which perceived itself as an elite, became the most powerful organization within the National Socialist state. During the war, it was responsible for carrying out the extermination of Europe's jews.

In the *Länder*, or federal states, the National Socialists appointed so-called Reich Commissioners and dissolved the state parliaments. By depriving the *Länder* and the local authorities of their autonomy, the National Socialists dismantled the federal structure established under Bismarck and turned Germany into a centralized unitary state. Following the death of Hindenburg, Hitler united the offices of President and Chancellor and designated himself "Führer of the German Reich". All civil servants and soldiers swore a personal oath of allegiance to the Führer. Already bound by their traditional sense of loyalty to the state, this served to tie them even more closely to Hitler.

Through its various mass organizations, the NSDAP gained control of political and social life in Germany. All other political, economic and cultural organizations were "coordinated", that is brought into line with the NSDAP's objectives. The trade unions were smashed, and the workers deprived of the right of association to defend their interests which they had fought for and won in the 19th century. The two sides of industry were incorporated into a single state-run organization: the German Labour Front. The freedom of workers to change jobs was restricted, and the Führer principle transferred to industry thereby strengthening the position of the employers. Although the National Socialists left the principle of capitalist private enterprise untouched, production was largely steered by the state. During the Second World War, the concentration camps and, ultimately, the whole of Europe ruled by Germany became a source of labour for the German armaments industry.

The National Socialists sought to overcome the latent antagonism between the concepts of "nationalism" and "socialism" by building a "people's community". In reality, they abandoned the idea of German nationalism and propagated a racialist ideology. Their attempt to gain a tight ideological hold on the entire German nation was best illustrated by their measures to organize young people. All existing youth organizations were disbanded, and replaced by the state-run "Hitler Youth", which became an instrument of Nazi education and pre-military training.

The international economic upturn from 1933 onwards contributed to the recovery of the German economy. The National Socialists initiated a programme of job creation, mainly in the field of public works. It did little to boost industrial production, but got the unemployed back to work, albeit for low wages. An initially covert programme of rearmament and the extension of the period of military service to two years further reduced unemployment. This achievement helped to ensure that the National Socialist regime met with little popular opposition to its policies.

The National Socialists financed their job creation and armaments programmes by issuing government bonds and, ultimately, by printing money. As a result, the level of public debt reached unprecedented levels. National Socialist economic policy from 1933 onwards served Hitler's secret plans for a war of conquest in the east which would bring a "final solution for Germany's future ... by extending our people's living space and enlarging its supply of food and raw materials". In 1936, he confidentially stated a dual objective: "Firstly, in four years the German army must be operational. Secondly, in four years German industry must be ready for war."

The National Socialists' foreign policy, which initially appeared to be a simple continuation of the revisionist policy of Weimar governments, secretly pursued this goal from the very beginning. For fear of war, the Western powers reacted cautiously, thereby enabling Hitler to continue his policy of aggression and expansion. Only after Germany's occupation of Czechoslovakia in the spring of 1939 did France and England opt for a more resolute stance by declaring their intention to stand by Poland. It was now clear that Hitler risked unleasing a large-scale war should he take any further step.

Antisemitism, whose spiritual and intellectual precursors were to be found in the 19th century, was already widespread in the Weimar Republic. A racial worldview was the centrepiece of Hitler's ideology. During the economic crisis, a feeling of being at the mercy of anonymous social forces had gripped broad sections of the population; the NSDAP now succeeded in transforming it into aggression towards the "world conspiracy of Jews and bolshevists". On coming to power, the National Socialists set about putting Hitler's ideas about these "enemies of the people" systematically into practice. Acts of violence against Jewish citizens and their property were the first step. They were followed by measures depriving them of any form of livelihood. Finally, during the war, the declared aim of the National Socialists became the annihilation of the "Jewish-Bolshevist elite" and of East European Jewry, and the acquisition of "living space" for the "Germanic master race".

The scope for effective resistance to the regime by political opposition groups was limited from the outset. The political left, sections of the bourgeois-conservative camp, and men of the Church and the military concurred in their rejection of Hitler's policies but owing to their political differences, and above all to the National Socialists' effective system of surveillance, they did not succeed in forming a united front against the regime. Only when faced with the consequences of impending military defeat, did a group of officers make an attempt to remove Hitler and thus, in the west at least, to bring the war to an end. However, the 20 July plot failed and the regime responded by liquidating all those involved. The remaining months of the war, now waged ever more ruthlessly and accompanied by an intensified reign of terror in Germany itself, claimed more lives than the years preceding 20 July 1944.

VI/251
NSDAP rally in
the Bürgerbräu
beer-hall in Munich
around 1923

1. The beginnings of the National Socialist movement

At the beginning of the 1920s, the National Socialist Workers' Party of Germany (NSDAP) was but one of a large number of nationalist-racialist splinter groups determined to resort to the most radical measures to fight the new democratic republic. Under the leadership of Adolf Hitler, who assumed a key position in the party as early as 1921, it initially geared all its efforts to organizing a putsch. But they came to nothing: the putsch ended in dismal failure in November 1923 with the crushing of the party's march to the Feldherrenhalle in Munich. Hitler's subsequent trial and imprisonment served only to enhance his prestige, however. He became the central figure on the nationalist right.

After his release in 1925 he set about completely rebuilding the party. He transformed the NSDAP into a tightly organized unit, and consciously set it apart from other groups in the nationalist-racialist camp. The party now focused on seizing power "legally" by mobilizing the masses and, not least, by taking part in elections. Above all, however, Hitler turned the NSDAP into an instrument fully obedient to his own political will.

When, from autumn 1929 onwards, the social and economic crisis in Germany dramatically deepened, the NSDAP was well placed, both organizationally and ideologically, to act as a reservoir for fanatics and those disappointed and embittered by the republic. The party rapidly became a mass protest movement whose ranks swelled as the crisis worsened. Politically, there no longer seemed to be any way round Adolf Hitler and the NSDAP.

VI/252
(opposite)
The NSDAP's
political programme
of 1920

Grundsätzliches Programm

der nationalsozialistischen

Deutschen Arbeiter-Partei.

Das Programm der Deutschen Arbeiter-Partei ist ein Zeit-Programm. Die Führer lehnen es ab, nach Erreichung der im Programm aufgestellten Ziele neue aufzustellen, nur zu dem Zweck, um durch künstlich gesteigerte Unzufriedenheit der Massen das Fortbestehen der Partei zu ermöglichen.

1. Wir fordern den Zusammenschluß aller Deutschen auf Grund des Selbstbestimmungsrechtes der Völker zu einem Groß-Deutschland.
2. Wir fordern die Gleichberechtigung des deutschen Volkes gegenüber den anderen Nationen, Aufhebung der Friedensverträge in Versailles und St. Germain.
3. Wir fordern Land u. Boden (Kolonien) zur Ernährung unseres Volkes u. Ansiedelung unseres Bevölkerungs-Ueberschusses.
4. Staatsbürger kann nur sein, wer Volksgenosse ist. Volksgenosse kann nur sein, wer deutschen Blutes ist, ohne Rücksichtnahme auf Konfession. **Kein Jude kann daher Volksgenosse sein.**
5. Wer nicht Staatsbürger ist, soll nur als Gast in Deutschland leben können u. muß unter Fremdengesetzgebung stehen.
6. Das Recht, über Führung u. Gesetze des Staates zu bestimmen, darf nur dem Staatsbürger zustehen. Daher fordern wir, daß jedes öffentlich Amt, gleichgiltig welcher Art, gleich ob im Reich, Land oder Gemeinde nur durch Staatsbürger bekleidet werden darf. — Wir bekämpfen die korrumpierende Parlamentswirtschaft einer Stellenbesetzung nur nach Parteigesichtspunkten ohne Rücksichten auf Charakter und Fähigkeiten.
7. Wir fordern, daß sich der Staat verpflichtet, in erster Linie für die Erwerbs- u. Lebensmöglichkeit der Staatsbürger zu sorgen. Wenn es nicht möglich ist, die Gesamtbevölkerung des Staates zu ernähren, so sind die Angehörigen fremder Nationen (Nicht-Staatsbürger) aus dem Reiche auszuweisen.
8. Jede weitere Einwanderung Nicht-Deutscher ist zu verhindern. Wir fordern, daß alle Nicht-Deutschen, die seit 2. August 1914 in Deutschland eingewandert sind, sofort zum Verlassen des Reiches gezwungen werden.
9. Alle Staatsbürger müssen gleiche Rechte u. Pflichten besitzen.
10. Erste Pflicht jedes Staatsbürgers muß sein, geistig oder körperlich zu schaffen. Die Tätigkeit des Einzelnen darf nicht gegen die Interessen der Allgemeinheit verstoßen, sondern muß im Rahmen des Gesamten u. zum Nutzen Aller erfolgen.

Daher fordern wir:

11. Abschaffung des arbeits- und mühelosen Einkommens.

Brechung der Zinsknechtschaft.

12. Im Hinblick auf die ungeheuren Opfer an Gut und Blut, die jeder Krieg vom Volke fordert, muß die persönliche Bereicherung durch den Krieg als Verbrechen am Volke bezeichnet werden. Wir fordern daher **restlose Einziehung aller Kriegsgewinne.**
13. Wir fordern die Verstaatlichung aller bisher bereits vergesellschafteten (Trust's) Betriebe.
14. Wir fordern Gewinnbeteiligung an Großbetrieben.
15. Wir fordern einen großzügigen Ausbau der Alters-Versorgung.
16. Wir fordern die Schaffung eines gesunden Mittelstandes und seine Erhaltung. Sofortige **Kommunalisierung der Groß-Warenhäuser** und ihre Vermietung zu billigen Preisen an kleine Gewerbetreibende, schärfste Berücksichtigung aller kleinen Gewerbetreibenden bei Lieferung an den Staat, die Länder oder Gemeinden.
17. Wir fordern eine unseren nationalen Bedürfnissen angepaßte Bodenreform, Schaffung eines Gesetzes zur unentgeltlichen Enteignung von Boden für gemeinnützige Zwecke. Abschaffung des Bodenzinses und Verhinderung jeder Bodenspekulation.
18. Wir fordern den rücksichtslosen Kampf gegen diejenigen, die durch ihre Tätigkeit das Gemein-Interesse schädigen. Gemeine

Volksverbrecher, **Wucherer, Schieber** usw. sind **mit dem Tode zu bestrafen,** ohne Rücksichtnahme auf Konfession und Rasse.
19. Wir fordern Ersatz für das der materialistischen Weltordnung dienende römische Recht durch ein Deutsches Gemein-Recht.
20. Um jedem fähigen und fleissigen Deutschen das Erreichen höherer Bildung und damit das Einrücken in führende Stellungen zu ermöglichen, hat der Staat für einen gründlichen Ausbau unseres gesamten Volksbildungswesens Sorge zu tragen. Die Lehrpläne aller Bildungsanstalten sind den Erfordernissen des praktischen Lebens anzupassen. Das Erfassen des Staatsgedankens muß bereits mit Beginn des Verständnisses durch die Schule (Staatsbürgerkunde) erzielt werden. Wir fordern die Ausbildung geistig besonders veranlagter Kinder armer Eltern ohne Rücksicht auf deren Stand oder Beruf auf Staatskosten.
21. Der Staat hat für die Hebung der Volksgesundheit zu sorgen durch den Schutz der Mutter und des Kindes, durch Verbot der Jugendarbeit, durch Herbeiführung der körperlichen Ertüchtigung mittels gesetzlicher Festlegung einer Turn- und Sportpflicht, durch größte Unterstützung aller sich mit körperlicher Jugend-Ausbildung beschäftigenden Vereine.
22. Wir fordern die Abschaffung der Söldnertruppen und die Bildung eines Volksheeres.
23. Wir fordern den gesetzlichen **Kampf** gegen die **bewußte politische Lüge** und ihre Verbreitung durch die Presse. Um die Schaffung einer deutschen Presse zu ermöglichen, fordern wir, daß:
    a) Sämtliche Schriftleiter u. Mitarbeiter von Zeitungen, die in Deutscher Sprache erscheinen, Volksgenossen sein müssen.
    b) Nichtdeutsche Zeitungen zu ihrem Erscheinen der ausdrücklichen Genehmigung des Staates bedürfen. Sie dürfen nicht in deutscher Sprache gedruckt werden.
    c) Jede finanzielle Beteiligung an Deutschen Zeitungen oder deren Beeinflussung durch Nichtdeutsche gesetzlich verboten wird, u. fordern als Strafe für Uebertretungen die Schließung einer solchen Zeitung, sowie die sofortige Ausweisung der daran beteiligten Nichtdeutschen aus dem Reich. Zeitungen, die gegen das Gemeinwohl verstoßen, sind zu verbieten. Wir fordern den gesetzlichen Kampf gegen eine Kunst- u. Literatur-Richtung, die einen zersetzenden Einfluß auf unser Volksleben ausübt u. die Schließung von Veranstaltungen, die gegen vorstehende Forderung verstoßen.
24. Wir fordern die Freiheit aller religiösen Bekenntnisse im Staat, soweit sie nicht dessen Bestand gefährden oder gegen das Sittlichkeits- u. Moralgefühl der germanischen Rasse verstoßen. Die Partei als solche vertritt den Standpunkt eines positiven Christentums, ohne sich konfessionell an ein bestimmtes Bekenntnis zu binden. Sie bekämpft den jüdisch-materialistischen Geist **in** und **außer** uns und ist überzeugt, daß eine dauernde Genesung unseres Volkes nur erfolgen kann von **innen** heraus auf der Grundlage:

Gemeinnutz vor Eigennutz.

25. Zur Durchführung alles dessen fordern wir die Schaffung einer starken Zentralgewalt des Reiches. Unbedingte Autorität des politischen Zentralparlaments über das gesamte Reich u. seine Organisationen im allgemeinen. Die Bildung von Stände- und Berufskammern zur Durchführung der vom Reich erlassenen Rahmengesetze in den einzelnen Bundesstaaten.

Die Führer der Partei versprechen, wenn nötig unter Einsatz des eigenen Lebens, für die Durchführung der vorstehenden Punkte rücksichtlos einzutreten.

München, den 24. Februar 1920.   Für den **Partei-Ausschuß:** Anton Drexler

Spenden und Beiträge sind zu richten an die Geschäftsstelle München: **Corneliusstr. 12** (Tel. 23620)

Geschäftsstunden 9—12 Uhr vorm., 2—6 Uhr nachm.

Münchener Plakatdruckerei, Schreiber & Hartl
Geschäftsstellen: Rosenthal 6 und Ledererstraße 3

P 00088 A

Beginnings in Bavaria

Until the putsch in November 1923, the NSDAP – founded in October 1919 as the German Workers' Party and renamed in March 1920 – was a nationalist-racialist splinter group whose activities were mainly limited to Bavaria. Its programme of February 1920, which Hitler would declare unalterable in 1926 but which was of little importance in terms of practical policy, combined a rejection of liberal parliamentary democracy with slogans attacking the Marxist left and the republic, a muddled anticapitalism, and a radical racialist antisemitism. This mixture conformed to the mood among large sections of the population in the first few crisis-ridden years of the republic, but its appeal waned during the ensuing phase of relative stability.

The party and its organizations

The NSDAP was a political party in name only. Strictly speaking, it was the organizational core of a broad-based movement consciously geared to "political struggle". As its undisputed leader, Adolf Hitler sought to mobilize mass support. In

VI/253
Title page of the first volume of Hitler's *Mein Kampf*

VI/254
Meeting of the NSDAP executive committee in Munich in 1928

VI/255
Hall used as
a rallying point by
the SA in Berlin
in 1932

doing so, he relied not only on the party's own private "army", the SA or *Sturmabteilung*, whose storm troopers largely spearheaded the struggle on the streets, but also on numerous party organizations set up to attract different sections of society, such as: the Hitler Youth, the especially successful National Socialist League of German Students, special associations for individual professional groups such as lawyers, doctors, teachers and creative artists, and the National Socialist Factory Cell Organization.

Leaders, members and voters

From the early 1920s, the real core of the NSDAP and its leadership was formed largely by young men belonging to the generation of front-line soldiers who had fought in the First World War. Politically radicalized and socially uprooted by the war and the revolutionary turmoil of the immediate post-war years, they were the type of men best epitomized by Hitler himself. After 1930, the ranks of the party began to swell, even though many new members would leave again soon afterwards. Although the number of new members from the middle and lower middle classes was disproportionately high, the NSDAP in fact drew its membership from all sections of society, including large numbers from the working class. As recent studies have shown, this also held true for the party's voters: the rise of National Socialism was the result not only of a process of radicalization among the middle classes but of the emergence of a broad protest movement cutting across class divisions.

VI/256
Reich Chancellor
Adolf Hitler with
members of his
cabinet in Berlin
in 1933

2. The "seizure of power"

On 30 January 1933, Adolf Hitler was appointed Reich Chancellor by Reich President Hindenburg. He headed a coalition government in which, to begin with, only two other National Socialists held office. The majority of ministers were independent conservatives, members of the German National People's Party (DNVP) and representatives of the *Stahlhelm*, a conservative ex-servicemen's organization. The Vice Chancellor, von Papen, and the chairman of the DNVP, Hugenberg, were convinced that they had successfully contained the National Socialists and would be able to use them for their own ends in effecting a turnaround in policy in line with their staunchly conservative aims.

But the events of 30 January, the jubilant crowds and the torch-lit parades of the SA, already showed that the political balance of power was in fact a very different one. The National Socialists spoke of a "seizure of power": in the following weeks, by taking unprecedentedly radical measures, they succeeded in eliminating their main political opponents and harnessing the ministerial civil service and the *Reichswehr* – both of which initially appeared capable of acting as powerful counterweights to the National Socialists – to their political ends.

The first repressive measures against the opposition were taken in early February. The SA and the SS, now with the formal backing of the state, intensified their reign of terror. Freedom of the press was restricted, the work of other parties obstructed, and the civil service purged of those unwilling to conform. The Reichstag fire on 27 February 1933 presented the National Socialists with an opportunity to accelerate this process dramatically. Although at the elections to the Reichstag on 5 March 1933 Hitler's government gained an adequate majority, he nevertheless demanded dictatorial powers from the Reichstag. With its adoption of a corresponding "Enabling Act" by a two-thirds majority on 23 March 1933, parliament itself sealed the fate of Germany's first democracy. The NSDAP newspaper, the *Völkischer Beobachter*, wrote in a editorial: "The parliamentary system has surrendered to the new Germany."

find an authoritarian answer to the severe economic and political crisis besetting the Weimar Republic, but this time with the mass support of the National Socialists. However, this new constellation gave the NSDAP a unique opportunity to combine the vast power concentrated in the hands of the Reich President and the presidential cabinets since 1930 with the tremendous dynamism and energy of an antidemocratic mass movement. It was this combination, and the skilful exploitation of each source of power in turn, which was at the root of the rapid establishment of the National Socialist dictatorship.

VI/257
Torch-lit parade
of the SA on
the evening of
30 January 1933

30 January 1933

Like his predecessors in office, the new Reich Chancellor, Adolf Hitler, headed a presidential cabinet. His appointment marked a further attempt by conservative circles to

The Reichstag fire

On the night of 27/28 February 1933, a fire broke out in the Reichstag Building. The plenary chamber and parts of the dome above it were engulfed by the flames. The

VI/258
The Reichstag building in flames on the evening of 27 February 1933

arson attack on this, the most prominent symbol of parliamentary democracy and the Weimar Republic, was the act of a solitary individual, the young Dutchman Marinus van der Lubbe. Nazi propaganda, however, blamed it on the Communists and used the fire as a pretext for taking more radical action against opponents of the regime.

Precisely because the Reichstag fire fitted in so well with the plans of the National Socialists, and was exploited by them so skilfully and to such lasting effect, the suspicion soon arose that they had laid the fire themselves. But even today, after many years of heated debate, there is no proof that this was the case.

VI/259 (opposite)
Emergency decree issue by the Reich President "to protect the people and the State" on 28 February 1933

Reichsgesetzblatt

83

Teil 1

| 1933 | Ausgegeben zu Berlin, den 28. Februar 1933 | Nr. 17 |

Inhalt: Verordnung des Reichspräsidenten zum Schutz von Volk und Staat. Vom 28. Februar 1933 ...... S. 83

Verordnung des Reichspräsidenten zum Schutz von Volk und Staat. Vom 28. Februar 1933.

Auf Grund des Artikels 48 Abs. 2 der Reichsverfassung wird zur Abwehr kommunistischer staatsgefährdender Gewaltakte folgendes verordnet:

§ 1

Die Artikel 114, 115, 117, 118, 123, 124 und 153 der Verfassung des Deutschen Reichs werden bis auf weiteres außer Kraft gesetzt. Es sind daher Beschränkungen der persönlichen Freiheit, des Rechts der freien Meinungsäußerung, einschließlich der Preßfreiheit, des Vereins- und Versammlungsrechts, Eingriffe in das Brief-, Post-, Telegraphen- und Fernsprechgeheimnis, Anordnungen von Haussuchungen und von Beschlagnahmen sowie Beschränkungen des Eigentums auch außerhalb der sonst hierfür bestimmten gesetzlichen Grenzen zulässig.

§ 2

Werden in einem Lande die zur Wiederherstellung der öffentlichen Sicherheit und Ordnung nötigen Maßnahmen nicht getroffen, so kann die Reichsregierung insoweit die Befugnisse der obersten Landesbehörde vorübergehend wahrnehmen.

§ 3

Die Behörden der Länder und Gemeinden (Gemeindeverbände) haben den auf Grund des § 2 erlassenen Anordnungen der Reichsregierung im Rahmen ihrer Zuständigkeit Folge zu leisten.

§ 4

Wer den von den obersten Landesbehörden oder den ihnen nachgeordneten Behörden zur Durchführung dieser Verordnung erlassenen Anordnungen oder den von der Reichsregierung gemäß § 2 erlassenen Anordnungen zuwiderhandelt oder wer zu solcher Zuwiderhandlung auffordert oder anreizt, wird, soweit nicht die Tat nach anderen Vorschriften mit einer schwereren Strafe bedroht ist, mit Gefängnis nicht unter einem Monat oder mit Geldstrafe von 150 bis zu 15 000 Reichsmark bestraft.

Wer durch Zuwiderhandlung nach Abs. 1 eine gemeine Gefahr für Menschenleben herbeiführt, wird mit Zuchthaus, bei mildernden Umständen mit Gefängnis nicht unter sechs Monaten und, wenn die Zuwiderhandlung den Tod eines Menschen verursacht, mit dem Tode, bei mildernden Umständen mit Zuchthaus nicht unter zwei Jahren bestraft. Daneben kann auf Vermögenseinziehung erkannt werden.

Wer zu einer gemeingefährlichen Zuwiderhandlung (Abs. 2) auffordert oder anreizt, wird mit Zuchthaus, bei mildernden Umständen mit Gefängnis nicht unter drei Monaten bestraft.

§ 5

Mit dem Tode sind die Verbrechen zu bestrafen, die das Strafgesetzbuch in den §§ 81 (Hochverrat), 229 (Giftbeibringung), 307 (Brandstiftung), 311 (Explosion), 312 (Überschwemmung), 315 Abs. 2 (Beschädigung von Eisenbahnanlagen), 324 (gemeingefährliche Vergiftung) mit lebenslangem Zuchthaus bedroht.

Mit dem Tode oder, soweit nicht bisher eine schwerere Strafe angedroht ist, mit lebenslangem Zuchthaus oder mit Zuchthaus bis zu 15 Jahren wird bestraft:

1. Wer es unternimmt, den Reichspräsidenten oder ein Mitglied oder einen Kommissar der Reichsregierung oder einer Landesregierung zu töten oder wer zu einer solchen Tötung auffordert, sich erbietet, ein solches Erbieten annimmt oder eine solche Tötung mit einem anderen verabredet;

2. wer in den Fällen des § 115 Abs. 2 des Strafgesetzbuchs (schwerer Aufruhr) oder des § 125 Abs. 2 des Strafgesetzbuchs (schwerer Landfriedensbruch) die Tat mit Waffen oder in bewußtem und gewolltem Zusammenwirken mit einem Bewaffneten begeht;

3. wer eine Freiheitsberaubung (§ 239) des Strafgesetzbuchs in der Absicht begeht, sich des der Freiheit Beraubten als Geisel im politischen Kampfe zu bedienen.

§ 6

Diese Verordnung tritt mit dem Tage der Verkündung in Kraft.

Berlin, den 28. Februar 1933.

Der Reichspräsident
von Hindenburg

Der Reichskanzler
Adolf Hitler

Der Reichsminister des Innern
Frick

Der Reichsminister der Justiz
Dr. Gürtner

Herausgegeben vom Reichsministerium des Innern. — Gedruckt in der Reichsdruckerei, Berlin.

VI/260
Political opponents
under arrest in 1933

Persecution of the opposition

The Reichstag fire offered the National Socialists a pretext for further intensifying the repressive measures they had already initiated against all forces opposed to the regime. On 28 February an emergency decree "to protect the People and the State" was issued by the Reich President. It suspended key basic rights and all constitutional guarantees. The deputies and leading functionaries of the Communist party, the KPD, were arrested, Communist and Social Democrat newspapers outlawed, and the election campaign activities of all other parties, in particular those on the left, massively disrupted. The SA and the SS, assigned the functions of an auxiliary police force in Prussia on 22 February, unleashed a systematic campaign of terror against political opponents. By mid-March more than 10,000 people had been arrested in Prussia alone.

Reichstag elections and the Enabling Act

New elections to the Reichstag took place on 5 March 1933 in a highly charged political atmosphere marked by deep legal uncertainty and overt terror. Despite the massive restrictions on political freedom, the NSDAP won only 43.9% of the votes. Together with the DNVP and the *Stahlhelm*, however, it still obtained a sufficient majority. But Hitler wanted to free himself

VI/261
Hitler and von Hindenburg, the Reich President, on the "Day of Potsdam", 21 March 1933

of all constitutional restraints and every form of parliamentary control. He tabled an Enabling Act which, with the support of the Centre party and the liberals, was passed on 23 March 1933 by a two-thirds majority in the Reichstag. Only the Social Democrats – the Communist deputies had already been excluded from the Reichstag – voted against this Act, which deprived Parliament of all its powers and abolished the system of parliamentary democracy.

VI/262
Hitler justifying the Enabling Act of 23 March 1933 to the Reichstag

3. *Gleichschaltung*

Following the elections in March, the institutions which once had formed the cornerstone of the democratic order swiftly fell victim to the emerging National Socialist dictatorship in a process of *Gleichschaltung* or "coordination". Step by step, all the organs of state and all the institutions of civil society were subjugated to the will of the regime. All political opponents were eliminated, and their organizations either compelled to cease their political activity or forcibly dissolved.

The methods used by the National Socialist to achieve this were always the same: pressure from above by the state machinery alternated with pressure from below on the streets; flagrant acts of open violence alternated with assiduous official efforts to maintain a semblance of legality by passing new laws and ordinances. The National Socialists were helped by the fact that many of the measures they took, especially against political opponents on the left, met with the broad approval of the conservative middle classes, who realized too late that the regime had no intention of exempting them from its policy of repression.

Reviewing progress in a speech on 6 July 1933, Adolf Hitler could note with satisfaction that the "total state" was nearing completion. A number of questions concerning the balance of power within the National Socialist camp itelf remained unresolved, however, in particular the relationship between the party leadership and the SA. On the 30 June 1934, a series of murders carried out on Hitler's orders put an end to any ambitions the leaders of the SA had to gain a share in wielding military power. The process of *Gleichschaltung* reached completion after the death of Reich President Hindenburg on 2 August 1934, when the offices of President and Chancellor were merged and the *Reichswehr* ordered to swear a personal oath of allegiance to the "Führer and Chancellor" Adolf Hitler.

Towards the "total state"

Immediately after the Reichstag elections, the process of "coordinating" the *Länder*, the constituent states of the Reich, began. Wherever the assumption of power by the National Socialist was resisted, the

VI/263
The judiciary brought into line with the NSDAP regime

VI/264
A unit of the SA
in front of the trade
union headquarters
in Munich on 2 May
1933

SA and the SS were sent in to create unrest, which was then taken as a pretext by the National Socialists to appoint a *Reichskommissar* or commissioner. On 9 March, the last *Land*, Bavaria, was forced to yield. Two laws enacted on 31 March and 7 April brought this process to a close: henceforth, each *Land* was was to be headed by a *Reichsstatthalter*, or governor, appointed by the central government. At the same time as dismantling the federal structures and abolishing the autonomy of local authorities, the National Socialists also set about "purging" the civil service and the judiciary. Under the Law on the Reestablishment of the Permanent Civil Service, enacted on 7 April 1933, any civil servant or judge who did not pledge his unconditional loyalty to the National Socialist state could be dismissed from office.

The end of the political parties

Having deprived the democratic parties of any political influence by passing the Enabling Act, in June and July 1933 the National Social-

ists took steps to close them down completely. The SPD, already in a state of internal collapse with its leaders having fled to Prague following the occupation of its offices on 10 May, was banned on 22 June. The other parties also found that they no longer had any political room for manouevre and were forced to opt for voluntary dissolution – the last two to do so were the Catholic Centre party and its Bavarian sister, the Bavarian People's Party (BVP), on 4 and 5 July. On 14 July 1933 a law was passed prohibiting the reestablishment of political parties – the National Socialist one-party state was complete.

The dissolution of the trade unions

Anxious to preserve their own organizational structures, the Free Trade Unions turned away from the SPD and sought to cooperate with the new rulers who, seemingly, complied: 1 May, the day which traditionally symbolized the workers' struggle, was declared a national holiday by, of all people, the

VI/265
Catholic bishops
and leading NSDAP
politicians in 1935

National Socialists. Hundreds of thousands of workers, including many trade union representatives, followed the regime's call. But the very next day, the unions' offices were occupied by the SA and the SS, their functionaries arrested and their assets seized. The old trade unions, reflecting a broad range of ideological positions, were replaced by a single organization, the German Labour Front.

VI/266
Hitler and the
Protestant "Reich
Bishop", Müller

The National Socialist state and the Churches

The Churches did not challenge the National Socialists' claim to absolute power either. The Protestant Church in particular willingly submitted to the National Socialist state – in line with its tradition as the Church closest to the state in Germany. Only a minority of Protestant priests, who formed the

Bekennende Kirche or Confessing Church, opposed this official stance. The Catholic Church was more resilient and succeeded in particular in preserving its unity as a religious community. The price it paid for this, however, was complete political abstinence. Indeed, with the concordat of 20 July 1933, concluded between the German Reich and the Vatican, the Catholic Church helped significantly to enhance the standing of the National Socialist regime among the Catholic population and on the international stage.

The Night of the Long Knives

From the summer of 1933 onwards, relations between the NSDAP leadership around Adolf Hitler and the SA under Ernst Röhm became increasingly tense. The SA, whose ranks had quickly swelled to over three million men, was eager to push ahead with the National Socialist "revolution" and saw itself as Germany's future army. These ambitions jeopardized not only the power bargain reached by the National Socialists with the *Reichswehr* but also Adolf Hitler's own position. On 30 June 1934, with the support of the SS and the *Reichswehr*, Hitler struck against the SA leadership: some 100 people were executed without trial, including conservative opponents of the National Socialist regime such as the last Chancellor of the Weimar Republic, General von Schleicher. The murders were justified in a subsequent law as an "act of self-defence" by the state.

VI/267
The *Reichswehr* swearing an oath of allegiance to Adolf Hitler on 2 August 1934

4. The Führer state

Adolf Hitler, the "Führer of the Nation", acquired vast personal power following the death of the Reich President. He was the head of state and the head of government, supreme commander of the *Wehrmacht*, as the *Reichswehr* was called from 1935 onwards, head of the judiciary and the leader of the party. National Socialist propaganda stressed the Führer's omnipotence and attributed every political success to him personally. But in retrospect, too, it cannot be overlooked that Hitler's *Weltanschauung*, or worldview, and the political programme he based upon it, did have a direct impact on developments in Germany under National Socialism. Neither the regime's racial policy nor its plans for a war of conquest and annihilation in the east were conceivable in this form without Hitler. To this extent, the Third Reich was characterized by the autocratic rule of one man.

On the other hand, National Socialist rule saw the emergence of a confusing array of parallel and competing authorities, special bodies, party organizations and offices of the *Gestapo*, the secret police, and the SS. Government in the Third Reich was characterized by power struggles, conflicts of jurisdiction, growing frictions and inefficiency, and the incipient breakdown of a well-structured system of public administration. Time and again, the administrative chaos gave leading figures in the party a chance to pursue goals of their own, and created a vacuum in which radical National Socialist policies could evolve without hindrance. Hitler himself refused either to be bound by any rational criteria of efficient government or to commit himself to a specific programme or any form of centralistic regulation. This very refusal safe-guarded his personal position and power, and ensured the achievement of his radical political goals. Dictatorship and administrative chaos were not contradictions but two sides of the same coin.

Adolf Hitler as the "Führer of the Nation"

Even before 1933, Adolf Hitler was the undisputed leader of the National Socialist movement. But after the "seizure of power" the stylization of his persona acquired a new dimension through Joseph Goebbels's perfectly orchestrated propaganda. The nimbus of the Führer was enhanced by every success, especially in combating the economic crisis and in the field of foreign policy. The veneration of Hitler by broad sections of the German population acquired an increasingly pseudoreligious quality. This faith in the Führer became the key force of integration in the Third Reich. It was also the main reason why many Germans were willing to follow the Führer into war and to support criminal policies without precedent in history.

The role of the Party

After seizing power, the NSDAP built up a network of organizations and suborganizations which covered both state and society like a web. In some cases they were established alongside existing institutions; in others they replaced them. The party and many of its influential leaders were the dynamic element in the National Socialist state. They undermined the established norms of government behaviour and the traditional division of powers. They were the key driving

VI/268
Nazi propaganda adorning the Brandenburg Gate in the run-up to the Reichstag elections of 5 March 1933

VI/269
Floodlit rally on the
Zeppelinfeld in
Nuremberg to mark
the NSDAP's nation-
al party conference
on 11 September
1936

forces behind the National Socialist revolution in society and the economy, and behind the system of racial and political persecution. From early on, therefore, the image of the NSDAP was negative, whereas Hitler – quite contrary to his actual role – was seen in a positive light as, ostensibly, an opponent of the radical elements in the party.

The SS state

Following the curbing of the SA's power in the "night of the long knives" on 30 June 1934, the SS, led by Heinrich Himmler and his deputy Reinhold Heydrich, emerged as the most powerful organization in the National Socialist state. Perceiving itself as the elite, also in racial terms, of the Third Reich, the SS most fully embodied the National Socialist doctrine and the principle of unconditional devotion to the Führer. The SS increasingly became a "state within the state", its leaders holding the most important reins of power in their hands. It was responsible for the Nazis' system of terror: it ran the concentration camps and was in charge of the political police, the *Gestapo*. The SS conducted the campaign of racial extermination and therefore bears the responsibility for the murder of millions.

VI/270
SS units assembled in full military gear in the stadium used for party rallies in Nuremberg

5. Persecution and resistance

Only by using force to repress those who held different political views were the National Socialists able to establish their dictatorship. Their persecution of political opponents began just a few days after their "seizure of power". But so, too, did the formation of resistance to the National Socialist regime.

To begin with, resistance was organized mainly by the Communists and the Social Democrats, who were also the primary targets of National Socialist persecution, and by individual representatives of the Churches. In this early phase of resistance, those involved had to contend not only with the brutal repressive measures of the regime but also with internal disputes and the broad public support Hitler enjoyed owing to his political success-

es. The opposition managed to establish isolated conspiratorial organizations, but not to form a broadly based and united resistance movement. A number of spectacular operations, such as the attempt to assassinate Hitler at the Bürgerbräukeller in Munich in 1938, were the work of individuals acting alone.

With the onset of war, conditions became even more difficult. The regime still enjoyed strong public support, surveillance of all political activity was tightened, and persecution intensified. Moreover, now that Germany was at war, any attempt to topple the government was bound to appear as an act of high treason – a dilemma which many in the officer corps in particular found difficult to resolve. De-

VI/271
Democratic politicians and journalists entering Oranienberg concentration camp on 10 April 1933

spite this, resistance now also began to grow in conservative circles and in the armed forces, which since 1933 had worked together loyally with the National Socialist regime. Most of the conspirators who, on 20 July 1944, made a last attempt to remove the dictator and to end the war came from the ranks of the military. Like so many others who openly opposed the regime, they paid for this with their lives.

Persecution of parliamentarians

From the very beginning, the regime's repressive measures were directed above all against members of the Reichstag and the state parliaments, or *Landtage*. For the Na-tional Socialists they, more than any other group, represented the hated Weimer Republic. But it was also often they who, even after the seizure of power by the National Socialists, spoke out against the regime, as in the SPD's courageous vote against the Enabling Act. In the first few months of 1933 alone, nine Reichstag deputies were murdered. By the end of the war, this figure had risen to over 100. It included primarily Communists and Social Democrats but also many deputies belonging to conservative parties. A far larger number of parliamentarians were arrested and spent long periods in prisons and concentration camps, where they suffered maltreatment and torture. Many were forced out of their professions or had to emigrate.

VI/272
Prisoners pushing a road-roller in Dachau concentration camp in 1933

VI/273
Prisoner caught
on the electric fence
surrounding a con-
centration camp

The system of terror

Soon after the "seizure of power" the National Socialists established an improvised system of repression. It included a large number of camps, some of them provisional, run by the SA and intended for political opponents taken into "protective custody". Under the supervision of the SS, this system was systematically expanded and developed in the following years. A network of concentration camps, whose inmates were subject to cruel maltreatment or brutally murdered, covered the entire country. Increasingly, the concentration camps were used to hold not only political prisoners but also "antisocial elements" and members of persecuted minorities: Jews, gypsies, homosexuals and others. During the war, the system of concentration camps was extended to the occupied territories, and the number of inmates increased from around 25,000 to several million.

VI/274
Members of the
"White Rose",
a student resistance
group, in Munich
on 23 July 1942

Emigration

One way to escape the process of coordination, or *Gleichschaltung*, intiated by the National Socialists was to flee abroad. For many, emi-gration was indeed the only way to reach safety from persecution. From the very beginning the emi-grants included not only politicians but also a large number of artists and scientists. There were often

VI/275
The briefing room
at Hitler's military
headquarters on
the eastern front
(the "Wolf's Lair")
following the assas-
sination attempt
on 20 July 1944

overlaps between these emigrants and Jewish emigration which, with some 500,000 people, was by far the largest group.

Most emigrants remained focused on Germany: they tried to continue the struggle against the National Socialist regime from abroad, or at least laid claim to representing "the other Germany". Despite this, efforts to establish an effective opposition movement in exile did not succeed.

pose a serious threat to Hitler. Their opposition to the regime was first roused in 1938, when it became increasingly clear that Hitler's foreign policy threatened the Reich's very existence. But several more years passed before, in the face of military setbacks and the murder of millions, the various opposition groups began to collaborate more closely. They plotted a coup d'etat and, on 20 July 1944, made an attempt on Hitler's life. The plotters

VI/276
Trial before the
Volksgerichtshof, or
"People's Court"

20th July 1944

Only late in the day did resistance to the regime begin to form in national-conservative circles. Because they held key positions in the civil service and the armed forces, they were the only group which could

were aware that they could no longer avert Germany's military defeat. For them, the true significance of their act was to show "before the world and before history" that there had been resistance in Germany to the National Socialist regime and its crimes.

6. The "people's community"

For most Germans at that time, the most appealing element of National Socialist propaganda was doubtless the notion of a *Volksgemeinschaft*, or "people's community". Like the utopian Marxist vision of a classless society, it brought together the most disparate expectations and aspirations.

Both forward- and backward-looking, the concept of a "people's community" was, on the one hand, an attempt to mask the deep divisions within modern society and, on the other, an expression of the desire to create, across persisting social fault-lines, a society of equals.

In this spirit, National Socialist policy, backed by a plethora of special campaigns, institutions and regulations, emphasized social equality and solidarity within the framework of the *Volksgemeinschaft*.

The old trade unions were replaced by the German Labour Front, which united all "workers of the brain and of the fist". The Hitler Youth, the Reich Labour Service and mili-

VI/277
Pamphlet advertising the first Volkswagen

VI/278
Collecting money for the *Winterhilfswerk*, a scheme to help people in need during the winter months

tary service were also intended to break down social barriers. The *Winterhilfswerk*, or winter aid campaign, was set up to foster solidarity with the weak in society.

A leisure and recreation organization, called Strength through Joy, was created with the aim of making it possible for the lower classes, too, to go on holiday or, later, to buy a car. On the other hand, however, it was quite clear that the "people's community" aimed to be anything but a pluralistic and democratic order in which latent conflicts in society would be resolved by establishing a fair balance between the interests and needs of different social groups. On the contrary: the ideological objective of the National Socialist "people's community" was to destroy all traditional social bonds, thereby making it easier for the regime to tighten its all-encompassing ideological hold on the population.

Modernity and anti-modernity in National Socialism

Contrary to the backward-looking nature of National Socialism, its corporative ideals, its attacks on modern industrial society, and its glorification of an essentially agrarian future, the practical policies it engendered often had a modernizing effect unintended by the regime.

Two factors were at work here: firstly, between 1933 and 1945 many of the traditional divisions in German society were overcome and important steps were taken in the field of social policy. Secondly, the regime could only prepare for, and later wage, war by implementing an intensive armaments programme which inevitably added great impetus to the process of industrialization and weakened traditional sectors of the economy.

The boundaries of the "people's community"

The boundaries of the "people's community" were clearly defined from the outset: only those who showed unequivocal political support for the National Socialist regime, and were considered "Germans" in accordance with its racial criteria, could belong to it. In this spirit, the Nuremberg Laws, a series

of racial laws promulgated in 1935, stated: "Citizens of the Reich shall be only those persons of German or related blood who by their conduct show that they are able and willing loyally to serve the German people and the German Reich." All other sections of the population were, in a certain sense, natural enemies of the "people's community" and, as such, at the mercy of the National Socialist regime and its murderous reign of terror.

VI/279
Presentation of the Volkswagen by Adolf Hitler in Berlin in 1939

7. Overcoming the economic crisis – armaments policy

The expectations the National Socialists faced on coming to power were particularly high in the economic field. In January 1933, more than 6 million people were registered as unemployed. Including their families, more than a third of all Germans were living from state benefits at the beginning of 1933.

The Hitler government did achieve a steady reduction in unemployment: in 1934 only 2.7 million people were still out of work; by 1937 the figure had fallen below the million mark. More than any other factor, the success of the National Socialists' economic policy helped to stabilize the regime.

The National Socialists were fortunate in that the economic upswing had already begun before their "seizure of power": from 1930 onwards, a diverse set of policy instruments had been developed to boost the economy and create jobs. The measures taken by the National Socialists to overcome the economic crisis were, however, inextricably linked with their policy of rearmament and their preparations for war. The Labour Service was used as a means to prepare young men for military service; the building of *Autobahnen*, or motorways, helped to increase military mobility in case of war; and government subsidies were targeted above all on the armaments industry.

To finance the economic upswing and its armament programme the regime resorted chiefly to issuing government bonds and, ultimately,

VI/280
Workers building a motorway on the bank of the river Main in Frankfurt lined up for roll-call in 1933

VI/281
Opening of a section of motorway near Frankfurt by Adolf Hitler on 19 May 1935

to printing money. The result was a level of government debt unprecedented in German history which, after the war, led to a total collapse of the currency and the need for a currency reform.

Combating unemployment

On assuming power, Hitler's government retained and expanded the job creation programmes already in place. By initiating emergency work programmes, setting up a "voluntary" labour service, reducing the number of women in work, and lastly, in 1935, introducing conscription and, as preparation for it, a *Reichsarbeitsdienst*, or compulsory labour service, the regime achieved a steady reduction in the number of people out of work. Employment policy was closely aligned with the regime's goal of building up its armed forces, however. The plans for the *Autobahnen*, for instance, were altered and expanded – at Hitler's personal behest – in order to comply with military requirements. It was only because the regime was

absolutely determined to expand its armed forces, and was willing to invest the increasing amounts of money required for this military build-up, that Germany managed to overcome the economic crisis more swiftly than other countries.

National Socialist economic policy

Contrary to the regime's ideological preference for small and medium-sized companies, and its anti-capitalist propaganda, the National Socialists did not introduce any form of state control of large-scale enterprises, department stores or banks. The economic system, based on market economics and the private ownership of the means of production, remained essentially unchanged. However, as the state began to intervene more in the distribution of scarce foreign exchange and raw materials, the economy became increasingly overlaid by forms of central planning. As war drew closer, the regime tightened its political grip on industry whilst continuing to give it preferential treatment economically. Although the leaders of industry criticized individual aspects of the National Socialists' economic policy, ultimately they submitted to the political will of the regime.

The armaments industry

Increasingly, the regime focused all its political and economic efforts on the arms build-up and on preparations for war. Following the introduction of conscription, the share of defence spending in total government expenditure – 4% in 1933 – rocketed to 50% by 1938. The needs of other sectors of the economy were increasingly ignored. This one-sided emphasis on the armaments industry led to substantial shifts in the structure of the economy as a whole. Whilst favouring large-scale enterprises in the armaments sector in particular, it neglected the consumer-goods industry made up largely of small and medium-sized companies. The government called upon industry and the general public to put up with certain difficulties and hardships by looking ahead to the benefits the coming war would bring.

VI/282
A tank leaving the
assembly line

8. Everyday life in the Third Reich

In the Third Reich there was no such thing as "normal" everyday life. National Socialist rule was underpinned by what amounted to a permanent state of emergency. Broad sections of the population did nevertheless see the first few years following the "seizure of power" as a return to normality. On the surface, life was in many ways more peaceful than it had been during the final turbulent years of the Weimar Republic. The immense political tensions of those years appeared overcome, and the economic and social problems which in many cases had threatened people's very livelihoods were gradually being solved. The National Socialist regime sought to reinforce this impression by not interfering in broad areas of everyday life or in the way people organized their leisure time. In the field of cultural affairs in particular, once the regime had eliminated its opponents it practised relative ideological restraint and consciously promoted apparently unpolitical entertainment through radio broadcasts, the cinema and sport. At the perfectly stage-managed Olympic Games of 1936, National Socialist Germany successfully presented itself to its own citizens and to the nations of the world as a "normal" and, peace-loving country.

All this was offset by the regime's overwhelming propagandistic presence in public life and its tight ideological hold on other important areas such as education. Both intensified considerably over the years and during the war. As people struggled with the devastations of nightly bombing raids and the omnipresent threat of death, propaganda and ideology reached such a pitch that they completely dominated the everyday life of German society. People could no longer retreat into private life, as many would have liked to do if only to escape the horrors of war.

VI/283
A fruit and vegetable market in Munich in 1936

VI/284
The Rosenstrasse in
Munich with flags
marking the Reichs-
tag elections of
29 March 1936

VI/285
Women sewing
swastika flags

Gleichschaltung in the field of culture

The National Socialists extended their policy of "coordination" of state and society to include culture. Freedom of the press was abolished, and a large number of writers and artists were forced into exile and deprived of their German citizenship. On 10 May 1933, "un-German" literature was burned on the Opernplatz in Berlin. Large exhibitions were organized to pour scorn on "degenerate art" and to propagate an "official" art which conformed with the official taste of the new regime. At the same time, however, the regime devoted a great deal of time and effort, mainly through the new media of cinema and radio, to promoting light entertainment. These ostensibly unpolitical films and broadcasts were

VI/286
Books being burnt
on the Opernplatz
in Berlin on 10 May
1933

VI/287
Morning assembly
and flag-raising at
a German school

very popular with a wide public. Together with continuity in the theatre repertoire and well-stocked bookshops, they played a key role in efforts to ensure people's loyalty to the regime.

Youth in the Third Reich

Even before coming to power in 1933, the National Socialists had sought to draw young people into their ranks: they perceived their movement as a youthful force and their struggle as a rebellion against the ossified social order of the older generation. Many young people were attracted by this ethos of youth. Following their "seizure of power", the National Socialists intensified their efforts in this area by taking a firm hold on education and seeking to achieve a growing degree of indoctrination in schools. The life of young people became increasingly regimented; they were required to pass through various youth organizations (*Jungvolk*, the Hitler Youth and the League of Ger-

man Maidens) and to complete labour service in the *Reichsarbeitsdienst* and military service in the armed forces. Youth camps and marching formations became the institutions through which the National Socialists aligned young people to their ideological aims. The result was a young generation which grew up believing in National Socialism and was willing to be led into war.

The role of women

The National Socialists had a deeply traditional view of the role of women: their lives should be restricted to taking care of the household and looking after their families and children. As far as possible they should no longer go out to work. Actual developments after 1933, however, only partially matched this ideological ideal: although many women were forced out of skilled jobs as a way of reducing unemployment, the overall number of women in gainful employment did not in fact fall. And during the war the regime was in any case forced to incorporate more women into the workforce. Moreover, the membership of girls and women in National Socialist organizations, as part of their everyday politicization and mobilization, itself contradicted the National Socialist ideal of female domesticity.

Everyday life during the war

The National Socialist regime took far greater pains than the governments of the other countries engaged in the war to demand as few sacrifices as possible from the civilian population. A ruthless policy of occupation and exploitation, combined with millions of forced labourers, ensured a sufficient but nevertheless ever more strictly rationed supply of food and other goods. However, as the Russian campaign faltered, leading to a sharp increase in front-line losses, and the Allied bombing raids began to devastate Germany's towns and cities, people could no longer escape the effects of war. At the same time, the regime intensified its reign of terror and political persecution. As the the war and its depredations intensified, most Germans were forced to struggle for their very survival.

VI/288
Female workers at an armaments factory during the war

9. Persecution and extermination of the Jews

From the early 1920s, a racialist worldview and hostility towards Jews were central elements of National Socialist ideology. Hitler himself was a committed racist and antisemite. In this respect, the NSDAP absorbed many prejudices long prevalent among broad sections of German society. But only the crisis-ridden years of the Weimar Republic created the conditions the National Socialists needed to translate widespread resentment towards the Jews into an aggressive programme of action against what they claimed to be a Jewish-Bolshevist "world conspiracy". After assuming power in 1933, the leadership and the grass-roots of the party, in a process of mutual radicalization, began putting their antisemitic ideas into practice. Initial attacks on Jewish citizens and their property were followed in April 1933 by the dismissal of Jews from the civil service and the judiciary. This was the first step in excluding Jews from an increasing number of professions and from virtually all spheres of public life. Under the "Nuremberg laws" of September 1935, the rights of Jewish citizens were radically curbed, and marriages between Jews and non-Jews prohibited. The aim of the organized pogrom of November 1938 was the final exclusion of Jews from all areas of commercial and economic life. It was soon followed by the first mass deportations to ghettos and camps.

As more and more areas of eastern Europe were conquered, the racial policies of the National Socialists became progressively more radical and led ultimately to systematic genocide. Following initial brutal measures against the Jewish popu-

VI/289
Slogans smeared across the windows of a Jewish shop in Frankfurt on 1 April 1933

VI/290
Poster calling for
a boycott of Jewish
shops in a Berlin
street on 1 April
1933

1146   Reichsgesetzblatt, Jahrgang 1935, Teil I

Reichsbürgergesetz.
Vom 15. September 1935.

Der Reichstag hat einstimmig das folgende Gesetz beschlossen, das hiermit verkündet wird:

§ 1

(1) Staatsangehöriger ist, wer dem Schutzverband des Deutschen Reichs angehört und ihm dafür besonders verpflichtet ist.

(2) Die Staatsangehörigkeit wird nach den Vorschriften des Reichs- und Staatsangehörigkeitsgesetzes erworben.

§ 2

(1) Reichsbürger ist nur der Staatsangehörige deutschen oder artverwandten Blutes, der durch sein Verhalten beweist, daß er gewillt und geeignet ist, in Treue dem Deutschen Volk und Reich zu dienen.

(2) Das Reichsbürgerrecht wird durch Verleihung des Reichsbürgerbriefes erworben.

(3) Der Reichsbürger ist der alleinige Träger der vollen politischen Rechte nach Maßgabe der Gesetze.

§ 3

Der Reichsminister des Innern erläßt im Einvernehmen mit dem Stellvertreter des Führers die zur Durchführung und Ergänzung des Gesetzes erforderlichen Rechts- und Verwaltungsvorschriften.

Nürnberg, den 15. September 1935,
am Reichsparteitag der Freiheit.

Der Führer und Reichskanzler
Adolf Hitler

Der Reichsminister des Innern
Frick

Gesetz zum Schutze des deutschen Blutes und der deutschen Ehre.
Vom 15. September 1935.

Durchdrungen von der Erkenntnis, daß die Reinheit des deutschen Blutes die Voraussetzung für den Fortbestand des Deutschen Volkes ist, und beseelt von dem unbeugsamen Willen, die Deutsche Nation für alle Zukunft zu sichern, hat der Reichstag einstimmig das folgende Gesetz beschlossen, das hiermit verkündet wird:

§ 1

(1) Eheschließungen zwischen Juden und Staatsangehörigen deutschen oder artverwandten Blutes sind verboten. Trotzdem geschlossene Ehen sind nichtig, auch wenn sie zur Umgehung dieses Gesetzes im Ausland geschlossen sind.

(2) Die Nichtigkeitsklage kann nur der Staatsanwalt erheben.

Nr. 100 — Tag der Ausgabe: Berlin, den 16. September 1935   1147

§ 2

Außerehelicher Verkehr zwischen Juden und Staatsangehörigen deutschen oder artverwandten Blutes ist verboten.

§ 3

Juden dürfen weibliche Staatsangehörige deutschen oder artverwandten Blutes unter 45 Jahren in ihrem Haushalt nicht beschäftigen.

§ 4

(1) Juden ist das Hissen der Reichs- und Nationalflagge und das Zeigen der Reichsfarben verboten.

(2) Dagegen ist ihnen das Zeigen der jüdischen Farben gestattet. Die Ausübung dieser Befugnis steht unter staatlichem Schutz.

§ 5

(1) Wer dem Verbot des § 1 zuwiderhandelt, wird mit Zuchthaus bestraft.

(2) Der Mann, der dem Verbot des § 2 zuwiderhandelt, wird mit Gefängnis oder mit Zuchthaus bestraft.

(3) Wer den Bestimmungen der §§ 3 oder 4 zuwiderhandelt, wird mit Gefängnis bis zu einem Jahr und mit Geldstrafe oder mit einer dieser Strafen bestraft.

§ 6

Der Reichsminister des Innern erläßt im Einvernehmen mit dem Stellvertreter des Führers und dem Reichsminister der Justiz die zur Durchführung und Ergänzung des Gesetzes erforderlichen Rechts- und Verwaltungsvorschriften.

§ 7

Das Gesetz tritt am Tage nach der Verkündung, § 3 jedoch erst am 1. Januar 1936 in Kraft.

Nürnberg, den 15. September 1935,
am Reichsparteitag der Freiheit.

Der Führer und Reichskanzler
Adolf Hitler

Der Reichsminister des Innern
Frick

Der Reichsminister der Justiz
Dr. Gürtner

Der Stellvertreter des Führers
R. Heß
Reichsminister ohne Geschäftsbereich

Das Reichsgesetzblatt erscheint in zwei gesonderten Teilen — Teil I und Teil II —
Fortlaufender Bezug nur durch die Postanstalten. Bezugspreis vierteljährlich für Teil I = 1,75 ℛℳ., für Teil II = 2,10 ℛℳ. Einzelbezug jeder (auch jeder älteren) Nummer nur vom Reichsverlagsamt, Berlin NW 40, Scharnhorststraße Nr. 4 (Fernsprecher: D 2 Weidendamm 9265 — Postscheckkonto: Berlin 96200). Einzelnummern werden nach dem Umfang berechnet. Preis für den achtseitigen Bogen 15 ℛ₰, zzgl. abgelaufenen Jahrgängen 10 ℛ₰, ausschließlich der Postdurchsuchungsgebühr. Bei größeren Bestellungen 10 bis 60 v. H. Preisermäßigung.
Herausgegeben vom Reichsministerium des Innern. — Gedruckt in der Reichsdruckerei, Berlin.

VI/291

The "Nuremberg Laws" of 15 September 1935

lation in Poland, from mid-1941 onwards the National Socialists set about the systematic annihilation of the Jews, first through mass executions and subsequently in the gas chambers of the extermination camps. In an act of historically unprecedented barbarity, more than half of the European Jews were killed by the end of the war.

The first stages of persecution

In early March 1933, hatred of the Jews manifested itself openly in increasing attacks and acts of violence against the Jewish population. Most were initiated by local NSDAP functionaries and the SA. With a three-day boycott of Jewish shopkeepers, lawyers and doctors beginning on 1 April, the party leadership sought to gain control of and channel this wave of antisemitic sentiment. At the same time, a number of laws were passed under which "non-Aryan" civil servants, professors, judges and public prosecutors were suspended from office, and Jewish doctors and lawyers restricted in practising their professions. In the following years, this discrimination was extended to ever more fields.

The Nuremberg laws

The process by which the Jewish population was deprived of its rights reached a provisional climax with the so-called Nuremberg laws, hastily enacted on Hitler's orders on 15 September 1935. Of these, the "Act on Reich Citizenship" established a distinction between "citizens of the Reich", who had to of "German or related blood" and who enjoyed full rights, and mere "subjects". The "Act on the Protection of German Blood and German Honour" imposed a ban on marriages and "extramarital relations" between Jews and non-Jews. "Racial defilement" was introduced as a new punishable offence of which hundreds of people were convicted in the following years.

of their livelihoods, and they even had to begin to fear for their lives. This external pressure strengthened the feeling of solidarity among Jews and their determination to assert themselves. It led to an intensification of Jewish cultural life and to the setting up of many self-help organizations.

By 1939, almost half of Germany's Jews had been forced to emigrate by the National Socialist rulers, although many of them did not succeed in finding safety from persecution for long.

VI/292
Sign at an entrance to a German village in 1935 warning Jews that they enter at their own risk

Jewish life under the swastika

Beginning in 1933, the German Jews were subject not only to increasingly oppressive government-backed discrimination but also to countless forms of everyday harassment. Their property was under threat, they were gradually robbed

The November pogrom

On 9 November 1938 the National Socialists took the assassination of a German diplomat by a 17-year-old Jew in Paris as a pretext for unleashing a massive wave of persecution throughout the Reich. In the so-called *Kristallnacht*, or "crystal

VI/293
A synagogue in
Frankfurt in flames
on 10 November
1938

night", thus named because of the splinters of broken glass left strewn across the streets, the police and SA troops ransacked, and partially looted, Jewish shops and burned down almost all Germany's synagogues.

More than 25,000 Jews were arrested, most of them being taken to concentration camps. A subsequent flood of official decrees further degraded and marginalized those Jews not yet in detention.

The November pogrom heralded the final stage of the National Socialists' persecution of the Jews.

Deportation and extermination

With the beginning of the Russian campaign in June 1941, resolute action was taken to make real Hitler's threat of January 1939, namely that a future war would lead to "the annihilation of the

VI/294
Deportation of Jews
in Baden-Baden
in 1942

Jewish race in Europe". Previous forms of persecution and provisional plans for expelling the Jews were superseded by the so-called "final solution of the Jewish question in Europe", the term used to denote plans for genocide in the minutes of the Wannsee Conference held on 20 January 1942. The annihilation of European Jewry was carried out systematically, initially through mass shootings by special units, the so-called *Einsatzgruppen*, and ultimately in extermination camps.

mination camps in Poland. The main camps were located at Auschwitz, Maidanek and Treblinka. Jews were taken there, mostly by rail in cattle waggons, from all occupied European countries. The majority of them – women and children in particular – were "selected" for death in the gas chambers on arrival; a slow and agonizing death through forced labour awaited the rest. The extermination camps continued to operate with a constantly increasing capacity until

VI/295
Mass grave at Auschwitz in 1945

Auschwitz

The murder of millions of Jews was perpetrated with almost inconceivable technical perfection in exter-

late 1944, shortly before they were liberated by the Red Army. In total, between 5 and 6 million Jews fell victim to the National Socialists' racial madness.

VI/296
Selection for
the gas chambers
at Auschwitz

10. Between revision and expansion

From the outset, the objective of National Socialist foreign policy was expansion. But in the first few years, the prevailing impression among the German public and abroad was that Hitler was merely continuing the efforts of governments of the Weimar years to achieve a revision of the Versailles Treaty. With its policy of ostensible restraint, the National Socialist regime attempted to bridge the critical first phase in power in which it had to reckon with foreign intervention without itself being adequately armed for a military conflict. The European powers allowed themselves to be deceived as to Hitler's true intentions. They were willing to accept Germany's violations of international treaties, and even to seek a new *modus vivendi* with the National Socialists. Step by step Hitler succeeded in shaking off the shackles imposed on Germany's armed forces by the Versailles Treaty, and in regaining for Germany the great power status it had lost in the wake of the first world war. Already in late 1933,

VI/297
Poster seeking support for Hitler in the referendum on the *Anschluss*, or annexation, of Austria in April 1938

Zug um Zug zerriß **Adolf Hitler** das **Diktat v. Versailles!**

1933 Deutschland verläßt den Völkerbund von Versailles!

1934 Der Wiederaufbau der Wehrmacht, der Kriegsmarine und der Luftwaffe wird eingeleitet!

1935 Saargebiet heimgeholt! Wehrhoheit des Reiches wiedergewonnen!

1936 Rheinland vollständig befreit!

1937 Kriegsschuldlüge feierlich ausgelöscht!

1938 Deutsch-Oesterreich dem Reiche angeschlossen! Großdeutschland verwirklicht!

Darum bekennt sich ganz Deutschland am 10. April zu seinem Befreier **Adolf Hitler**

Alle sagen: **Ja!**

Germany announced its withdrawal from the League of Nations. In 1935 the Saarland rejoined the Reich following a referendum in which 90% of the population voted for Germany. In the shadow of the enhanced prestige brought by this victory, the regime introduced compulsory military service. In 1936, the year in which the Olympic Games took place in Germany, the German army marched into the demilitarized Rhineland. With the *Anschluss*, or annexation, of Austria in March 1938, Germany reached the borderline which separated a policy of revision from a policy of territorial expansion.

Hitler's foreign policy programme

In *Mein Kampf* Hitler had already stated categorically that, in the foreign policy field, he would not be content merely to reestablish Germany's pre-1914 borders and its position as a great power. He created a close nexus between foreign policy and racial policy, and considered their prime objective to be the conquest of "living space" in eastern Europe for the "Germanic master race". He reaffirmed this goal in a secret address to high-ranking army officers on 3 February 1933. By contrast, in his so-called peace speech delivered to the Reichstag on 17 May 1933 and intended for public opinion at home and abroad, he stressed the continuity of foreign policy and his desire for a peaceful balancing of interests.

Cooperation and confrontation

Initially, Hitler endeavoured to counter foreign mistrust of his regime and to prevent Germany's complete isolation. To this end, the new government stressed continu-

ity by making no changes to the staff of the diplomatic service headed by Foreign Minister von Neurath. The regime achieved one of its first foreign policy successes with the signing of the Concordat between Germany and the Vatican on 20 July 1933. On 26 January 1934, it went on to sign a non-aggression pact with Poland, the country with most to fear from an increasingly assertive revisionist policy on the part of Germany. On the other hand, Hitler seized every opportunity gradually to dismantle the old order established at Versailles. As early as 14 October 1933, Germany declared its withdrawal from the League of Nations.

VI/298
Election propaganda in a Munich street in the run-up to the referendum and Reichstag elections on 12 November 1933

VI/299
Jubilant crowds
on the Heldenplatz
in Vienna during
Hitler's speech on
15 March 1938

Rearmament

Behind the veil of an ostensibly co-operative foreign policy, the National Socialist regime took resolute steps to build up its armed forces. By the autumn of 1934, Germany had already once again built up a 250,000-strong army, and the newly established air force, the *Luftwaffe*, was also a considerable fighting force. With the introduction of compulsory military service in March 1935, this military build-up – a flagrant violation of the Versailles Treaty – was made public. The protests by the other European powers were muted. On the contrary, the signing of a naval convention between Germany and Great Britain in June 1935 placed the policy of rearmament on a firm diplomatic footing. The way was now clear for Germany to cast off the remaining shackles imposed by the Versailles Treaty.

11. The road to war

Hitler led National Socialist Germany single-mindedly and unerringly into war. He was in absolutely no doubt that his foreign and racial policy objectives could only be achieved by military means. War also became increasingly unavoidable as a result of Germany's massive military build-up and the resultant one-sidedness of National Socialist economic policy.

As a possible constellation or alliance allowing Germany a free hand for a large-scale war of conquest in the east Hitler envisaged an understanding with England, entailing a division of spheres of influence between Great Britain, as the old colonial world power, and Germany as the new continental world power. However, the regime's unbending determination to shake up what it perceived as an ossified international order, thereby enhancing Germany's power as a resurgent nation, almost inevitably encouraged it to join forces with those other two countries likewise seeking agressively to expand their sphere of influence: Italy and Japan.

For a long time Great Britain and France did virtually nothing to counter the attacks by Hitler's Germany and its allies on the international order established at Versailles. As late as September 1938 they still attempted to preserve peace by giving in to Hitler on the issue of the Sudetenland. Only German action against Bohemia and Moravia a few months later prompted the Western powers to review their policy and to pledge their assistance to Poland and other eastern and southeastern European countries in case of a German attack. The next aggressive step by Germany was bound therefore to lead to war. It came on 1 September 1939 with Germany's invasion of Poland.

VI/300
The Munich conference on 29 September 1939

VI/301
Powerless Czech
citizens protesting
as German troops
enter Prague in
March 1939

Berlin, Rome, Tokyo

Despite their ideological affinities, Germany and Italy were initially divided on a number of issues, and particularly on the question of Austria. Only with the onset of Italy's war of conquest in Abysinnia, which heightened tensions with England and France, were the "Fascist" powers prompted to seek closer alignment. The new fronts were reinforced during the Spanish civil war in which both Germany and Italy intervened on the side of the rebels led by General Franco. In November 1936 the Italian dictator

VI/302
The signing of
the non-aggression
treaty between
Germany and the
Soviet Union on
23 August 1939

Mussolini referred for the first time to an "axis" between Rome and Berlin. The system of alliances for the forthcoming war was sealed on 25 November 1936 with the signing of the Anti-Comintern Pact between Germany and Japan, to which Italy acceded a year later.

The Munich Agreement

After the *Anschluss* or annexation of Austria, the expansionist ambitions of the National Socialist regime focused on Czechoslovakia. Hitler had plans for military action drawn up. At the same time, the Sudeten Germans were instrumentalized as an "explosive device" within Czechoslovakia itself. In September 1938, with the situation on the verge of war, England, France and Italy acquiesced to Germany's demands in the so-called Munich Agreement. Czechoslovakia was forced, without any say in the matter, to cede the Sudetenland to Germany. Through their compliance the Western powers, and in particular the British Prime Minister Neville Chamberlain, made one last effort to bind Germany into a new pan-European order. But soon after, in March 1939, German troops marched into Bohemia and Moravia in a flagrant breach of the Munich Agreement.

The outbreak of war

From late 1938 onwards, German policy focused increasingly on Poland, Germany's neighbour to the east. In return for concessions on bilateral issues, Germany offered Poland an alliance against the Soviet Union as well as territorial gains in the east. When the Polish government rejected this offer, Hitler, unperturbed by the Anglo-French guarantees given to Poland, resolved to seek a military solution. At the same time, he sought a temporary understanding with the Soviet Union, which led ultimately to the signing of a German-Soviet non-aggression pact on 23 August 1939. In a secret protocol, the two dictators, Hitler and Stalin, agreed on the partition of Poland and on the boundaries of their respective spheres of influence. A few days later, German troops crossed the border into Poland.

VI/303
German troops advancing in Poland in September 1939

VI/304
Hitler with field
marshalls appointed
following the victory
over France in September 1940

12. World power or doom

The Second World War began with swift victories for the German armed forces, both against Poland in autumn 1939 and against the countries of northern and western Europe in spring 1940. More than ever before, Hitler and the whole German leadership were convinced of the superiority of the German people and the Germanic race. They were determined to establish a world empire of unprecedented dimensions.

Following the invasion of the Soviet Union in June 1941, what had already begun under German rule in Poland became patently obvious: on Hitler's orders the war in the east was to be conducted not only as a war of conquest but also as one of racial annihilation. The systematic liquidations carried out by special German units claimed millions of victims among Jews, the Polish elites and Communist functionaries in the Soviet Union. Millions lost their lives as prisoners of war or as a result of inhuman treatment by the German occupying forces.

Militarily, however, the German armed forces became overstretched after the invasion of the Soviet Union. The United States entered the war in December 1941, and fighting continued on other fronts in southeastern Europe and Africa. The German defeat in the battle of Stalingrad in January 1943 marked the turning point of the war. Faced with the superior might of the allied powers, the German troops were from then on gradually forced to retreat. The "total war" proclaimed by the National Socialists in February 1943 ended, having claimed millions of lives and having led to the collapse of the German Reich and the complete devastation of the country, on 8 May 1945 with Germany's unconditional surrender.

Swift victories

Following the invasion on 1 September 1939, Poland only succeeded in stemming the tide of superior German forces for a few weeks. In the Polish campaign, Hitler achieved his first *Blitzkrieg* victory. Although Britain and France responded to the German attack by declaring war on 3 September, they failed to establish a second front. This was conducive to Hilter's military strategy. In separate campaigns, the German army, the *Wehrmacht*, succeeded in first subjugating Poland, then occupying Denmark and Norway from April 1940, and finally, after violating the neutrality of the Benelux states, in conquering France in May and June 1940 and repulsing British troops from the continent. However, Hitler's attempts over the following months either, as he had originally calculated, to reach an arrangement with England, thereby freeing his hands for a war in the East, or to force its to its knees militarily came to nothing.

The war against the USSR

On 22 June 1941, the Germans unleashed their surprise attack on the Soviet Union. Code-named "Barbarossa", this campaign was planned by Hitler and his generals as another *Blitzkrieg* or "lightning war". But in contrast to the war in

VI/305
Shooting of hostages by a German officer in the Yugoslavian town Pancevo in April 1941

VI/306
Starving Russian
prisoners of war
begging for bread

VI/307
The eastern front
near Moscow in
January 1942

the west, its aim was not only one of military conquest but also, in the truest sense of the word, one of physical annihilation. The Communist leaders were to be murdered, the population decimated, and the country's industrial and agricultural base destroyed. Initially, the *Wehrmacht* again succeeded in penetrating deep into enemy territory. But, in December 1941 the German offensive ground to a halt outside Moscow. Despite renewed advances in the summer of 1942, German losses and the stubborn resistance of the Soviet troops finally dispelled any illusions of an eventual German victory.

VI/308
German soldiers
advancing on Stalin-
grad in the summer
of 1942

The turning point of the war

By summer 1942, German domin-
ion over foreign territory had
reached its peak. But long front-
lines and superior opposing forces
imposed demands that exceeded
the capacity of Germany's army, its
arms industry and its supply of raw
materials. The Soviet Union, Great
Britain and the USA came together
to form a united "anti-Hitler coalition". They agreed that Germany
should be beaten on the field of
battle and forced to accept an "unconditional surrender". The turning
point of the war was heralded in
November 1942 by the British

VI/309
German dead at
Stalingrad in Febru-
ary 1943

VI/310
American bomber
aircraft during a raid
on Berlin in 1945

communists alone; the economy was restructured along the lines of a socialist planned economy which entailed the collectivization of land and the nationalization of banks and key industries. These developments ultimately led to the establishment of an East German state, the German Democratic Republic (GDR), on 7 October 1949.

During the 1950s the division of Germany steadily deepened, which put an end to hopes that national unity might soon be restored. In the Federal Republic a fierce battle ensued concerning the country's political orientation. Under the leadership of Chancellor Konrad Adenauer, those who favoured a Federal Republic firmly oriented towards the West finally prevailed and in 1955 the Federal Republic became an equal and sovereign partner in the Western community of states. In a series of countermoves, the GDR was gradually incorporated into the Soviet-dominated Eastern bloc and ultimately became a full member of the Warsaw Pact in 1955. The inner German border marked the dividing line between the militarily powerful Eastern and Western blocs. German soldiers on both sides of the border also helped to maintain the status quo and thus contributed to the two German states pursuing very different paths.

Once initial difficulties had been overcome, West Germany embarked on a period of unparalleled economic growth. Owing to the urgent need for reconstruction after the devastation of the war years and supported by the sustained global economic upturn, the West German economy continued to flourish into the 1960s. All sections of the population soon experienced a steady improvement in their standard of living. The "economic miracle" not only allowed solutions to be found rapidly to the enormous social problems left behind by National Socialism and the war, but also provided the material conditions under which a tight social security net could be established. Above all, however, the continuing economic boom and the absence of serious social tensions gave West Germany's postwar democracy the domestic stability which the Weimar Republic had so grievously lacked.

The situation in East Germany, however, contrasted starkly with that in the West. In the GDR a largely Soviet-style communist dictatorship emerged which was sustained by violence and terror. In 1952 and in the years which followed, East Germany's communist party, the Socialist Unity Party (SED), sought openly to "build Socialism" within the framework of a planned economy. In two major phases, at the beginning and end of the 1950s, agriculture was collectivized and industrial enterprises and trading concerns were converted into state-owned companies. Although the efforts to build up the new system were to some degree successful, living conditions improved only very slowly. Popular discontent began to grow and reached its peak in an uprising on 17 June 1953. Soviet tanks were deployed, and the insurrection was brutally crushed. During this period more than 100,000 people were leaving the GDR for the West each year. It was not until the Berlin Wall was built on 13 August 1961, and the border with the West effectively sealed, that the GDR achieved stability as a state. Nevertheless, the East German economy increasingly lagged behind that of West Germany. While the SED leadership sought to achieve international recognition for the GDR as a state in its own right, support grew in the Federal Republic for a change of course in policy on Germany.

The 1960s were a time of transition for the Federal Republic. The first sharp economic downturn and the ensuing crisis which faced the Erhard government in the autumn of 1966 were considered so serious that the CDU/CSU and the SPD agreed to form a coalition for a limited period in order to overcome the difficulties. There was also, however, an increasing willingness to adapt the political and social order built during the postwar years to the changed conditions. The desire for a new start manifested itself in two ways: first in the student-led protest movement of the late 1960s, and secondly in the government changeover of 1969 when a Social Democrat became Federal Chancellor for the first time.

In foreign policy, the priority of the Social-Liberal government was to establish good-neighbourly relations with the Federal Republic's Eastern European neighbours. The treaties concluded with the Soviet Union, Poland, Czechoslovakia and the German Democratic Republic provided for the renunciation of force, recognized the conditions which had resulted from the Second World War, and brought practical improvements for the people in both parts of Germany. There was considerable opposition to this policy in both German states which only began to diminish when Erich Honecker succeeded Walter Ulbricht as SED leader in the GDR in 1971 and when the Brandt/Scheel government was re-elected in the Federal Republic in 1972. The signing of the "Treaty on the Basis of Relations between the Federal Republic of Germany and the

German Democratic Republic" in East and West Germany the following year marked the beginning of a new era in which there was a modus vivendi between the two states.

Domestic reform in West Germany was brought to an end in the autumn of 1973 by the onset of the first oil crisis, which heralded a political turnaround in West Germany. The Social-Liberal coalition under Helmut Schmidt, who became Chancellor in May 1974, sought to limit the effects of the global recession on the Federal Republic. It introduced programmes to stimulate the economy and create jobs and sought to pursue an internationally coordinated economic policy. However, because of the ongoing economic crisis and the rise in East-West tension following the Soviet invasion of Afgha-nistan in 1979, the Social-Liberal coalition fell apart. On 1 October 1982 a coalition government was formed by the CDU/CSU and the FDP under the leadership of Chancellor Helmut Kohl. It set about reorganizing economic and social policy. Thanks in part to the global economic upturn, the new government succeeded in bringing about a return to real growth by implementing financial and social policies to boost recovery. It was unable, however, to overcome the problems of an emerging structural crisis caused by technological change and growing international competition in certain sectors of industry.

Across the inner-German border there was a perceptible revival in the political and economic fortunes of East Germany under the leadership of Erich Honecker. Once the international community had finally recognized the GDR as a state, the SED began to adopt a more open and flexible stance. Although there were improvements in the supply of goods and services, they soon proved almost impossible to finance. From the end of the 1970s, it became increasingly clear that the Eastern bloc states were unable to keep pace with structural changes in the economy and technology without exhausting their resources entirely. The opposition movement in the GDR gradually acquired more continuity in terms of its organization and leadership, notwithstanding the oppression it faced. Yet the SED leadership, unlike the Soviet leadership under Mikhail Gorbachev, showed no desire to introduce thoroughgoing economic or political reforms. In the autumn of 1989, the GDR was thrown into a profound internal crisis. The pro-democracy movement swept the country, prompting the downfall of the one-party communist system and ultimately leading, after the first free elections to the People's Chamber, to the unification of the two German states on 3 October 1990.

VII/312
American troops
entering Bensheim
in Hesse, 27 March
1945

1945–1955: Division

1. The Germany of the victors

The occupation of the entire German Reich by Allied troops, unconditional surrender by Germany and the assumption of supreme authority by the USA, Britain, France and the USSR put the final seal on military defeat and showed that Germany had become a pawn on the chessboard of the victorious powers.

During the war, the anti-Hitler alliance had already agreed on the outlines of a European postwar order and on a series of measures for dealing with Germany. Large areas of the Reich to the east of the Rivers Oder and Neisse were to be detached from the country and placed under Polish or Soviet administration; the remaining area was to be divided up into four zones of occupation, with Berlin being treated as a separate entity and governed jointly by the Four Powers. Responsibility for governing the whole of Germany was assigned to an Allied Control Council composed of the commanders-in-chief of the Four Powers.

For the rest, however, the unity of the Allies was limited to their resolve to prevent Germany from ever again waging another war and to remove all vestiges of the National Socialist regime. Even the agreements reached at the Potsdam Conference, including the decision to treat Germany as a single economic

VII/313
Soviet troops
entering Berlin-
Schöne-berg,
April 1945

unit and to build a new democratic system, merely gave a rough outline of joint aims and could not hide fundamental conflicts of interest.

The Allied Control Council therefore soon proved incapable of reaching decisions on most questions and its responsibilities were increasingly transferred to the commanders-in-

VII/314
Liberation of
concentration camp
inmates in Dachau,
29 April 1945

chief and the military governments in the individual occupation zones. The plan for German central administrations was vetoed by France, while economic unity fell victim to the disputes over reparations, which were demanded above all by the Soviet Union.

With regard to political democratization, the prime objective of each occupying power was to establish an order in line with its own political system. In this way the four zones began to go their separate ways, thus prompting a development which was to eventually lead to the division of Germany.

Between liberation and occupation

The reaction of the German population to the advance of the Allied troops varied considerably, depending on their political views and on which of the Four Powers was occupying their area. The hour of defeat was also the hour of liberation and the eradication of an inhuman dictatorship. Yet the combination of liberation and occupation also marked the dilemma which was to face Allied and German politics in the years to come: while the victors were determined to impose their

VII/315
Bodies in Nordhausen concentration camp after its liberation, 1945

VII/316
Refugees making
their way west-
wards

will, they also wanted to establish a democratic order, and while the German side sought to represent German interests, it was also prepared to cooperate loyally with the occupying powers.

A society in collapse

When the war ended Germany lay in ruins. The economy had collapsed, and almost all transport and communications links had been destroyed. Millions of people, Germans and foreigners alike, were on the move, all searching for relatives and a new home. There were evacuees who had fled bomb attacks and advancing troops; refugees and expellees who had been forced to flee their ancestral homes; former slave labourers, concentration camp inmates and prisoners; and soldiers who had been released from military service. For most of

VII/317
Plenary session
of the Potsdam Con-
ference, July/August
1945

them, their main concern was to survive and overcome starvation and destitution. Within a few weeks of the end of the war, however, these preoccupations gave way to a determination to rebuild the country and make a fresh start.

The policies of the occupying powers

The policy on Germany pursued by the victorious powers reflected a mixture of very different interests: their security needs and their de-

VII/318
Soviet army
entering Gera,
2 July 1945

mands for reparations, their desire to incorporate all or part of Germany into their own spheres of influence, and their readiness to establish a new democratic order in Germany, for which they each developed their own particular strategy based on their own political system. Against the background of their disputes over global issues, this led to tensions which made it possible to reach compromise solutions only for a short transitional period until around the end of 1946. The system of occupation, the division of Germany into four zones, the right of veto held by each of the victorious powers, and the relationship between the Allied Control Council and the commanders-in-chief of the zones, which had never been properly clarified, also did little to facilitate the development of a coherent policy of occupation.

Denazification

Punishment for the crimes committed under National Socialist rule and the removal of all active Nazis from their jobs were among the top priorities of the victorious powers. Nevertheless, only the trials of the leading war criminals at Nuremberg were conducted jointly by the Allies. The actual denazification programme was approached differently in each zone. The Soviet Union considered it to be primarily part of a restructuring process along communist lines. By contrast, denazification in the Western zones, and in

VII/319
The courtroom at the Nuremberg War Crimes Trials, 1945/46

the American zone in particular, was treated as a question of individual guilt and of re-education. In the course of the reconstruction process and with the onset of the Cold War, these policies were pursued less and less rigorously. Denazification was finally abandoned in 1948, falling short of the high expectations which had been placed in it.

VII/320
Denazification questionnaire used in the American zone of occupation

MILITARY GOVERNMENT OF GERMANY
Fragebogen

A. PERSONAL / A. Persönliche Angaben

B. SECONDARY AND HIGHER EDUCATION / B. Grundschul- und höhere Bildung

C. PROFESSIONAL OR TRADE EXAMINATIONS / C. Berufs- oder Handwerksprüfungen

D. CHRONOLOGICAL RECORD OF FULL TIME EMPLOYMENT AND MILITARY SERVICE / D. Chronologische Aufstellung jeglicher Hauptanstellungen und des Militärdienstes

E. MEMBERSHIP IN ORGANIZATIONS / E. Mitgliedschaften

41. NSDAP
42. Allgemeine ##
43. Waffen-##
44. Sicherheitsdienst der ##
45. SA
46. HJ einschl. BDM
47. NSDStB
48. NSKOB
49. NS Frauenschaft
50. NSKK
51. NSFK
52. Reichsb. der deutschen Beamten
53. DAF
54. KdF
55. NSV
56. NS Reichsb. deutsch. Schwestern
57. NSKOV
58. NS Bund Deutscher Technik
59. NS Ärztebund
60. NS Lehrerbund
61. NS Rechtswahrerbund
62. Deutsches Frauenwerk
63. Reichsbund deutscher Familie
64. NS Reichsb. für Leibesübungen
65. NS Altherrenbund
66. Deutsche Studentenschaft
67. NS Reichsstudentenbund
68. Deutscher Gemeindetag
69. NS Reichskriegerbund
70. Reichsdozentenschaft
71. Reichskulturkammer
72. Reichsschrifttumskammer
73. Reichspressekammer
74. Reichsrundfunkkammer
75. Reichstheaterkammer
76. Reichsmusikkammer
77. Reichskammer d. bildend. Künste
78. Reichsfilmkammer
79. Amerika-Institut
80. Deutsche Akademie München
81. Deutsches Auslandsinstitut
82. Deutsche Christen-Bewegung
83. Deutsche Glaubensbewegung
84. Deutscher Fichte-Bund
85. Deutscher Jägerschaft
86. Deutsches Rotes Kreuz
87. Ibero-Amerikanisches Institut
87. Institut zur Erforschung der Judenfrage
88. Kameradschaft USA
89. Osteuropäisches Institut
90. Reichsarbeitsdienst (RAD)
91. Reichskolonialbund
92. Reichsluftschutzbund
93. Staatsakademie für Rassen- und Gesundheitspflege
94. Volksbund für das Deutschtum im Ausland (VDA)
95. Werberat d. Deutschen Wirtsch.
  Others (Specify) andere:
96.

VII/321
Propaganda for
the referendum in
Saxony, 30 June
1946

VII/322
Konrad Adenauer in front of the ruined city hall building in Cologne, 1945

2. Continuity and a new beginning

The year 1945 did not usher in a completely new beginning. Admittedly, given what the German people had experienced during the National Socialist dictatorship and in view of the destruction, material and otherwise, which had been wrought, there was at first an almost universal conviction that the only way to ensure a better future for Germany was to make a completely new start. The occupying powers, moreover, represented a source of fresh inspiration. At the same time, however, the efforts to establish a new economic, social and political order were influenced by personalities and political ideas which were in many respects closely linked to the Weimar Republic or even older traditions.

The new political parties which began to emerge soon came to play a key role in this process. Although the party system overcame the fragmentation of the Weimar peri-od, it nevertheless reflected the main historical currents of German politics. Alongside the Communist Party (KPD), which under the leadership of Walter Ulbricht and his supporters essentially followed the line dictated by Moscow, the Social Democrats (SPD), led in West Germany by Kurt Schumacher and the so-called "Hanover Circle", were the first party successfully to reorganize themselves and to develop a programme which was widely accepted. By contrast, the CDU and CSU, which had been newly founded by forces from the Catholic, liberal and conservative camps, were only later able to agree on a uniform programme and policy. Lastly, the two wings of liberalism, which had been represented by different parties since 1866/67, merged to form the Free Democratic Party (FDP) in the Western zones and the Liberal-Democratic Party (LDP) in the Soviet zone.

The central feature of the "new beginning" was the process of restoring a democratic political system, starting with the communes and then moving on to the *Länder*, or federal states. Although there were some ideological differences between the parties, and although they had different views on the future relationship between the federation and the *Länder*, they were able to reach a consensus on the structure of the political system. They disagreed strongly, however, on the kind of economic system to be introduced. The Social Democrats in particular fought for a parliamentary democracy based on a socialist economy. The Liberals favoured a market economy and the maintenance of existing forms of private ownership. The CDU/CSU, on the other hand, reflected a wide spectrum of opinion, ranging from those who were moderately socialist in outlook to committed advocates of market economics. It was not until 1948/49, when steps were underway to establish the Federal Republic in the western part of Germany, that the supporters of a social market economy prevailed. Moreover, it was only at this stage in the process of division that the fronts and balance of power were firmly established.

A fresh start?

In the first few weeks of the Allied occupation political groups began to emerge, most of which followed in the footsteps of those who had resisted Hitler's regime. Transcending traditional party-political boundaries, they put their efforts into seeking the immediate creation of a new democratic order. In the Soviet sphere of influence, however, the desire for unity demonstrated by these antifascist groups was soon exploited and made to fit communist objectives. The Western occupying powers turned their attention in the first instance to rebuilding the administration. They relied for help largely on German politicians who were known to them from the Weimar Republic or who had been recommended to them by the churches,

VII/323
Berlin tram with banner promoting the Antifascist Block, 1945

VII/324
Meeting in Schumacher's office in Hanover, 1946

VII/325
Meeting of the CDU/CSU working group in Frankfurt am Main, April 1948

which were assumed to have a clean record. Under strict supervision by the occupying powers, steps were taken to reintroduce newspapers and broadcasting services and thus lay the foundations of a new democratic way of life.

The founding of parties and trade unions

On 10 June 1945 – not least with the aim of influencing political developments throughout Germany – the Soviet Union became the first

VII/326
Wilhelm Pieck,
Otto Grotewohl and
Walter Ulbricht at
the joint SPD and
KPD party confer-
ence when the two
parties were merged
to form the SED,
21/22 April 1946

VII/327
Meeting of the
executive commit-
tee of the Liberals
in Frankfurt am
Main, 3 November
1947

occupying power to sanction the establishment of political parties and trade unions. Moving more slowly, the Americans and the British followed suit in the late summer, and so did the French towards the end of the year. Following short-lived attempts to form alliances on the left and right, four parties were granted licences in all zones, with only a few regional exceptions: the SPD and KPD were newly founded, the Liberals regrouped themselves under various names (Free Democratic Party (FDP), Liberal-Democratic Party (LDP), German People's Party (DVP)) and two new parties were formed by Catholic and Protestant Christian Democrats, the CDU and its Bavarian sister party, the CSU. Having been put under intense pressure to do so, the communists and Social Democrats in the Soviet zone merged in April 1946 to form the Socialist Unity Party of Germany (SED) which from then on increasingly began to lay claim to political leadership.

VII/328
Opening of the
Constituent Assembly in Württemberg-Baden, July 1946

As the political parties were being formed, workers began to set up ideologically neutral trade unions in each sector of industry, which were free from party-political affiliations. In the eastern zone, however, they soon fell under the control of the SED.

The establishment of the *Länder*

In all zones, the boundaries of the *Länder*, or federal states, were redrawn in 1945/46, not least because of the break-up of Prussia. The boundaries laid down by the

VII/329
Demonstration by
the "antifascist
police" in Leipzig,
September 1945

VII/330
Hungry children at
a food distribution
point in Berlin, 1947

occupying powers still apply today, both in the western part of the Federal Republic, with the exception of the south-west, and in the east of the country where they were re-established after unification. The *Länder* played a prominent role, particularly in the American and French zones, where they were rapidly established as political units organized in keeping with the rules of parliamentary democracy and were granted extensive powers. Having initially introduced a more centralized form of government in their zone, the British authorities soon adopted the American and French model of zonal organization with the result that federal structures became a determining factor in the political order of the Federal Republic.

In 1947 the *Länder* in the Soviet zone were also formally granted democratic constitutions, but the key positions in the ministries were soon filled by communists. Increasingly, all important decisions came to be taken by the SED leadership and the central authorities in Berlin, in consultation with the occupying power.

Reconstruction and nationalization

Many barriers had to be overcome before the reconstruction which everyone longed for could commence in postwar Germany. War damage in the industrial sector was compounded by the dismantling of industrial equipment by the Allies. Moreover, the lack of raw materials, transport problems and grave food shortages stood in the way of a new beginning. The economy had also suffered lasting damage owing to the collapse of the Reichsmark and the widespread lack of goods. Rationing and the black market were part and parcel of everyday life. In circumstances like these it

VII/331
"Rubble women"
in Berlin, 1945

was not only the communists and Social Democrats who considered reconstruction along socialist lines to be the only possible solution. Many members of the CDU also favoured nationalization, land reform, the extension of employee participation and state intervention in the economy. A majority of the population in Saxony voted in favour of nationalization; in Hesse the introduction of a clause on nationalization in the state constitution received widespread support;

and in North Rhine-Westphalia a majority of members of the state parliament voted to nationalize the coal-mining industry.

A new cultural beginning

Having been denied the right to free speech and the opportunity to engage in any form of artistic activity for so long, many people positively craved culture. Long queues formed outside theatres, concert

VII/332
Soviet soldiers uncovering the statues of Goethe and Schiller in Weimar, July 1945

halls and cinemas. Sales of books and periodicals rocketed. Although material circumstances were often difficult, cultural life soon began to flourish again. Many artists and writers, who had fled the National Socialists and escaped abroad, returned to Germany. Even those who had stayed in Germany but had retreated into private life spoke out in public once again. In literary and journalistic circles the desire for a fresh start was particularly strong. Writers and journalists were therefore quick to criticize the course of developments after the war, arguing that too many postwar policies simply marked a return to the past. Yet, as in other areas of postwar reconstruction, the efforts to rebuild cultural life were also inspired by a desire to return to the positive traditions of German history and culture. The centenary celebrations of the revolution of 1848/49 and the bicentenary of Goethe's birth in 1949 were an opportunity to recall Germany's democratic legacy and the values represented in German classicism.

VII/333
Banner welcoming the author Thomas Mann to Weimar, 1949

VII/334
Passers-by viewing the window display in Rosen's antiquarian bookshop in Berlin, 1947

3. On the way to division

In 1945 the German Reich de facto ceased to exist. From the outset, the victorious powers were unable to agree on a common occupation policy and in this way to preserve the economic and political unity of Germany. The division of Germany was provisionally sealed by the Cold War, the origins and causes of which extended far beyond Germany and its specific problems.

The Soviet Union considered the protests against its conduct in Eastern Europe and the refusal to meet communism. This new course was most clearly reflected in the Marshall Plan for the economic reconstruction of Western Europe, which also aimed to end France's special role in respect of policy on Germany.

After the failure of the Four-Power Conference in London in December 1947, the steps necessary to establish a West German state were rapidly taken. The Soviet Union responded by taking corresponding measures in its zone and by at-

VII/335
Conference of Allied foreign ministers in Moscow, March/April 1947

its demand for reparations to be evidence that the capitalist countries were pursuing a policy of encirclement and it subsequently sought quite openly to strengthen its supremacy in Eastern Europe. In response to these expansionist policies, the United States abandoned its earlier line, which was based on the delimitation of spheres of interest and partial cooperation. On 12 March 1947, the American President proclaimed the Truman Doctrine, which marked the beginning of a policy aimed at containing tempting to exert pressure on the West. Following the currency reform and the adoption of a constitution by the Parliamentary Council, the Federal Republic of Germany was officially proclaimed on 23 May 1949. A few months later, on 7 October 1949, an East German state, the German Democratic Republic, also came into being.

Most German politicians found it difficult to accept that Germany was no longer a united country and that the economic and political recovery of the three Western zones could only be achieved in this way. They finally went down this route because they thought that a democratic and economically prosperous Federal Republic would act as a magnet for the rest of Germany, thereby leading to reunification after a few years.

In East Germany, as before, the communists were not the only ones to be active politically. The ostensible support for national unity shown by the Soviet Union and the SED induced many democratic politicians, trade unionists, writers and artists who opposed the division of Germany to harbour illusions about future developments in the Soviet zone. Yet in the years leading up to the establishment of the GDR it became increasingly evident that the proclamations made by the "People's Congress Movement" in support of national unity were a front for the rigorous enforcement of communist doctrine in all areas of society. Rather than becoming the more democratic and more welfare-oriented heart of the future Germany nation, as the SED claimed, the GDR turned into a Soviet-style communist dictatorship.

VII/336
Poster promoting
the Marshall Plan,
1948

The Cold War

In the course of 1946, the global confrontation between two ideologically opposed power blocs, the first signs of which had already become apparent towards the end of the war, began increasingly to determine the future shape of Europe. An "Iron Curtain", as Churchill put it, came down along the borders of the territories dominated by the Soviet Union. Germany became the focal point of the Cold War. Against the background of this global confrontation, the differences between the Allies over how to treat Germany became insurmountable.

After the failure of the foreign ministers' conference in Moscow in April 1947, the United States took the initiative: with the support of Britain and later also of France, the Western zones were gradually integrated into the Western system, both economically and politically. All German attempts to salvage the ever-diminishing prospect of national unity failed because of the power-political situation and because differences within Germany too had become unbridgeable.

The Marshall Plan and currency reform

The United States and Britain, concerned about the serious economic situation and the growing tension in relations with the USSR, resolved to give priority to the economic recovery of the Western zones. The first step they took was to merge their zones to form the British-American Bi-Zone on 1 January 1947. The second step was the announcement by the American Secretary of State George C. Marshall in June 1947 of the launching of an economic aid programme for Europe which incorporated the three Western zones but in which, as expected, the East did not participate. The third step was the currency re-

VII/337
Demonstration against the Marshall Plan in East Berlin, 1 May 1948

Selbst kurbelten uns'ren Betrieb wir an und brauchten keinen Marshall=Plan!

VII/338
Distribution of
new Deutschmark
notes in Munich,
20 June 1948

form of 20 June 1948 which saw
the replacement of the Reichsmark,
which had become practically
worthless, by the new Deutschmark. At the same time, rationing
was largely abolished. All three
steps not only served to promote
an economic upturn in the Western
zones but also ensured that an early decision was taken in favour of
the market-oriented policies ad-
vanced by Ludwig Erhard. However,
they also had the effect of deepen-
ing the divide between East and
West.

The failure of four-power policy

The creation of the British-American Bi-Zone and, in particular, the
introduction of the Marshall Plan,
which was directed against the Soviet Union, speeded up the division
of Germany. It became increasingly
clear that talks between the four
powers were merely being held for
appearances' sake. On 20 March
1948, perceiving that the plans to
create a West German state were
gradually acquiring a more concrete form, the Soviets left the Al-

VII/340
Police from East
and West Berlin
in Bernauer Strasse
at the boundary be-
tween the eastern
and western sec-
tors, spring 1949

lied Control Council, the supreme authority of the occupying powers for Germany as a whole. The East-West confrontation reached its climax in the dispute over Berlin, which was divided into four sectors. The Soviets reacted to the currency reform in the Western zones by closing all the approaches to West Berlin by rail, road and water on 24 June 1948. The Western powers responded with the Airlift. For eleven months, until 12 May 1949, the city, which had a population of two million, was supplied exclusively from the air. It was during this time, due to communist pressure and aggression, that the split in Berlin's political life was cemented. The spheres of power in Berlin and Germany were thus clearly delimited.

VII/341
Demonstrators
storming the new
city hall in Berlin,
6 September 1948

VII/339
(opposite)
Plane carrying
supplies during
the Berlin Airlift
seen above a street
in West Berlin,
1948/49

VII/342
The three western
military governors
at the handing-over
of the Frankfurt
Documents, 1 July
1948

From Frankfurt to Bonn

VII/343
Final vote on
the Basic Law in
the Parliamentary
Council, 8 May
1949

In the Frankfurt Documents of 1 July 1948 the Western powers invited the minister-presidents in their zones to draw up a constitution for a West German state. The German politicians reluctantly agreed, not least because they were concerned about the Berlin blockade. On 1 September 1948 the Parliamentary Council began its work. Its 65 members – 27 each from the SPD and the CDU/CSU, five from

VII/344
The first Federal
Government after
being sworn in,
20 September 1949

the FDP and two each from the KPD, the German Party (DP) and the Centre Party – were elected from the state parliaments. Following lengthy negotiations, during which the compromises reached on the German side were repeatedly jeopardized by the military governors' demands for an extension of the rights of the *Länder*, a large majority of the Parliamentary Council – 53 Members against only 12 from the CSU, DP, KPD and Centre Party – voted to adopt the Basic Law for the Federal Republic of Germany. After receiving the approval of the military governors and state parliaments the new constitution was proclaimed at an official ceremony on 23 May 1949, thus marking the foundation of the Federal Republic of Germany.

From the People's Congress to the GDR

Towards the end of 1947, the SED inaugurated a "People's Congress for Unity and Just Peace". The stated purpose of the People's Congress was, as its name implied, to promote national unity and draw up a constitution for the whole of Germany. In reality, however, its delegates were not democratically elected and therefore had no democratic legitimacy. The People's Congress therefore served primarily to strengthen the power of the SED in the Soviet zone and ultimately to bring about the establishment of an East German state. In March 1948, a German People's Council comprising 400 delegates – 100 from the Western zones – was elected by

VII/346
Handing-over of
administrative au-
thority by the Soviet
army to the East
German govern-
ment, 10 October
1949

the Second People's Congress which was now a permanent organ of state. The People's Council then arranged for a constitution to be drafted – a process which lasted until October 1948 – and adopted the resulting document by unanimous vote on 19 March 1949. In May 1949 the Third People's Congress was elected for the first time under the single-list system. Notwithstanding widespread vote-rigging, only two thirds of ballots were in support of official candidates. On 7 October 1949, the Third German People's Council voted unanimously to bring the constitution into force, thus officially marking the establishment of the German Democratic Republic.

VII/347
Wilhelm Pieck,
President of the
GDR, inspecting
an honorary guard
of the East German
police, 11 October
1949

VII/345
(opposite)
Sitting of the
German People's
Council in East
Berlin, 7 October
1949

4. Western and Eastern integration

The promulgation of the Basic Law of the Federal Republic of Germany in May 1949 and of the East German constitution in October 1949 by no means marked the completion of the process leading to the emergence of two fully fledged states within Germany. The scene had indeed been set for such a development but the internal structure of both states had still to be worked out in detail and the question of external sovereignty remained unresolved.

In West Germany, the first elections to the Bundestag on 14 August 1949, when a centre-right coalition of the CDU/CSU, the FDP and the DP won by a narrow majority, played an important part in determining the future political course of the Federal Republic. In the domestic sphere the government continued to pursue a policy of social market economics, while in foreign affairs Chancellor Adenauer sought to achieve West Germany's integration into the Western alliance on an equal footing with other states. However, economic difficulties and daunting social problems caused a considerable degree of political uncertainty during the early years of the Federal Republic. Domestic and foreign policy were subjects of fierce contention among the political parties. It was not until the Bundestag election of 1953, when the governing coalition won by a large majority and thus consolidated its position, that the initial years of crisis were overcome.

In East Germany, although the authorities contrived to maintain the illusion of a multi-party system, there was growing evidence that the GDR was being turned into a replica of the Soviet Union. On the political front the CDU and the LDP lost what remained of their inde-

VII/348
Assembly-line production of Volkswagen cars, 1949

VII/349
Unemployed men
in an employment
office after the cur-
rency reform of
1948

pendence. Just like the mass organizations, which had already been brought into line with the SED's objectives, they now merely served to safeguard the power of the Party. Any form of opposition, especially within the ranks of the SED itself, was crushed with the utmost ruthlessness. Under the slogan "learning from the Soviet Union is a lesson in victory", a one-sided economic policy was pursued which gave priority to heavy industry. Consequently, although production figures rose, living standards improved only marginally. As these problems worsened the situation became increasingly critical and finally led to the workers' uprising of 17 June 1953.

Hence, in 1953 key decisions were taken on both sides of the inner-German border. The Federal Republic decided to go down the route of economic prosperity and political stability, and allied itself closely with the West. The GDR, opted to secure by force a Soviet-style system of government and social order. The treaties concluded in 1955 put the finishing touches to the process of Eastern and Western integration and set the seal on the division of Germany.

The policy of the "social market economy"

The policy of social market economics introduced by Ludwig Erhard in the Frankfurt Economic Council at the same time as the currency reform faced its first major test in the early years of the Federal Republic. Erhard's conservative financial policy and export-oriented economic policy were designed above all to encourage investment while, at least initially, holding down domestic consumption. Erhard was thus prepared to accept temporary social imbalances. Although high growth rates were occasionally achieved in the early years, unemployment continued to rise and wage levels remained low. This difficult phase was mastered only because of the restraint shown by the trade unions. From 1952/53 onwards, broad sections of the population benefited from the economic boom in the form of significant increases in real incomes.

The "building of Socialism" in the GDR

The object of economic policy in the GDR, as proclaimed publicly by the SED at its Second Party Congress in July 1952, was to "build Socialism" within the framework of a planned economy. Even before the foundation of the GDR in 1949 steps had already been taken in this direction. As early as 1945 land

reform was introduced, initially with the support of all the political parties, which expropriated owners of large estates and divided up the land into new farms. From 1952 onwards, many farmers who were unable to make a living independently were forced into collectives. The number of state-owned enterprises in the industrial and commercial sectors also grew significantly – a major factor in this process being the gradual return of "Soviet joint stock companies" to German ownership. However, the goal of creating a socialist system not only involved changing the structure of ownership; its main feature was the introduction of central planning for all areas of economic activity, starting with the Two Year Plan in 1949 and continuing, on a more extensive scale, with the Five Year Plan introduced in 1951. Crucially, and despite the fact that the necessary conditions were lacking, the GDR gave priority to developing a heavy industry of its own while neglecting those sectors of industry which were of greater long-term value and produced consumer goods.

VII/350
Hennigsdorf iron works as a state-owned company, 1946/47

VII/351
(opposite)
Poster promoting the first Five Year Plan in the GDR, 1952

BAUTEN DES FÜNFJAHRPLANES

EISENHÜTTENKOMBINAT OST (EKO)
Aus sowjetischem Erz und polnischer Kohle
wird deutscher Friedensstahl

VII/352
Constituent sitting
of the Bundestag,
7 September 1949

The stabilization of parliamentary democracy

VII/353
Theodor Heuss
being sworn in as
Federal President,
12 September 1949

The stability of the political system in the Federal Republic was by no means guaranteed in the early years. Political extremists on both right and left posed a threat to the political order. The government was, however, ultimately able to hold extremism in check, for instance by banning certain parties. On the other hand, the electoral successes achieved by the large number of new refugee and regional movements indicated a worrying trend towards party fragmentation – a phenomenon which prompted intense internal struggles within the CDU, the CSU and the FDP. Nevertheless, the rapid economic upturn and the five-per-cent clause – which meant that parties needed to poll at least 5 per cent of the vote to be represented in parliament – helped to halt this tendency and, in the Bundestag elections of 1953, set in motion a massive trend towards a three-party system. The governing CDU/CSU in particular, which achieved an absolute majority in the Bundestag, showed itself to be capable of integrating a broad range of political views. Thus, towards the end of 1953, the Swiss political author Fritz René Allemann noted with satisfaction, in his book of the same title, that "Bonn is not Weimar".

VII/354
Parade in East
Berlin, 1950

The transition to SED rule

According to the provisions of the East German constitution, which in many ways was modelled on that of the Weimar Republic, the newly established German Democratic Republic was a liberal state which guaranteed fundamental rights and a separation of powers, and where a democratically elected parliament was the supreme organ of state. Yet the emergence of a growing personality cult around Lenin, and especially Stalin, revealed that the GDR was steadily assuming the characteristics of a Soviet-style single party state. Two major factors in this development were the elections to the People's Chamber in May 1950, held on the single list system, which was accepted by the CDU and the LDP, and the fact that the mass organizations, in particular the Free German Youth (FDJ) and the Free German Trade Union Federation (FDGB), became instruments for the promotion of SED

Jeder bekenne sich durch seine Unterschrift zum Wahlprogramm der Nationalen Front !

VII/355
Election poster
for the National
Front of the GDR,
1950

aims. Any sign of opposition was dealt with ruthlessly. The particularly heavy-handed terror tactics employed during this early phase were largely the work of the Ministry of State Security. This ministry, known as the Stasi, was set up on 8 February 1959 and was directly answerable to the SED Politbüro. The judicial system also played a major part in this process by conducting show trials and prosecuting thousands of people for their political beliefs.

within a few years. In the GDR too a "national construction programme" was launched, although the destruction was on a smaller scale in the east. In both parts of Germany, however, a great many interesting buildings which could and should have been preserved were torn down during reconstruction.

The characteristic features of many town and city centres were lost as existing buildings were replaced by uniform modern facades and traf-

VII/356
The newly built Stalin-Allee, January 1953

The reconstruction of towns and cities

Owing to the devastation Germany had suffered during the war, one of the foremost political tasks after 1945 was the reconstruction of towns and cities. Housing was needed for millions of refugees, expellees and people who had been made homeless by bombing. In the Federal Republic the construction of publicly-assisted housing went some way towards eliminating the most serious housing shortages

fic-friendly street systems. In both East and West Germany, the changes towns and cities underwent owed a great deal to planning strategies which had the rehabilitation and reorganization of urban areas as their objective.

While in the Federal Republic these changes came about largely as a result of the rapid pace of reconstruction, in the GDR they were a direct result of communist ideology – as illustrated, for example, by the demolition of the royal palace in Berlin.

VII/357
New council build-
ing in Nuremberg,
1953

Social policies in the aftermath of the war

At the end of the war both German states were faced with enormous social problems. Millions of war victims, invalids, widows and orphans were in need of food, clothing and accommodation. The greatest social problem, however, was that of trying to integrate expellees and refugees. In 1950 around 8 million people in the Federal Republic fell into this category and at least 3 million in the GDR. Al-

though refugees and expellees suffered poverty and privations in the early years, when they often spent long periods in camps and were without work, most were eventually able to establish themselves with the help of government programmes. In the Federal Republic the success of these efforts was also borne out by the fact that the expellees' party, the Alliance of Expellees and Disenfranchised Persons (BHE), failed to clear the 5-per-cent hurdle in the 1957 elections and was thus no longer repre-

VII/358
Refugee camp in
Schleswig-Holstein,
1945

VII/359
First visit by Chancellor Adenauer to the High Commissioners, 21 September 1949

sented in the Bundestag. The democratic parties joined forces to ensure that compensation was made for the crimes committed by the National Socialists particularly against the Jews. The Federal Republic not only compensated individuals for the suffering they had endured but also made payments to the State of Israel.

VII/360
Signing of the Bonn Conventions in Bonn, 26 May 1952

The rearmament debate

The Federal Republic was the scene of a passionate debate concerning the orientation of the Federal Republic in the foreign policy field. Chancellor Adenauer believed that through close alignment with the USA as a world power and through western European integration,

VII/361
Demonstration in
East Berlin, 1 May
1953

which enjoyed enthusiastic support in most countries, the Federal Republic would be able to achieve the equal status at international level it still lacked. Adenauer was convinced that the key to achieving this objective was to propose that West Germany be rearmed. Concerned as they were about the war in Korea, the Western powers greeted this proposal with considerable interest. The main opponents of a course of this kind were the Social Democrats led by Kurt Schumacher. Central to the debate was the question of whether the security of the Federal Republic could be guaranteed and reunification eventually achieved only by integrating the Federal Republic into the West, or whether the goal of national unity should be made an absolute priority and any step avoided which would further deepen the division between the two states. On 26 and 27 May 1952, in the face of fierce domestic opposition in the Federal Republic, the Bonn Conventions, which ensured that the Federal Republic became a sovereign state, were signed, as was the Treaty on the Establishment of a European Defence Community (EDC).

End to hopes of national unity

While West Germany was pursuing this course, the GDR was engaged in a massive propaganda campaign in support of German unity. In March and April 1952 the Soviet Union made another attempt to

VII/367
Herbert Wehner
delivering his
keynote speech
on foreign policy
in the Bundestag,
30 June 1960

triggered another dramatic rise in the number of East Germans fleeing the GDR. The SED leadership felt that the open border in Berlin threatened the very existence of the East German state. When the Soviet Union's attempt to force the withdrawal of the three Western allies from West Berlin failed, the SED decided that the border between the GDR and West Berlin should be hermetically sealed. The building of the Berlin Wall on 13 August 1961, which provoked protests but no intervention from the Western powers, and the Cuban missile crisis of 1962, when the USA successfully averted a Soviet threat, served as final confirmation of the status quo.

VII/368
Signing of the
Treaties of Rome,
25 March 1957

VII/369
Konrad Adenauer
and the French
President, De Gaulle
after signing the
Franco-German
Friendship Treaty
in Paris, 22 January
1963

The policy of European integration

Following the decisions of 1955, the political controversy over foreign and defence policy in the Federal Republic gradually subsided. Fierce arguments nevertheless continued to flare up from time to time over whether or not the Bundeswehr should have a nuclear capability. From 1959/69 onwards the Social Democrat opposition also came to accept the Federal Republic's integration into the Western alliance. On the German question the Adenauer government became even more vigorous in asserting its claim that it had the sole right to represent Germany. It also adopted the Hallstein Doctrine, which embodied this principle and was designed to prevent the recognition of the GDR by third countries.

VII/370
Communist Party
leaders at the 20th
Congress of the So-
viet Communist Par-
ty, 28 February
1956

In the field of European politics, the failure of attempts to set up a European Defence Community and "Europeanize" the Saarland prompted a new course in economic integration. The result was the establishment of the European Economic Community (EEC) with six member states in 1957. Besides cultivating close ties with the USA, as the leading power in the West, the Federal Republic developed a particularly close relationship with France. This relationship intensified when General de Gaulle became President and culminated in the Franco-German Friendship Treaty of 1963.

gold, showed a hammer and a pair of compasses encircled by ears of corn. Now a sovereign state, the GDR henceforth had an army of its own and joined the Eastern European alliance system as an equal partner. Even after Stalin's death, however, the Soviet Union continued to set the agenda in all policy areas in East Germany. Not only did the Soviet leadership determine East German foreign policy, but the SED followed the example of the Soviet Union and adhered to the guidelines laid down by the Soviet Communist Party in every aspect of domestic policy too. In the sphere

VII/371
Defence Minister General Stoph handing over the regimental flag to the first regiment of the National People's Army of the GDR, 30 April 1956

The position of the GDR in Eastern Europe

The GDR also acquired a new measure of statehood in 1955. This was symbolized not least by a new state flag which, in addition to the traditional colours of black, red and

of economic policy, the GDR was obliged, as a member of Comecon (Council for Mutual Economic Assistance), to align itself increasingly with the division of labour in operation in Eastern Europe whose primary function was to serve the requirements of the Soviet Union.

VII/372
Workers celebrating
the production of
the five millionth
Grundig radio, 1957

The "economic miracle"

The cornerstone of political and social stability in the Adenauer era was the extraordinary economic upswing, which lasted for more than fifteen years. Thanks to annual growth rates of around 10% in real terms, the Federal Republic, which only shortly before had been a country ravaged by war, rapidly became the third strongest industrial country in the world. By the early 1950s, people had already started to talk of an "economic miracle" in Germany, particularly those who were observing developments from abroad. The 1950s were also a decade of profound structural change, the full extent and consequences of which became apparent only gradually. In trade and industry, small and medium-sized firms were increasingly displaced by large companies, new industrial centres sprang up and improvements in the transport network changed the landscape and the urban environment. As a consequence of these developments, many areas of life were fundamentally transformed.

VII/373
(opposite)
German Trades
Union Congress
poster promoting
the five-day week,
1954

Structural changes in the GDR economy from 1955 to 1961

During the second half of the 1950s the economic development of the GDR appeared to stabilize. Although heavy industry was progressively expanded under the Second Five Year Plan, the consumer goods industry caught up. Food supplies became more plentiful and ration cards were finally abolished in 1958.

These relatively promising economic developments, however, led the SED to believe quite unrealistically that East Germany could, as they put it, "catch up with and over-take" the Federal Republic by 1961. Despite the fact that the economy was clearly in crisis – the Five Year Plan had to be scrapped in 1959 and was replaced by a new Seven Year Plan – a new stage was launched in the efforts to achieve the "victory of Socialist relations of production".

At the beginning of 1960 almost all independent farmers were coerced into joining collective farms. In trade and industry too collectivization was intensified. The stepping up of the nationalization programme was a key factor in the dramatic rise in the number of people fleeing the GDR.

VII/374
Presidium of
the 5th SED Party
Congress with party
leader Walter Ul-
bricht at the podi-
um, 10 July 1958

VII/375
Model of a rocket
at a meeting of
the Young Pioneers,
21 August 1961

VII/376
Delegates at the SPD Party Conference in Bad Godesberg, 15 November 1959

The "Chancellor democracy"

Chancellor Adenauer was so successful in performing the functions of head of government, who plays a particularly important role under the constitution, that the term "Chancellor democracy" was coined. His success was due not only to his skill in the field of foreign policy but also to his ability to hold together a coalition made up of extremely heterogeneous forces and use it to his advantage. However, after the dynamic early years, government policy, which came to be

VII/377
Demonstration concerning the Spiegel affair, October 1962

VII/378
Portrait of
Konrad Adenauer
by Oskar Kokosch-
ka, 1966

VII/379
Federal Chancellor
Konrad Adenauer
giving his resigna-
tion speech in the
Bundestag, 15 Octo-
ber 1963

completely dominated by the Chancellor, began to appear more and
more rigid towards the end of the
1950s. Both the SPD, which declared its support for Western integration and the social market economy in its Godesberg Programme,
and the FDP, which became an opposition party in 1956 and survived
a serious internal crisis, went
through a successful process of renewal. Yet the authority and dominance of the Chancellor, who by
this time was into his eighties,
came increasingly to be seen as a
paralysing element. It was not,
however, until October 1963 that
Konrad Adenauer finally announced
his resignation after 14 years in office.

The consolidation of SED rule

In the wake of the 20th Congress of
the Soviet Communist Party in February 1956, when some acknowl-
edgement was made of the crimes
committed during the Stalinist era,
the SED was confronted with a new
set of political guidelines. The at-

tempt by the SED leadership to
keep de-Stalinization in the GDR
within tight bounds met with resistance from opposition elements
within the party and the Politburo
itself. In the course of 1957/58,
however, internal opposition was
progressively eliminated. This effectively ensured that party chairman
Walter Ulbricht, who was now the
focus of a growing personality cult,
played a leading role for a long
time thereafter. In 1960, Ulbricht's
hold on power was further consolidated when, following the death of
the East German President, Wilhelm Pieck, he took over as chairman of the newly founded Council
of State. As the influence of the
CDU and LPD – the so-called bloc
parties – gradually declined, mass
organizations were given an increasingly important role to play in
SED strategy over this period. It fell
to the Free German Youth (FDJ)
and the Free German Trade Union
Federation (FDGB) in particular, as
organizations whose membership
ran into millions, to integrate broad
sections of the population into the
SED state.

VII/380
Head of a statue
of Stalin in Bu-
dapest, 1956

The building of the Berlin Wall
on 13 August 1961

In late 1958, the Soviet Union, buoyed by its successes in the field of space exploration, took the initiative with regard to policy on Germany and demanded the withdrawal of the Western powers from Berlin. However, the Soviet ultimatum met with an unequivocal refusal from the West. The growing international tension within and around Berlin, together with the

VII/381
SED leader Walter
Ulbricht (seated)
on his election
as Chairman of
the Council of State,
People's Chamber,
12 September 1960

VII/383
The Brandenburg
Gate on the morn-
ing of 13 August
1961

domestic problems in the GDR, led in 1960/61 to a dramatic rise in the already vast numbers of refugees. The SED leadership could see no way of stopping the mass exodus other than by closing off the border with West Berlin. In the night of 12/13 August the East German police, task forces and army troops put up barbed wire along the border between East and West Berlin. In the weeks that followed they erected a wall in its place. Although the Western powers were careful to ensure that their rights in relation to Berlin and Germany as a whole were not undermined they did not intervene to prevent the building of the wall itself. Like the Cuban missile crisis in the following year, the Berlin crisis helped set the seal on the status quo.

VII/384
American President,
John F. Kennedy,
visiting the Berlin
Wall, 26 June 1963

VII/382
(opposite)
The Berlin Wall
under construction,
13 August 1961

VII/386
Employees in
a savings bank,
around 1960

my, however, there was a marked decrease in the number of workers and in the percentage of self-employed persons in agriculture, trade and commerce. Underpinned by social policy reforms, West Germany now appeared to be evolving into a society with a steadily growing industrial workforce. Although the differences in income between the upper and lower classes actually increased during this period, the growing general prosperity and the resulting mass consumption substantially narrowed the gap in the lifestyles of all classes. Within this context, distinct "waves" of consumption reflected the West German population's predominant needs: after the upsurge in demand for food, clothing and then housing, the trend switched, after the late 1950s, to travel and holidays. At the same time, the motor car increasingly came to be regarded as the main status symbol. Finally, television, as a new source of information and entertainment, brought about lasting changes in all areas of life.

VII/387
Placards advertising
an exhibition in
Düsseldorf, 1952

VII/388
Miners taking
a break, around
1960

A new society?

From the outset, it was the intention of the communist leadership in the GDR to create a new social order – a workers' and farmers' state. As a result of the policies of socialization and collectivization, and exacerbated by the large numbers of people fleeing to the West, the GDR, in terms of its social development, evolved into a society of dependent paid employees to a far greater extent than the Federal Republic – although in contrast to the West, this process was associated with a significant "levelling down".

Above the industrial and agricultural workforce there emerged a class of functionaries – a phenomenon specific to the GDR – which was privileged in many ways. Another notable feature was the large share of women in work, amounting to almost 90%. Otherwise, however, in terms of its social development the GDR generally remained fixated on the West German model. Compared with West German standards of prosperity and consumption, to which the aspirations and demands of the GDR population were orientated, East German society long continued to be beset by shortages.

VII/389
Member of
a "housewives'
brigade" at
Brandenburg steel-
works, summer
1960

VII/390
Neonazi graffiti on
Jewish gravestones,
1964

Shadows of the past

In the 1960s, a number of events increasingly focussed attention on the legacy of the National Socialist past: the trial of Adolf Eichmann in Jerusalem; the trial in Frankfurt am Main of SS guards from the Auschwitz concentration camp; and the stormy debate in the Federal Republic on the question of extending the statute of limitations for Nazi crimes, which was eventually supported by a large majority in

VII/391
Protest against
the Second Federal
Party Conference
of the NPD, 1967

Parliament. However, these events did not play a particularly significant role until the National Democratic Party, founded in 1964, scored surprising successes at the polls, not least as a result of the economic crisis. The rise of neo-Nazi forces awakened memories, especially abroad, of the last years of the Weimar Republic.

By contrast, the SED took the view that, as an anti-Fascist state, the German Democratic Republic was not affected, in terms either of policy or of personnel, by the National Socialist past.

At the same time, it attempted to use anti-Fascism as a weapon in the political confrontation with the Federal Republic.

VII/392
Anti-Fascist
demonstration
in East Berlin,
1964

VII/393
Demolition of
a disused mine
in the Ruhr

VII/394
"Is the economic
miracle over?" –
cover picture of
Der Spiegel
3 January 1966

From Erhard to the Grand Coalition

Ludwig Erhard succeeded Adenauer as Federal Chancellor in what initially appeared to be an unchanged political environment, an impression which seemed to be confirmed by his victory at the polls in autumn 1965. His term of office however, proved to be a difficult period of transition. In addition to a number of problems in the foreign policy field, economic developments played a key role in this respect. In 1966, there was a general downturn in the economy, firstly in the Ruhr region as a result of the coal crisis, and then in the Federal Republic as a whole. The unexpected successes of the neo-Nazi NPD at the polls during this period gave rise to serious doubts about the ability of the Federal Republic's political system to withstand crises. By autumn 1966, the economic and political problems were considered so serious that the formation of a Grand Coalition, consisting of the CDU/CSU and the SPD, was seen as the only solution to the crisis.

VII/395
East German
soldiers at a border
crossing point

VII/396
Propaganda to
boost productivity,
East Berlin,
1967

The GDR under Ulbricht

After the building of the Berlin
Wall, Walter Ulbricht – who simultaneously held the posts of First
Secretary of the SED, Chairman of
the Council of State and Chairman
of the National Defence Council –
was at the height of his power. The
GDR's economy had stabilized, underpinned by the introduction of a
"New Economic System of Planning
and Management" which gave the
volkseigene Betriebe, or national-
ized enterprises, greater autonomy
and introduced more performance
incentives. Economic policy, however, had to be partially modified in
1967 after conflicting both with Soviet economic interests and with
the SED's claim to centralized control. In other areas, too, such as
cultural policy, a hardening of SED
policies could once more be observed after the mid-1960s. The
more discussion there was in Bonn
about policies on relations between
the two German states, the more
the GDR pursued a policy of demarcation from the Federal Republic
and underlined its independence as

a state, particularly with its Nationality Law in 1967 and its new Constitution of 1968. Yet its efforts to gain international recognition still met – at least initially – with very limited success.

which it had previously been impossible to find the necessary majorities in Parliament, were also addressed. These were the constitutional rules applicable in a state of emergency, the reform of the con-

VII/397
Kurt Georg Kiesinger and Willy Brandt after agreeing to form a Grand Coalition

Crisis management and reform policies

From the outset, the Grand Coalition of CDU/CSU and SPD was intended to be a temporary alliance which aimed to solve certain specific problems. Its first key task was to overcome the economic crisis. To this end, Economics Minister Karl Schiller (SPD) and Finance Minister Franz-Josef Strauss (CSU) were responsible for devising a range of new policy instruments which succeeded, as early as 1968, in bringing about real economic growth once more. Problems requiring a change in the Constitution, for

stitutional rules on public finance, and the new regulations governing relations between the federation and the *Länder* in the fields of education and health.

This comprehensive adjustment of the instruments of state to the requirements of a highly industrialized society must be regarded as the Grand Coalition's main achievement. However, the Federal Government's overwhelming parliamentary majority gave rise to concerns about the very future of parliamentary democracy, which in turn contributed substantially to the stormy protests witnessed during this period.

VII/398
Economics Minister
Karl Schiller and
Finance Minister
Franz Josef Strauss

Changing social values in West and East

In the 1960s, a fundamental shift in values could be observed in the Federal Republic, as well as in other Western countries. It was triggered by, and associated with, vehement criticism of society in literature and the social sciences and the emergence of new types of music. Large numbers of young people turned against their parents' lifestyles and patterns of behaviour, rejecting the central role of the family, prevailing sexual morality, all forms of authority and traditionalism, and the preoccupation with consumerism and achievement. They also rejected the official doctrine of anti-Communism and West Germany's political ties to the USA. Starting from within the universities, this conflict was fuelled by criticism of the war being waged by the USA in Vietnam and the policies of the Grand Coalition; it culminated in 1967/68 in a wave of demonstrations and, in some cases,

violent protests, which only gradually subsided after the change of government in 1969. In the GDR, young people once again followed the Western example in certain superficial respects, but in general, their very different situation meant that a change in values did not occur there until much later.

VII/399
International
youth festival in
East Berlin, July/August 1973

VII/400
Demonstration
against the
Vietnam War on
the Kurfürstendamm
in Berlin, 18 Febru-
ary 1968

7. The change of power and the new *Ostpolitik*

After twenty years of CDU/CSU government, a change of power took place in the Federal Republic in 1969, arousing considerable attention both at home and abroad. In March 1969, the SPD's candidate, Gustav Heinemann, had won the presidential elections with the support of SPD and FDP voters. After the Bundestag elections in September 1969, Willy Brandt became the first Social Democrat to take office as Federal Chancellor. Brandt led a Social-Liberal coalition whose majority in the Bundestag was slender, however.

From the outset, a guiding principle – if not the key element – of the work of this alliance was its determination to supplement the policy of Western integration with a policy of accommodation with the Federal Republic's Eastern European neighbours. There were two major motives and objectives underlying the new *Ostpolitik*.

Firstly, there was the Federal Republic's international position: the supporters of *Ostpolitik* were convinced that the Federal Republic needed to adapt to the growing trend towards dètente in East-West relations and thus to widen its own scope for action in the foreign policy field.

Secondly, they focussed on the unity of the German nation: tangible improvements in relations with the GDR, and especially more intensive contacts between ordinary people, would, it was felt, counteract the growing tendency for the two German states to drift apart, and thereby keep the German question open.

Negotiations were soon initiated but met with considerable resistance and criticism on both sides. The GDR leadership, in particular, realized that this was an opportunity to achieve recognition and thus overcome its isolation in the foreign policy field; at the same time, however, it was also aware that its internal stability could be jeopardized if it were to open up too much to the West. It therefore attempted to slow down the process of *Ostpolitik*. It was not until Ulbricht was replaced by Honecker in May 1971 that this obstacle was largely removed.

In the Federal Republic, large sections of the population, as well as the majority of the CDU/CSU opposition, found it extremely difficult to abandon the fundamental principles on which the Federal Republic's relations with its Eastern European neighbours and the GDR had hitherto been based. They found it especially difficult to accept the proposed policy of recognising the GDR as a state and the Oder-Neisse line as the border with Poland. The passionate debates on these issues did not subside until the Social-Liberal coalition's clear victory in the Bundestag elections in November 1972.

The Eastern treaties, however, enabled considerable progress to be made towards the normalization of relations between the Federal Republic and the Eastern bloc countries. The treaties enhanced the Federal Republic's scope for action in the foreign policy field and also contributed substantially to the general process of East-West dètente.

For the two German states, the Treaty on Basic Relations between the FRG and the GDR, concluded in 1972 after almost two decades of tense confrontation and a complete absence of political dialogue, marked the beginning of a new era of regulated, "normal co-existence".

VII/401
President Heine-
mann handing
Chancellor Willy
Brandt his letter
of appointment,
21 October 1969

VII/402
The Brandt-Scheel
cabinet in front
of Villa Hammer-
schmidt, 22 October
1969

1969 – a change of power

Growing tensions within the Grand Coalition in 1968/69 heralded an imminent change of government. In particular, the presidential elections in March 1969 – in which the Social Democratic candidate, Justice Minister Gustav Heinemann, finally defeated the CDU/CSU candidate, Defence Minister Gerhard Schröder, after a prolonged battle for the FDP's votes – was seen as a signal in this direction. Although neither the SPD nor the FDP committed themselves publicly at this stage, it was generally assumed, even before the Bundestag elections on 28 September 1969, that the SPD and FDP might well form the next Federal Government. On the night of the elections, on the basis of a slender majority, Willy Brandt and

Walter Scheel, chairmen of the SPD and FDP respectively, agreed in principle to form a coalition government. On 21 October 1969, Willy Brandt was elected Federal Chancellor by a narrow majority, with 251 votes. The second republic had proved its ability to effect a change of government on the basis of democratic procedures.

From Ulbricht to Honecker

In the GDR, too, the change of government in Bonn was accompanied by high expectations. Yet the surprising departure of Walter Ulbricht from the post of First Secretary of the SED on 3 May 1971 was precipitated not by the GDR citizens' discontent with their own government but by Ulbricht's increasingly inde-

VII/403
Walter Ulbricht
on his 78th birth-
day, 30 June 1971

pendent political stance vis-à-vis the Soviet Union. The GDR's leadership's uncompromising attitude towards the Federal Republic's new *Ostpolitik*, in particular, had aroused the displeasure of the Soviet Union and other East European countries. Under Ulbricht's successor, his long-standing heir-apparent Erich Honecker, the SED not only unconditionally recognized the leading role of the Soviet Union once more, especially in foreign and economic policy. In the wake of the Polish workers' unrest of 1970, the new party leadership was also at pains to respond to a greater extent to the social and material interests of GDR citizens in the lower income brackets.

VII/404
Erich Honecker
after his election
as First Secretary
of the SED Central
Committee at the
8th Party Congress,
15 June 1971

The opening to the East

In his policy statement on taking office, Chancellor Brandt declared that the new Federal Government was willing to move beyond earlier offers of a renunciation of force and recognize the status quo in Europe, including the existence of the GDR as a state. Initial talks with the GDR leadership took place in Erfurt and Kassel, but foundered as a result of its insistence that the GDR should be recognized as a state under international law. However, Brandt's closest foreign policy

VII/407
Signing of the
Four-Power Agree-
ment on Berlin,
3 June 1972

advisor, State Secretary Egon Bahr, succeeded in reaching agreement in talks with the Soviet Union. The Treaty of Moscow, signed on 12 August 1970, was the centrepiece of the system of treaties negotiated by the Social-Liberal government with a number of Eastern European countries. Its clauses on the renunciation of force and respect for the territorial integrity of all states in Europe within their existing borders were later to form the key elements in subsequent treaties concluded with Poland, Czechoslovakia and the GDR. The Four-Power Agree-

VII/408
Signing of the
Treaty on the
Basis of Relations
between the
Federal Republic
of Germany and
the German Demo-
cratic Republic in
East Berlin, 21 De-
cember 1972

VII/409
Chancellor Willy
Brandt receiving
the Nobel Peace
Prize, 10 December
1971

VII/410
Demonstrations
in Bonn against
the Eastern treaties,
1972

ment on Berlin was also linked to the Treaty of Moscow. It eased transit traffic to West Berlin, enabled West Berliners to visit the Eastern sector of the city and the GDR, and confirmed West Berlin's ties with the Federal Republic.

Parliamentary disputes over the Eastern treaties

From the outset, the treaty negotiations were accompanied by heated domestic policy disputes in the Federal Republic which were just as ac-

rimonious as the debates about Western integration in the early 1950s. With the commencement of the parliamentary ratification process in late 1971, these disputes entered a crucial phase. They became even more impassioned when some members of the governing have never been fully clarified. Finally, after German legal reservations had been recognized in a "joint resolution of the German Bundestag" and the "letter on German unity", the CDU/CSU majority was willing to abstain in the vote on the Eastern treaties, thereby en-

parties joined the opposition camp, thereby jeopardizing the SPD/FDP coalition's majority. However, the CDU/CSU's attempt to have its leader, Rainer Barzel, elected Federal Chancellor by means of a vote of no confidence failed by a narrow margin under circumstances which abling them to be ratified by the Bundestag on 17 May 1972. After a bitterly contested election campaign, the Social-Liberal coalition emerged considerably strengthened from the early elections to the Bundestag which took place on 19 November 1972.

VII/411
Chancellor Willy Brandt and Vice-Chancellor Walter Scheel on the eve of the general elections, 19 November 1972

1973–1990: From co-existence to reunification

8. Two German states

After the conclusion of the Eastern treaties, which coincided at international level with the settlement of other conflicts, principally the Vietnam War, the 1970s were symbolized by the general improvement in East-West relations which resulted from the policy of détente. The objective officially promoted by both sides was that the two blocs – and therefore the two German states as well – should live in peaceful co-existence, despite all their political and ideological differences and the mutual threat posed by the military build-up on each side.

In the wake of détente, the GDR experienced a political and economic upturn in the early 1970s. Having finally achieved international recognition as a state, the GDR appeared, under Erich Honecker's new leadership, to be adopting a policy of greater openness and flexibility. In the economy, too, there were substantial improvements in the supply of consumer goods. By 1976/77, however, this upward trend – achieved at the price of burgeoning foreign debt and a dependency on hard currency – ended abruptly when the Eastern bloc countries also began to feel the effects of the global recession. Furthermore, after the Conference on Security and Co-operation in Europe (CSCE), the SED regime faced growing demands for respect for human rights. The GDR leadership responded to this nascent opposition by resorting once again to more repressive tactics.

The Federal Republic also benefited from the general improvement in East-West relations, especially in the fields of foreign and trade policy. However, a far more significant factor in shaping West German development in the 1970s was the far-reaching economic, financial and domestic policy changes triggered by the first oil crisis in 1973. There was now neither the money nor the inclination for large-scale reform programmes. The political

VII/412
Foreign Minister Walter Scheel addressing the UN General Assembly, 19 September 1973

EP. DEM. ALLEMANDE   DANEMA   REP. FED. D'ALLEMA

VII/413
Chancellor Helmut
Schmidt and Erich
Honecker, Chairman
of the GDR Council
of State, at the
CSCE conference
in Helsinki, 1 Au-
gust 1975

establishment was entirely preoccu-
pied with the task of steering a safe
course through the hazards posed
by world-wide economic recession.
The transition between these two
phases was highlighted by changes
in the leadership of the Social-Liberal coalition. In May 1974, Brandt
and Scheel were succeeded by Helmut Schmidt as the new Federal
Chancellor and Hans-Dietrich Genscher as Federal Foreign Minister.
In the 1970s, the links and contacts
between the two German states
continued to develop, albeit in an
ambivalent way. On the one hand,
the new treaties created opportunities for more personal contacts between ordinary citizens. On the other hand, it was impossible to ignore
the fact that more than twenty-five
years after the end of the war, Germans in East and West were increasingly beginning to settle into
their own way of life and focus on
their own problems within their
separate states, especially now that

the division of Germany had also
been confirmed by treaty. As the
numerous historical accounts which
are now being published confirm,
many people had come to regard
the "provisional" Federal Republic,
in particular, as a permanent feature of the German landscape.

Coexistence

The accession of the two German
states to the United Nations on
18 September 1973 confirmed the
new political situation in Germany
in the eyes of the entire international community. Despite some
setbacks and disappointments, the
Federal Republic and the GDR had
made some progress towards a
normalisation of their relations,
bringing tangible benefits to their
citizens. For the GDR, the way was
now clear for the international
recognition which it had craved for
so long. Within a few years, almost

every country in the world would establish diplomatic relations with East Berlin. At the same time, the SED leadership vigorously pursued a policy of demarcation vis-à-vis the Federal Republic and sought to underline the permanence of its existence as a state. In 1974, for example, all references to Germany and reunification were expunged from the GDR Constitution. "Coexistence" with the GDR, regulated by treaty, extended the Federal Republic's scope for action in the foreign policy field too. It was now able to intensify its relations – especially its economic links – with the Eastern bloc countries and throw off the shackles imposed by its previous claim to be the sole diplomatic representative of Germany as a whole.

Honecker – a new beginning?

The change in the SED leadership was accompanied by a clear shift in the general political climate. In order to integrate the population more fully into the state, the GDR leadership aimed to improve material living conditions, introduced new social policy measures and increased the opportunities for citizens' participation, for example in parents' groups, in local representative bodies, or through jury service. In an effort to inject new blood into the Politburo, older members were replaced by much younger colleagues, and a more liberal stance was adopted on a number of cultural issues. At the World Youth Festival in 1973, too, the regime made a concerted effort to

VII/414
Official opening of the Palace of the Republic in East Berlin, 1976

demonstrate openness. None of these measures, however, signified a relaxation of the SED's hold on power. On the contrary, despite the adoption of more flexible approaches in some areas, there was a clear tendency, under Honecker's leadership, for the decision-making process to become more centralized. Following the introduction of a more intensive policy of demarcation vis-à-vis the West, an increasingly ideological stance could also be observed in many areas, notably the education system. In 1976/77, the clampdown on the opposition, which had gained momentum as a result of the CSCE, demonstrated clearly that the SED had not abandoned its repressive policies.

VII/415
Reception for Soviet Communist Party chief Leonid Brezhnev in East Berlin, October 1974

VII/416
Robert Havemann, outspoken critic of the SED regime, in front of Fürstenwalde County Court, 14 June 1979

VII/417
Demonstration
against the classifi-
cation of abortion
as a criminal of-
fence, 1975

Domestic reforms

The Social-Liberal coalition came to power in 1969 with plans for fundamental reforms in domestic policy too. Its guiding principle was summed up by Chancellor Brandt in his government policy statement, when he called on West Germans to "accept the challenge of more democracy". The reform programme ranged from liberalizing and modernizing the legal system to extending the social security network, strengthening co-determination in the workplace and improving the education system. However, due to the heated controversies sparked off by Brandt's *Ostpolitik*, the bulk of the reform programme drawn up in 1969 could not be implemented until after 1972. Even then its progress was gradual and fell short of some of its original ob-

jectives. Its lack of progress was due to differences of opinion between the SPD and FDP, and to objections by the CDU/CSU majority in the Bundesrat and the Federal Constitutional Court about key aspects of the reform legislation. Most importantly, deteriorating economic conditions imposed financial constraints on the reform plans.

Global economic dependencies

Even as early as 1970, the financial framework for reform-oriented policies was becoming increasingly constrained. Germany was also becoming more and more dependent on general trends in the global economy, which impacted first and foremost on the foreign exchange

VII/418
Otto Brenner, chairman of the Metalworkers' Union, speaking on co-determination, October 1968

VII/419
Federal Chancellor Willy Brandt and his aide Günther Guillaume, later unmasked as an East German spy, April 1974

VII/420
The first Schmidt-
Genscher cabinet
with Federal Presi-
dent Gustav Heine-
mann, 16 May 1974

markets. In 1974/75, all the Western industrialized nations plunged into severe economic crisis as a result of the oil price shock in 1973. In an effort to limit the effects of this crisis, the Federal Government launched a series of programmes to stimulate the economy and employ-

ment. At the same time, Western governments worked together – at world economic summits, through regular meetings of finance ministers, and also within the framework of the European Monetary System – in efforts to establish new forms of economy policy which would be co-

VII/421
The first world
economic summit
in Rambouillet near
Paris, 1975

VII/422
Ban on Sunday
driving during the
oil crisis, winter
1973

ordinated on an international scale. Nonetheless, the following years were dogged by high unemployment, soaring inflation rates and burgeoning national debt. In the political debate, therefore, doubts were increasingly voiced about the economic benefits of state-funded programmes to stimulate the economy. Indeed, some observers emphasized that there were limits to growth, from the ecological point of view too, and called for a fundamental reappraisal of the hitherto unchallenged commitment to growth per se.

Apparent stability

Under Honecker, the SED announced a new economic course based on "the indivisible unity of economic and social policy". In line with this principle, economic development would henceforth focus particularly on the material interests of the working population. This new set of objectives, however, did not prevent the SED from abruptly nationalizing the small companies which until then had continued to operate under partial government control; it was forced to accept a deterioration in the supply of consumer goods as a result. In addition to a general rise in incomes and a package of social policy measures designed primarily to improve the situation of working women, the key element of the new policy was housing.

By 1975, 600,000 new housing units had been constructed. However, the high expenditure on consumption and social welfare under Honecker resulted in soaring foreign debt. This became a serious problem when the GDR, too, was hit by the global shortage of oil and raw materials at the end of the 1970s.

VII/423
Leipzig trade fair

VII/424
Celebration to mark
the completion of
the three millionth
flat built since 1971,
12 October 1988

VII/425
Opera director
Walter Felsenstein
at a rehearsal in
the Comic Opera
in Berlin

Two states, one culture?

The apparent finality of Germany's division into two separate states gave rise, in the 1970s, to debates about what the German people had in common. After decades of division, what held the German nation together? Had a new and separate sense of identity evolved in the two states? Alongside more intensive personal contacts between citizens, their shared culture, expressed above all through their common language, was identified as a unifying factor. In addition to the classical heritage, and despite some cultural differences which were heightened by the new forms of alternative culture emerging in the West, many contemporary writers, musicians and other artists continued to appeal to large sections of the population in both German states. These crossborder cultural ties were unwittingly strengthened in 1976/77 when increasing numbers of prominent cultural figures were expelled from or chose to leave the GDR. On the other hand, the SED leadership made enormous efforts to promote the emergence of a specific GDR identity by consciously reviving certain historical traditions. Yet in the West, too, the number of those who, seeking to move away from a national orientation, saw the Federal Republic's *raison* d'être in its commitment to the Western values of the democratic constitutional state was growing.

VII/426
GDR singer Wolf Biermann giving a concert in Cologne, November 1976

9. Crisis and change

In December 1979, after a decade of improved East-West relations, two events occurred within a very short space of time which soon came to symbolize the end of dè-tente. They were NATO's dual-track decision, which was the Western Alliance's response to the USSR's decision to deploy new intermediate-range nuclear missiles (SS-20s) in East Germany and Czechoslovakia, and the Soviet invasion of Afghanistan. The USA, in particular, reacted by adopting a radical shift in policy towards the Soviet Union, especially after its new President, Ronald Reagan, took office in 1981. This crisis in international relations coincided with a further sharp increase in oil and raw materials prices which plunged the entire global economy into deep recession.

These twin challenges sparked off heated domestic policy debates in the Federal Republic. In response to NATO's policy of force modernization, a broad-based protest movement sprang up, extending even into the government camp. The conflict between economic and ecological concerns was heightened by fresh competition from the Greens, a new force in the party-political landscape. Above all, however, the Schmidt-Genscher government found it increasingly difficult to agree on appropriate economic and financial policies to deal with the crisis. As a result, the SPD/FDP coalition finally collapsed on 17 September 1982.

On 1 October 1982, a coalition government of CDU/CSU and FDP took office under Chancellor Helmut Kohl. Its primary objective was to overcome the recession through a package of new economic and financial policy measures. The ensuing period of economic recovery was also a time of rapid technological change in all the Western in-

VII/427
The scene of the abduction of Hanns Martin Schleyer, president of the Employers' Association, 5 September 1977

dustrialized countries as computers became an increasingly familiar feature in every area of life. Economic development was characterised increasingly by prosperity in tandem with structural crisis. The Federal Republic's foreign policy, and especially its relations with the GDR, were dominated by the need to maintain continuity. Even after 1982, the Federal Republic's integration into the Western community, coupled with an *Ostpolitik* designed to achieve a balancing of interests, continued to be the twin pillars of West German foreign policy. For this reason, the Kohl-Genscher government implemented the NATO dual-track decision in the teeth of fierce opposition at home, but was at pains not to jeopardize the progress achieved in previous years in its relations with the GDR.

The GDR, too, was disinclined to use the Afghanistan crisis or the change in government in Bonn as a reason to impose a freeze on its relations with the Federal Republic. Indeed, as a tacit *quid pro quo* for West German loans, it announced that it was prepared to dismantle the self-firing mechanisms on the border with the Federal Republic and improve travel opportunities for GDR citizens. A key factor in these decisions, however, was the massive economic problems faced by the GDR as a result of the second oil crisis, which could only be papered over, slowly and painfully, with a injection of Western finance. Technological change, in particular, was proving an increasingly insurmountable challenge for the GDR and other Eastern bloc countries.

Terrorism

From the early 1970s, the Federal Republic was confronted with the international problem of terrorism. The terrorist attacks reached a cli-

max in 1977 with the assassinations of Federal Prosecutor-General Siegfried Buback; Jürgen Ponto, president of the Dresdner Bank; and Hanns Martin Schleyer, president of the Employers' Association; as well as the hijacking of a Lufthansa aircraft. The Federal Government and the opposition worked together closely in an attempt to resolve the crisis but engaged in a heated debate on the methods which were appropriate to combat terrorism. Some critics felt that the more stringent legal provisions and new policing measures introduced undermined the rule of law. In autumn 1977, the Federal Government made it clear that it would never give in to terrorist blackmail and the number of attacks sharply decreased. Nonetheless, the threat of terrorist violence has persisted ever since.

VII/428
Wanted poster for terrorists belonging to the Baader Meinhof Group, 1971/72

VII/429
Smog sign warning
of increased air pol-
lution

Environmental degradation and nature conservation

In the 1970s, environmental protection emerged as a key issue in the political debate in the Federal Republic. More and more people felt that air and water pollution, traffic noise and large-scale construction projects posed a fundamental threat to the environment and their quality of life. Although the Federal Government's environmental policies had achieved considerable progress, they had nonetheless failed to keep pace with the grow-

VII/430
Water pollution
near a factory
in Wolfen, Saxony
Anhalt

VII/431
The burnt-out shell
of the Chernobyl
nuclear reactor
after the accident
on 26 April 1986

ing problems in many areas. The construction of new nuclear power stations and nuclear waste disposal facilities in particular triggered public concern and protests, especially after the Chernobyl disaster in 1986. On the basis of radical demands from the environmental lobby, the Greens gradually emerged as a new party-political force. They had been represented in many *Land* parliaments since 1979 and entered

VII/432
Press conference
given by the Green
party in Bonn,
27 September 1982

the Bundestag in 1983. In the GDR, too, severe environmental degradation was becoming increasingly obvious despite numerous official denials, and ecological issues were a key factor in the emergence of the opposition movements there.

Afghanistan in the same month marked the end of the thaw in East-West relations. The two German states now faced a difficult question: under these new conditions, could they safeguard all the positive achievements of the years

VII/433
Chancellor Helmut Schmidt with Erich Honecker, Chairman of the GDR Council of State, in Güstrow Cathedral, 12 December 1981

The end of dètente

By the end of the 1970s, the Western nations were viewing the Soviet Union's intensified armaments programmes with growing concern. In December 1979, not least on the initiative of Chancellor Schmidt, NATO threatened to deploy American intermediate-range nuclear missiles in Europe if the USSR were not willing to dismantle its new SS-20 missiles. The Soviet invasion of

of dètente? Furthermore, as the arms race entered a new phase, there was widespread anxiety about the threat it posed to peace, especially in Germany, which was a key deployment site as well as a target for many different types of nuclear missiles. Faced with opposition from the broad-based peace movement, it was only with difficulty that the Schmidt-Genscher government maintained its scope for action in the foreign policy field.

VII/434
Peace demonstra-
tion in Bonn,
10 October 1981

VII/435
Coalition talks between the CDU/CSU and FDP, September 1982

A change of government in Bonn

VII/436
Helmut Kohl, after his election as Federal Chancellor, with his predecessor, Helmut Schmidt, 1 October 1982

After 1979/80, the Federal Republic found itself in the grip of a second global recession, triggered by soaring oil and raw materials prices. The Social-Liberal coalition once more obtained a majority in the Bundestag elections on 5 October 1980. However, the impact of global recession heightened the tensions between the coalition part-

ners, especially on matters relating to economic and foreign policy. These differences of opinion, and the serious tensions within the SPD parliamentary group, finally led to the collapse of the Schmidt-Genscher government amid mutual recriminations on 17 September 1982. Coalition talks, accompanied by heated wrangling within the FDP, then took place between the CDU/CSU and FDP, leading to an agreement that these parties

VII/437
Robots being
used to weld car
body work at the
Opel works in Rüs-
selsheim, 1987

should form a new government. On
1 October 1982, the leader of the
opposition, Helmut Kohl, was elected Federal Chancellor through a
constructive vote of no confidence.
His newly-formed coalition adopted
a number of initial measures and
decisions, notably on budgetary
policy, before calling early elections
to the Bundestag. When the country went to the polls on 6 March
1983, a clear majority endorsed the
change of government.

From crisis to recovery

The new coalition of CDU/CSU and
FDP saw the task of overcoming
the severe economic crisis as its
main priority. It aimed to improve
the conditions for economic development by consolidating public finance, cutting social expenditure,
reforming the pensions system and
providing increased tax relief. Bol-
stered by an outstanding exports
performance, it succeeded in re-es-

VII/438
Demonstration
in Bonn by the Met-
alworkers' Union
in support of
the 35-hour week,
28 May 1984

tablishing real economic growth and cutting the inflation rate. However, unemployment continued to be a problem; although its upward progress had been halted, it remained stable at a high level. In the 1980s, therefore, economic development continued to be ambivalent and economic policy remained a contentious issue between government and opposition.

Despite the overall upturn in the economy, the structural crisis in traditional industrial sectors, such as ship-building, mining and the steel industry, remained entrenched. The substantial increases in incomes enjoyed by large sections of the population contrasted sharply with the social problems affecting some employment sectors and regions facing structural decline.

Leisure, holidays, freedom to travel

With growing prosperity and shorter working hours, holidays became a particularly valued aspect of life in the Federal Republic as early as the 1950s, and West Germans soon began to spend many of their vacations abroad. The importance of holidays and leisure continued to grow substantially in the wake of further massive reductions in working hours and an upsurge in global tourism. In an attempt to keep pace with these trends, which were common to all the modern industrialised countries, the GDR also introduced a wide range of leisure-time and holiday activities for its citizens. However, they were organised entirely by the state in line with predetermined objectives, e.g.

VII/439
German-language signs in the Spanish resort of Torremolinos

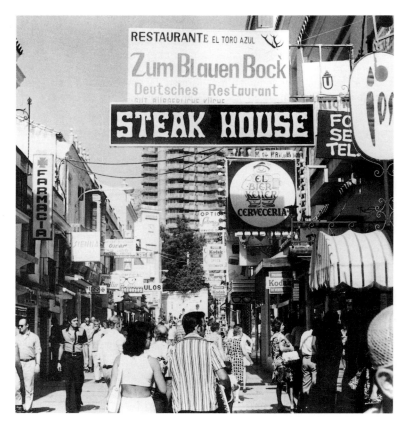

VII/440
A Trabant in front
of a weekend cot-
tage (dacha) in
the GDR

to encourage citizens to "engage in culturally meaningful leisure-time pursuits". The opening of the borders with Poland and Czechoslova-kia at the end of 1971 was intend-ed to fulfil GDR citizens' growing desire for more opportunities for in-dividual travel abroad, although re-strictions were later re-imposed. Even the introduction in the 1980s of more liberal provisions on travel to Western countries could do little to alter the fundamental dilemma inherent in SED policy: for the ma-jority of GDR citizens, freedom to travel was still the single most im-

VII/441
Pensioners at
Friedrichstrasse
station in East
Berlin

portant issue, both personally and politically, and the denial of this right was seen as the GDR regime's most basic flaw.

Youth between resignation and unrest

Following the years of political unrest around 1968, young West Germans were overcome by a widespread feeling of resignation in the 1970s which was heightened by the lack of career prospects for the baby-boom generation. Many young people reacted by becoming single-mindedly careerist, while others experimented with alternative lifestyles which resulted in the alienation of some groups of young

people from the established political cal parties. In the GDR, children and young people were integrated from an early age in a state-run system of education and child-care which was designed to mould them into good socialist citizens. Most young people, however, regarded the system with scepticism or even rejected it entirely. The more young people identified with the GDR as a state, the more critically they questioned why the GDR was not prepared to show confidence in its young people and give them greater opportunities to make their own choices. The continued denial of even the most minor freedoms encouraged many young people to adopt an oppositional approach to the regime.

VII/442
Disco at a club run by the East German Free German Youth organization, 1977

The resources run out

By the end of the 1970s, the GDR, too, was hit by global recession. Soaring raw materials costs could no longer be offset by increased production and exports, especially after the Soviet Union cut crude oil supplies in 1981. Furthermore, it was becoming increasingly evident that key areas of the GDR's economy were in crisis: its infrastructure was obsolete and it had failed to update its industrial plant in line with modern production needs. Billions of marks of investment were pumped into future-orientated technologies, such as the computer sector, but failed to compensate for years of neglect. Indeed, in some areas this merely compounded the problem. The shortage of resources was particularly acute in urban housing areas, where belated efforts to maintain and renovate old housing stocks were now undertaken.

Faced with growing economic problems, the GDR stepped up its efforts to acquire hard currency at every conceivable opportunity. During the 1980s, the Deutschmark increasingly emerged as the second currency of the GDR; for example, it could be used in the "Intershops" to purchase scarce or luxury items unavailable elsewhere. This influx of hard currency was a mixed blessing: whereas the DM stabilized the GDR's economy in the short term, it also undermined the socialist economic system.

VII/443
Old blast furnaces in Eisenhüttenstadt

VII/444
Dilapidated indus-
trial machinery
at Wolfen Photo-
chemical Combine,
December 1989

10. The end of division

Although the end of the division of Germany certainly would not have come about without external influence on the Eastern bloc countries, especially the GDR, it was by no means the outcome of a deliberate Western policy; rather, it was to a far greater extent the result of a gradual process of internal erosion. When the new leader of the Communist Party of the Soviet Union, Mikhail Gorbachev, cautiously embarked on his reform policies in 1985, the gerontocratic SED leadership under Erich Honecker soon responded by focussing on measures to prevent the spread of reform to the GDR. It thereby broke the fundamental law on which the GDR was built, namely unquestioning obedience to Moscow's policies. It became apparent, particularly from the flood of applications for exit visas, the increased activities of the opposition movements and, finally, a fresh wave of refugees to the West, that the GDR was sliding into deep domestic crisis, which finally reached a climax soon after the celebrations to mark its fortieth anniversary. When the borders to the West were opened on the evening of 9 November 1989, the SED had no alternative but to relinquish its political leadership of the GDR.

Most of the opposition groups were initially in favour of a democratic reform of the GDR. The "Round Table", which gave the new parties and groups their first opportunity to influence government policy alongside the "block parties" and the SED, was charged with the task of dismantling the state security apparatus, drafting a democratic constitution and overseeing free elections to the People's Chamber. Yet, at demonstrations in November 1989 calls were already being heard, first sporadically and then ever more

VII/445
The first meeting between Chancellor Kohl and the leader of the Communist Party of the Soviet Union, Mikhail Gorbachev, in Moscow, 12 March 1985

frequently, for rapid unification with the Federal Republic. The protesters' slogan "We are the people" soon became "We are one people". However, the results of the first democratic elections to the People's Chamber on 18 March 1990 clearly showed that the vast majority of GDR citizens regarded unification with the Federal Republic as the only possible solution to the GDR's acute economic, social and political problems.

Faced with this situation, Germany's European neighbours and, also, the Soviet Union showed an almost surprising willingness – despite some reservations – to give their political blessing to a united Germany. In a general climate of détente, solutions to the numerous problems arising under international law, including the issue of a united Germany's membership of NATO, were hammered out in negotiations between the Four Powers and the two German states, and, to a lesser extent, in direct talks between the Federal Republic and the Soviet Union. It thus proved possible to avoid the potential danger of an internationalization of the German question, for instance within the framework of the CSCE.

For the Federal Republic and the GDR, there were two key stages on the road to unification. On 1 July 1990, the two German states merged to form a single economic area, with the Deutschmark as a common currency. Political unity was completed three months later, on 3 October 1990, when the GDR acceded to the Federal Republic under Article 23 of the Basic Law. Its accession was regulated by a comprehensive Unification Treaty.

VII/446
Erich Honecker, Chairman of the GDR Council of State, inspects the guard of honour at the Federal Chancellery in Bonn, 7 September 1987

VII/447
Erich Honecker receiving a delegation from the Protestant Church of the GDR, 6 March 1978

Change in Eastern Europe

The reform policies introduced from 1985 onwards by the new leader of the Communist Party of the Soviet Union, Mikhail Gorbachev, were an attempt to respond to the growing signs of crisis in the Soviet sphere of influence. They marked the beginning of fundamental political change in Eastern Europe. At domestic policy level, a rigorous settling of accounts with Stalinism was intended to open up new ways forward in politics, the economy and society. In its foreign relations, the USSR embarked on a policy of détente and cooperation with the West, withdrawing its troops from Afghanistan and signalling its willingness to conclude comprehensive agreements on disarmament. In Eastern Europe, Poland and Hungary were the first countries to exploit the greater scope for action which the new Soviet policy afforded them; they gradually embarked

on the process of establishing a democratic and pluralist system on the Western model. By contrast, the SED leadership in the GDR became increasingly entrenched in its efforts to distance itself from all calls for reform.

The opposition in the GDR

Throughout the GDR's forty-year history, many diverse forms of opposition had sprung up and had always been violently suppressed. From the 1970s onwards, however, the opposition in the GDR developed greater continuity in terms of its personnel and organization. The opposition groups in the cultural field, which had been particularly active at almost every stage, were now strengthened by new initiatives which met under the aegis of the Church and focussed primarily on peace and environmental policy. In particular, the younger genera-

VII/448
Prayer vigil in the
Gethsemanekirche
in East Berlin for
people unjustly im-
prisoned, October
1989

VII/449
Erich Honecker
and the leader of
the Soviet Commu-
nist party, Mikhail
Gorbachev, on the
VIP rostrum

VII/450
Military parade
to mark the 40th
anniversary of
the founding of
the GDR, 7 Octo-
ber 1989

tion which had grown up in the GDR began to voice growing criticism of a state which did not tolerate even those forms of opposition which conformed with the system. Despite the successful efforts of the state security service to infiltrate some of these opposition groups and the harsh treatment often meted out to opposition members, the movement continued to swell in numbers, in parallel to the political development elsewhere in Eastern Europe until 1989.

Reform or revolution?

In 1989, when both German states celebrated their fortieth anniversary, the division of Germany still appeared to be permanent and stable. Yet in the weeks preceding the fortieth anniversary of the GDR, the SED leadership under Erich Honecker found itself in an increasingly precarious political position. As thousands of GDR citizens left the country via Hungary and Czechoslovakia, the opposition movement in the GDR grew stronger by the day. Only a few days after the official anniversary celebrations, hundreds of thousands of people met in peaceful protests against the Communist system of oppression. On 18 October 1989, Erich Honecker was replaced as First Secretary of the SED. Yet the new state and party leadership under Egon Krenz also proved unable to stabilize the situation. The opening of the GDR's borders on the evening of 9 November 1989 paved the way for a radical restructuring of the GDR on the basis of democracy.

VII/451
Monday demonstration in Leipzig,
16 October 1989

VII/452
The Brandenburg
Gate, 10 November
1989

VII/453
Marchers carrying banners calling for German unity at a Monday demonstration in Leipzig, 11 December 1989

Unification

The political upheavals in the GDR put the issue of German unity firmly on the agenda. It became increasingly apparent that what the majority of GDR citizens had in mind was not so much a reform of the existing system as the rapid integration of the GDR into a larger, democratic and economically prosperous Germany. After negotiations

VII/454
Constituent sitting of the first freely elected People's Chamber, 5 April 1990

between Chancellor Kohl and General Secretary Gorbachev in the Caucasus, even the Soviet Union no longer had any fundamental objection to this option. Negotiations were initiated at international level to clarify the problems arising under international law in connection with German unification. In the wake of the first free elections to the People's Chamber of the GDR, a democratic system and a market

VII/455
Meeting of the foreign ministers of the Four Powers and of the two German states in Bonn, 5 May 1990

VII/456
German-Soviet negotiations on German unification, the Crimea, 15 July 1990

Kommt die DM
bleiben wir
kommt sie nicht
geh'n wir zu ihr!

VII/457
Demonstrators call-
ing for monetary
union

economy were established to create the internal conditions for the
unification of the two German
states. A number of treaties between the Federal Republic and the
GDR regulated the specific steps to
national unity. The most important
of these agreements were the
Treaty on Economic, Monetary and
Social Union, with effect from 1 July 1990, and the Unification Treaty,
which was signed on 31 August
1990. On 23 August 1990, the People's Chamber voted by a two-
thirds majority in favour of the
GDR's accession to the Federal Republic of Germany on 3 October
1990.

VII/458
Signing of the
Unification Treaty
in East Berlin by
Wolfgang Schäuble,
West German Interi-
or Minister, and
Günther Krause,
parliamentary state
secretary to the
East German pre-
mier, 31 August
1990

VII/459
Celebrations in
front of the Reichs-
tag Building to mark
the accession of the
GDR to the Federal
Republic, 2/3 Octo-
ber 1990

VII/460
First sitting of
the all-German
Bundestag in the
Reichstag Building
in Berlin, 4 October
1990

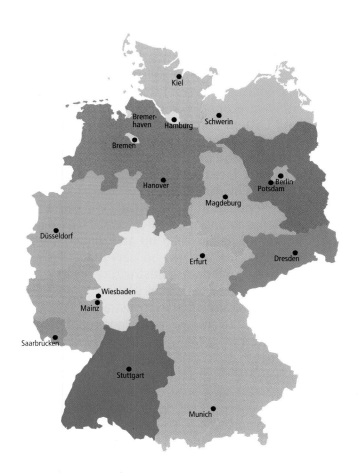

The Federal Republic since 1990

The Path
to the Present

VIII. The path to the present

In the 1990s internal and external developments in the Federal Republic have been determined above all by the direct and indirect consequences of the major upheavals of the year 1989. The collapse of the communist sphere of power opened up for many people, not only in the reunified Germany, prospects of a democratic future in freedom which had appeared unthinkable for many decades. Yet, at the same time, as a result of the wide economic and social differential between Western and Eastern Europe and the often conflicting claims of various nationalities to self-determination, it also caused a host of new political problems.

Internally, the country faced the daunting task of creating uniform living conditions in all the *Länder*, or federal states, of the enlarged Federal Republic. In the first place this was a material problem: immense financial resources were required to assume a vast burden of debts, clean up and modernize old industries in the former GDR and set up new industries and businesses there, create a modern infrastructure, include the citizens of the former GDR in the social security system and establish an efficient local and state administration and a legal system based on the rule of law. These funds could only be raised by drastically increasing taxes and other fiscal charges for all citizens; the fact that, despite this, it has not been possible to avoid a great deal of social hardship in the new *Länder* has caused widespread discontent in East and West, which underlines the great political, social and cultural differences resulting from the division of the country for a period of forty years. It is becoming ever more apparent that overcoming these differences will be no less difficult than creating an economic and social balance.

In international politics there were in some cases excessive expectations that, with the collapse of the Soviet Union and the Eastern bloc dominated by it, tensions between states would decrease and more peaceful developments would begin. These expectations were soon shattered by political reality. Though the international community no longer faced a global nuclear threat, it was – perhaps to a greater extent than ever before – called upon, as a result of acts of aggression by individual states, old and new conflicts between states and numerous internal conflicts, to provide humanitarian assistance and in many cases also to make a military contribution to restore peace. In view of this situation, international organizations to which the Federal Republic has belonged for a long time, such as the UN, NATO, the European Union, the Council of Europe and the OSCE, have acquired new responsibilities.

Moreover, the task of responding to these challenges in the domestic and foreign policy fields has been made even more difficult by unfavourable economic developments, in the course of which unemployment has risen drastically and substantial deficits in public budgets have had to be offset by increasing taxes and other fiscal charges and cutting expenditure. On account of both the considerable financial burden and the fierce competition on world markets, the polical debate in the Federal Republic is increasingly concerned with measures and laws intended to enhance the performance of the German economy and adjust the social state to the changed conditions.

The current political debate focusses on how, in view of this multitude of internal and external problems, the fundamental principles underlying the political and social system in Germany, which have hitherto been accepted by a large majority of the population, can be upheld and successfully further developed. It is perhaps more difficult than ever before in the history of the Federal Republic to predict the course and outcome of this debate.

Developing the new *Länder*

Only after unification of the two German states did the full extent of the tasks involved in building up the economy of the new *Länder* gradually become apparent: a huge legacy not only of a financial nature had to be coped with. The transport and communications system and the administrative structure had to be adapted to the requirements of a modern industrial society. Moreover, because the markets in Eastern Europe no longer existed and the production facilities were completely outdated, the process of economic restructuring proved far more difficult than could have been foreseen at the outset, particularly

VIII/461
Production of the last Trabi in Zwickau on 30 April 1991

since, with the slowing down of the economy from autumn 1992 onwards, companies tended to be less willing to make major investments in the new *Länder*. Despite all the successes achieved and the unmistakable signs of economic recovery, so far it has not been possible to create sufficient jobs. Whereas the younger generation appear to have

cussions on whether the new unity should be based solely on adoption of the constitutional, economic and social system of the Federal Republic in the new *Länder* or whether it should also be the result of a fundamental reform of this system and of an – at least partial – balance between East and West. However, in many cases not only the need for

VIII/462
Demonstration in Leipzig against mass unemployment in the new federal states on 6 April 1991

good prospects, many older workers are jobless or find only temporary work. Despite all the financial efforts, a high social price has had to be paid for integration of the new *Länder* into the Federal Republic.

The struggle for inner unity

Even during the reunification process there were extensive dis-

economic and administrative efficiency but also the burden in terms of personnel and structures left over from the period of communist dictatorship militated against such a balance. Still, the decision of the German Bundestag, taken by a narrow majority, that Berlin should be the German capital was indicative of an intention that developments in the Federal Republic of Germany should not in future proceed just as before in every respect. However,

VIII/463
Vote in the
German Bundestag
on the future capital
on 20 June 1991

VIII/464
Files in the archives
of the former State
Security Service of
the GDR in Norman-
nenstrasse in Berlin

many citizens of the former GDR felt that their specific achievements and values were not sufficiently accepted in the Federal Republic of Germany. Yet there are signs that attitudes at least among the younger generation in East and West are becoming increasingly similar.

A new Europe

After the collapse of the Iron Curtain, European unification initially continued to follow the course already mapped out. At the beginning of 1993 total freedom of movement for people, goods and services was achieved in the "Euro-

VIII/465
Summit meeting
of European heads
of government
in Maastricht on
9/10 December
1991

pean Union". With the accession of Austria, Finland and Sweden to the EU on 1 January 1995, almost all Western states were now members. However, since the decisions taken in Maastricht in December 1991 all debates have focussed on the introduction of a single European currency. It presupposes an unprece-dented degree of economic and po-litical coordination among the part-ner countries and would therefore substantially strengthen integration too. Yet, given the manifold inter-nal and external problems con-fronting them, most member coun-tries are finding it difficult to create the conditions for introduction of

VIII/466
Russian President
Boris Yeltsin and
American President
Bill Clinton at the
World Economic
Summit in Naples
on 9 July 1994

VIII/467
Outside Hamburg
aliens registration
office

the single currency. Moreover, the European Union also faces the major political task of including the new democracies of Eastern Europe in the integration process.

Germany and the new world order

In the light of the increasing number of international problems, the united Germany too faces new

challenges. More than any other Western country, the Federal Republic has sought to support the process of change in Eastern Europe politically and financially. Despite the population's basic willingness to help, the large number of refugees from many trouble spots in the world is placing a strain on public budgets and has led to social tension and even violence against foreigners. Finally, Germany's partner countries expect it to partici-

VIII/468
Federal Defence
Minister Rühe
visiting German
UN units in Split
in Croatia on
29 August 1995

VIII/469
Demonstration
against redundan-
cies in Duisburg
in 1992

pate in the peace-keeping operations of the United Nations not only
financially – as was the case in the
war against Iraq – but also by providing its own auxiliary personnel
and troops. The constitutional restrictions on military missions
abroad, which were in part a consequence of Germany's history,
provoked a protracted domestic
controversy – units of the Federal
Armed Forces have since taken part
in UN operations in Cambodia, So-
malia and former Yugoslavia.

The social state in crisis?

Since the 1980s it has become increasingly apparent that, even in
favourable economic conditions,
the jobless total no longer falls
drastically and full employment is
not achieved. This development,
which has been exacerbated by the
process of restructuring in the new
federal states, reflects the tremendous pace of technological change
and the increasing competition
from Eastern European countries

VIII/470
Demolition work
at a Brandenburg
steel mill in 1995

and the rising industrial nations in Asia. At the same time, high unemployment and the cost of reunification result in higher taxes and larger social security contributions, which increase the cost of labour and reduce net incomes. Many companies respond by taking incisive rationalization measures and extending their international activities. Both management and labour and the Government and opposition are increasingly divided over the question whether the acute economic crisis can be overcome by means of further reductions in working hours, measures to stimulate the economy and limited amendments to social security legislation or whether a radical reform of the economic and social system of the Federal Republic is required.

VIII/471
Federal President
Roman Herzog
being sworn in
on 1 July 1994

Parliamentary Berlin

Parliamentary Berlin

The various parliaments and the parliamentary system were only gradually able to establish their place in the political and social life of Berlin alongside the Hohenzollern monarchy and the institutions on which it depended, primarily the bureaucracy and the military. The United Diet, an assembly of delegates from the provincial parliaments, which marked the beginning of parliamentary history in Berlin in the spring of 1847, was dissolved after only two months on account of its oppositional stance. Even the Prussian National Assembly, which was elected after the Revolution of March 1848, failed in its efforts to give Prussia a liberal constitution. Following the successful counterrevolution, King Frederick William IV, acting on his own supreme authority, decreed the constitution. As was to be expected, it placed severe restrictions on the Lower House, the Chamber of Deputies, which was elected on the basis of the three-class electoral system. The Upper House, the Chamber of Peers, whose members were appointed by the King, provided an additional counterweight. It was not until after the founding of the Reich that the disputes between the parliamentary majority and the executive – its members were appointed by the King – which reached their climax in the Prussian constitutional conflict between 1862 and 1866, began to subside. The new Reichstag that had been elected by universal, equal suffrage, still had no real powers, but the growing responsibilities assigned to the state and the increasing volume of legislation to be dealt with slowly but surely strengthened Parliament's influence. Public interest focused increasingly on the Reichstag.

These political developments were clearly reflected in Berlin's parliamentary architecture. Whereas the early parliaments were housed in buildings designed for other purposes, such as halls in the Royal Palace, in the Singakademie or the Schauspielhaus on Gendarmenmarkt, the two Prussian Chambers were provided with their own quarters in about 1850. However, both of these buildings, like the first domicile of the Reichstag in Leipziger Strasse, were modified only to the extent necessary for parliamentary use and remained more or less inadequate temporary accommodation. Not until 1894 was the Reichstag able to move into the building designed by Paul Wallot on Königsplatz. A few years later, the Chamber of Peers and the Chamber of Deputies moved into buildings in Leipziger Strasse and Prinz-Albrecht-Strasse respectively.

These monumental and representative buildings were unmistakable evidence that Parliament had established itself in Berlin.

However, it was not until the revolution of 1918/19, following defeat in World War I, that Parliament assumed full political responsibility. The Weimar Constitution made the Reichstag the focal point of the country's democratic system and made the Reich Government, too, dependent on enjoying the confidence of a parliamentary majority. The Prussia of the landed gentry, the Junker, had become "red" Prussia, a republican bulwark with a coalition government led by the Social Democrats. Virtually all social groups focused their expectations and demands on Parliament and the political parties. But the readiness to reconcile conflicting interests through parliamentary procedures, which had never been very strong at the best of times, was weakened still further in the final crisis-ridden years of the Weimar Republic. From 1930 onwards the Cabinet was appointed by the Reich President and the Reichstag was frequently dissolved, which increasingly undermined Parliament's authority. When the Reichstag building went up in flames, this symbolized the end of parliamentary democracy in the Weimar Republic. Under the Nazi dictatorship, the Reichstag ceased to have anything in common with a democratic parliament.

When the war ended in 1945, Berlin's parliamentary buildings and large parts of the capital and of the German Reich lay in ruins. The red flag of the Soviet Union was flying on top of the Reichstag. Parliamentary democracy had to be completely rebuilt in Germany. From the very start, the Western sectors of Berlin were included in this process of reconstruction in the three Western occupation zones. Under the Basic Law, the Federal Republic's constitution, Berlin was represented by its own Members in the German Bundestag, though they had only limited voting rights. For a long time, the division of Germany deprived Berlin of its status as the capital and parliamentary centre of Germany. But the reestablishment of German unity in October 1990 has provided the city with an opportunity to renew its ties with the tradition of parliamentary democracy. The Reichstag Building is once again set to become the seat of Germany's national parliament.

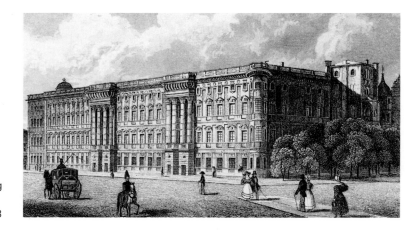

472
The Royal Palace
in Berlin, where
the official opening
of Parliament took
place up until 1918

I. 1847 – 1870: Parliaments in opposition

The first parliaments

473
Sitting of the United
Diet in the White
Hall of the royal
palace in Berlin in
spring 1847

Prussia's, and hence Berlin's, parliamentary history began on 11 April 1847 with the formal opening of the United Diet in the Royal Palace in Berlin. King Frederick William IV had agreed to convene the Diet in response to increasingly vocal demands for an assembly representing the whole of Prussia. However, it merely had the power to approve the levying of taxes. It was dissolved after only

two months when the majority of the assembly attempted to extend the Diet's powers and make it a true parliament.

The temporary success of the March 1848 Revolution also led to the election of a Prussian constituent National Assembly based on universal suffrage. This election was held simultaneously with the elections to the Frankfurt National Assembly on 1 May 1848. Howev-

474
The Singakademie, designed by Schinkel and built between 1825 and 1827

475
The Prussian National Assembly met in the Singakademie in spring and summer 1848

476
Beginning in
September 1848,
the National Assem-
bly convened in
the Schauspielhaus
on Gendarmen-
markt

477
In the wake of
the successful
counter-revolution,
the National Assem-
bly was driven out
of the Schauspiel-
haus on 11 Novem-
ber 1848 and finally
dissolved on 5 De-
cember of the
same year

er, the deliberations on a new constitution failed to lead to an agreement between King and Parliament. When the counterrevolutionary forces gained the upper hand in
the autumn of 1848, the Prussian
National Assembly was dissolved
by force. Acting on his own

supreme authority, Frederick William IV gave the country a constitution by royal decree.

The constitution, which was later
unilaterally revised several times by
the King, provided for the election
of a Lower House, the Chamber of
Deputies, which had only limited

478
The building on
the Dönhoffplatz
where the Prussian
Chamber of
Deputies met

powers in respect of the levying of taxes and the passage of legislation. For decisions to be legally valid, the consent of the Crown and both Chambers was required. The inferior status of Parliament in the eyes of the executive was also apparent from the cramped and inhospitable buildings in which the Chamber of Deputies was accommodated almost until the turn of the century.

Under the Prussian constitution, the Upper House, the Chamber of Peers, was mainly conceived as a counterweight to the Chamber of

479
Plan of the
Prussian Chamber
of Deputies, built
originally as a no-
bleman's mansion
in 1775, taken
from an English
book on parliamen-
tary architecture

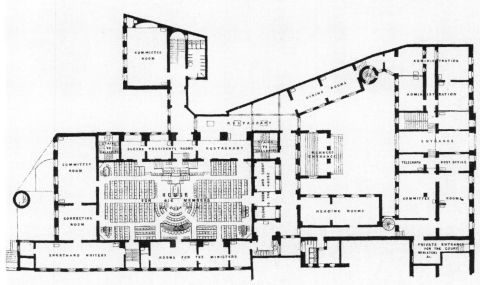

PLAN OF PRINCIPAL FLOOR.

480
The Prussian Chamber of Peers moved into a former nobleman's mansion at Leipziger Strasse 3

481
Between 1867 and 1870 the Reichstag of the North German Confederation convened in the plenary chamber of the Prussian Chamber of Peers

Deputies. This explains why originally half, and later all, of its members were appointed by the King. The majority of the conservative *Junker* proved to be reliable supporters of the executive, which was accountable only to the King and protected above all the interests of the aristocracy.

The parliamentary system under the Prussian monarchy

The Chamber of Deputies was elected indirectly by universal, but unequal suffrage and there was no secret ballot. The voters were divided into three classes according to the amount of taxes they paid. The

482
Bismarck during
a sitting of the
Prussian Chamber
of Peers in 1862

small number of people with large incomes (4% of the population) were thus able to nominate as many members of the electoral college and deputies as the large majority of small taxpayers (80% of the population). For decades, though, this electoral system was largely responsible for the liberal majorities in the Chamber as the middle class in particular became increasingly affluent.

The deputies enjoyed increasing popular support. By 1862 the turnout at elections had increased to 34%, which, considering the three-class electoral system, was remarkable. A large proportion of the parliamentarians came from the educated middle class. The liberal opposition was primarily made up of civil servants, especially those with a legal background. In the early stages of the constitutional conflict over a reform and expansion of the army, they formed the German Progress Party, which could always rely on the support of the Berlin constituencies.

After the abortive Revolution of 1848/49 the tension between Crown and Parliament subsided only briefly. In the late 1850s the Liberal opposition redoubled its efforts to assert and extend parliamentary rights. A serious conflict arose between Parliament and the King's executive over the constitutional implications of Bismarck's plans to reform the army. It was not resolved until 1866/67, when, for the sake of national unity, the National Liberal forces and Bismarck reached a compromise.

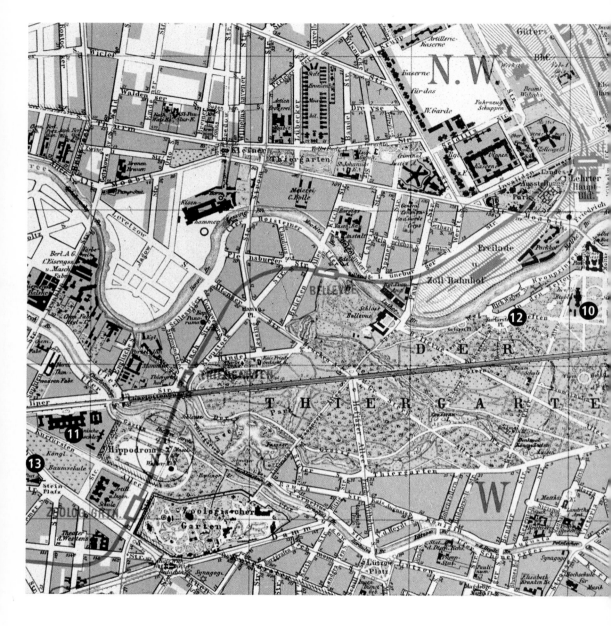

1.   Royal Palace

2.   Singakademie

3.   Schauspielhaus on
     Gendarmenmarkt

4.   Prussian Chamber
     of Deputies at Leipziger
     Strasse 75

5.   Prussian Chamber
     of Peers at Leipziger
     Strasse 75

6.   Provisional Reichstag
     building at Leipziger
     Strasse 4

7.   Reichstag Building on
     Königsplatz

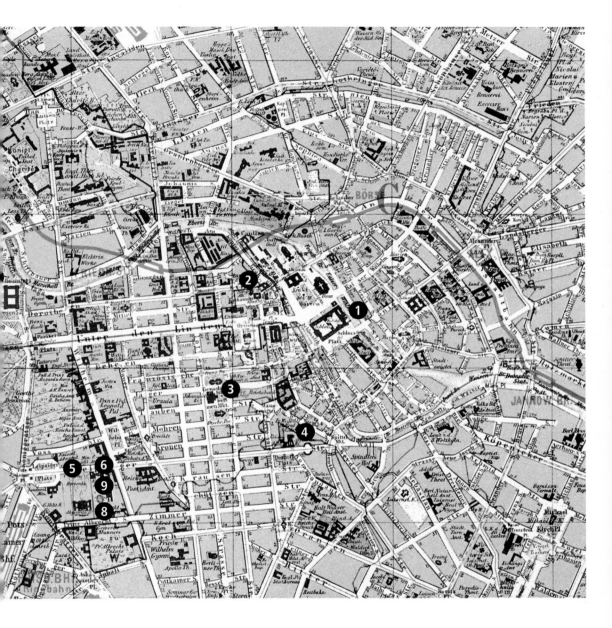

8. New Prussian Lower
Chamber at Prinz-Albrecht-
Strasse 5

9. New Prussian Upper
Chamber at Prinz-Albrecht-
Strasse 5

10. Kroll Opera House on
Königsplatz

11. Main building of the
Technical University

12. Congress Hall

13. Ostpreußenhalle
at the foot of the Radio
Tower

II. 1871 – 1918: Consolidation of parliamentarism

Parliament under the Empire

Under the constitution of the North German Confederation of 1867, which, four years later, was adopted largely unchanged for the newly founded German Reich, the Reichstag was the main constitutional organ alongside the Prussian King, the hereditary head of the Confederation. However, its political influence was limited for the most part to legislation, which included the power of the purse, whereas the government was almost exclusively dependent on the monarch. As a result, a strong Chancellor like Bismarck was able to exert decisive influence on the policies of the German Reich.

The Reichstag was elected directly by universal, equal suffrage and in a secret ballot. Bismarck had opted for this system as a means of fighting the Liberals. The candidates obtaining an absolute majority of the votes – if necessary, a second ballot was held – were elected. This system favoured parties with regional strongholds but disadvantaged the Social Democrats, especially since the constituency boundaries had not been redrawn to allow for the process of urbanization and the growth of densely populated industrial centres.

The Reichstag did not meet in permanent session. It was convened by the Emperor only once or twice a year for sessions which lasted several weeks. Although, formally, it was subdivided into seven groups determined by lot, from the very start the conduct of parliamentary business was mainly in the hands of the parliamentary groups. They generally nominated the speakers for plenary debates and the members of the committees and commissions, which play such an important role in the legislative process. In practice, therefore, the Reichstag was an instrument of modern party democracy and it in-

483
In the summer of 1871 the Reichstag moved into temporary premises at Leipziger Strasse 4

creasingly became the focal point of public interest.

During the years of the Empire, the executive slowly but surely became increasingly dependent on Reichstag majorities. Parliament's influence increased above all as a result of the ever greater responsibilities assigned to the state and the –

Parliament buildings

Following its early sessions in the building of the Prussian Chamber of Deputies, the Reichstag met for more than 20 years in a provisional building, the former Royal Prussian Porcelain Manufactory, which had been hastily converted for this pur-

consequently – ever broader scope of legislation. However, Parliament was excluded from real power until the hour of Germany's defeat in the First World War. The continuing split between Parliament and Government was a major obstacle to the development of parliamentary democracy in Germany.

pose in the summer of 1871. All plans for new and permanent parliament buildings were delayed for many years as a result of the tense relationship between Government and Parliament and because the site proposed in 1871, on the eastern side of the Königsplatz, was initially not available.

484
Sitting of the Reichstag in the provisional Reichstag building, the former Royal Porcelain Manufactory, around 1872

485

The Reichstag Building on Königsplatz, completed in 1894.

After protracted negotiations for the plot of land and two competitions to find the best design, work on the new Reichstag building began at long last in 1884. The winning entry was submitted by the Frankfurt architect Paul Wallot, who, departing from the tradition-al, classical type of building, developed a, in contemporary terms, modern style which reflected the aspirations of the Reich. The Reichstag took ten years to build and was completed on 5 December 1894. Parliament was given a monumental, representative building

486

The Reich Chancellor, Georg Michaelis, delivering his inaugural speech in the Reichstag on 19 July 1917

487
The new building
housing the Pruss-
ian Chamber of
Deputies in Prinz-
Albrecht-Strasse

which was not, however, suitable in every way for the conduct of parliamentary business by parliamentary groups and committees.

The two Prussian Chambers, too, were able to move into new quarters in the 1890s. New parliament buildings were constructed on a double plot between Leipziger Strasse and Prinz-Albrecht-Strasse, part of which had previously been occupied by the Chamber of Peers and the provisional Reichstag building. They replaced the totally inadequate accommodation dating back to the middle of the century.

488
After the Reichstag
moved into its new
building on Königs-
platz, the new
Prussian Chamber
of Peers was built
on the site at
Leipziger Strasse 3
and 4

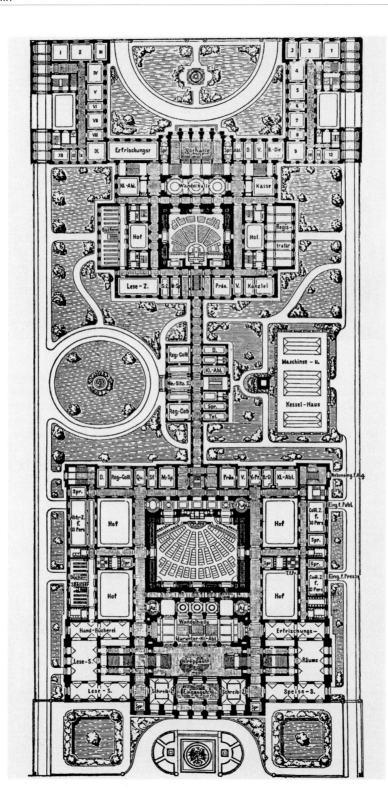

489
The double plot
of land between
Leipziger Strasse
and Prinz-Albrecht-
Strasse showing
the buildings of
the Prussian Cham-
ber of Peers (top)
and the Prussian
Chamber of
Deputies (bottom)

Parliament and parliamentarians in Berlin

Berlin's political and social life during the years of the Empire was dominated by the monarchy and the upper class, especially the military. The relative weight of the monarchy and of Parliament was most strikingly manifest in the annual solemn opening of the Reichstag. The ceremony was not held in Parliament itself, as in England for instance, but in the White Hall of the Royal Palace. Amidst the trappings of court ceremony and the many glittering uniforms, the deputies almost appeared to be mere supernumeraries.

The great majority of deputies came to Berlin only when the Reichstag was in session. The parliamentary groups met regularly in inns and restaurants in the vicinity of the Reichstag building. Sometimes receptions were given for them, with Bismarck's parliamentary "soirées" being particularly famous. Though the leading figures in the Reichstag of course belonged to Berlin's upper class, Parliament and its Members had very little impact on social life in the capital of the Reich.

Even after the founding of the Reich, Berlin's constituencies remained for many years firmly in the hands of the left-wing Liberals. By voting for the Liberals, large sections of Berlin's middle class expressed their political reservations about the Hohenzollern monarchy. However, the political scene changed as Berlin developed into an industrial metropolis with a growing working class and pronounced social disparities. First, the north and northeastern constituencies and then, from the mid-1890s onwards, all the constituencies in the capital switched their allegiance to the Social Democrats.

490
Ludwig Windhorst, of the Centre party, at a soirèe hosted by Bismarck in May 1879

III. 1919 – 1945: The heyday and decline of parliamentarism

Parliament as the centre of democracy

After the collapse of the monarchy and the authoritarian state in the revolution of 1918, two alternatives were available for shaping the political order: a system of councils, or parliamentary democracy. In December 1918 the National Congress of Workers' and Soldiers' Councils

In the years of the Weimar Republic, the Prussia of the landed gentry, the *Junker*, who had been the mainstay of the Hohenzollern monarchy, became "red" Prussia, a republican bastion with an SPD-led coalition government formed by the Social Democratic Party, the centre party and the Liberals. The comparative political continuity in the Prussian Diet – there were no in-

491
Sitting of the Reich Congress of Workers' and Soldiers' Councils in the Prussian Chamber of Deputies in December 1918

met for a time in the Prussian Chamber of Deputies. However, the leaders of the Social Democrats under Friedrich Ebert were able to assert themselves over the more radical groupings, with the result that elections were held for a constituent national assembly. The die had thus been cast for a system of parliamentary democracy.

stances of early dissolution of Parliament or frequent changes of government – made a major contribution towards the temporary stabilization of the Republic.
The Weimar Constitution made the Reichstag the centre of the country's democratic order. Its legislative powers were no longer circumscribed by the Reichsrat, which was

492
(opposite)
"Reichstag Sitting in 1930: Breitscheid Speaks", painting by Annot

made up of the representatives of the *Länder*, or states. Above all, however, the Government was now fully dependent on enjoying the confidence of a parliamentary majority. On the other hand, the strong position of the Reich President and the exceptional powers he was granted under the constitution reflected reservations about parliamentary democracy which had their roots in the tradition of the authoritarian state. In the final stages of the Weimar Republic this was to have fatal consequences.

made it difficult to form governments that could rely on stable majorities in Parliament.

Berlin society in the years of democracy

Berlin had become a European metropolis with four million inhabitants. It was an economically thriving city with busy traffic, glittering facades, colourful advertisements and large department stores. Berlin's special culture in the 1920s

493
The visitors' gallery in the Reichstag Building in October 1930

By enfranchising women and introducing a system of proportional representation, the Weimar Constitution removed all the inequalities of the previous electoral system: henceforth, all votes were to have equal weight and determine the composition of Parliament. However, this form of electoral justice produced many small parties and

was manifest in the cafés and in the city's nightlife, in the theatre, literature and art, and in the abundance of modern buildings. However, to a far greater extent than before the First World War, life in the city was also marked by political conflicts and controversies.

During the Weimar Republic, the political expectations and demands of nearly all social groups focused on Parliament and the parties. In Berlin itself, the elections to the Reichstag and to the Prussian Diet continued to be dominated by the workers' parties. Indeed, from 1930 onwards the Social Democrats were even overtaken by the German Communist Party. However, the parties were still not fully committed to reconciling their conflicting interests through parliamentary procedures, and they were even less prepared to do so in times of crisis.

The young Republic was vehemently attacked by extreme left and right-wing groups who consistently exploited all the freedoms and possibilities afforded by a pluralistic democratic order. Right-wing extremists, in particular, did not even shrink from assassinating leading democratic politicians. Manifold emotional and political reservations about the Weimar Republic weakened the ranks of its supporters.

Political crisis and the end of parliamentary democracy

The grave political and social conflicts besetting the Weimar Republic were exacerbated by the world economic crisis of 1929. Instead of being settled in Parliament, they were increasingly fought out in the street. In the elections of 1930 and 1932, left-wing and above all right-wing, anti-democratic forces polled more votes than the parties which supported the Republic. Conservative circles around President von Hindenburg sought to exploit the crisis in order to reshape the political order along anti-parliamentary, authoritarian lines.

From 1930 onwards the country was ruled by cabinets appointed by the Reich President, which increasingly restricted the Reichstag's possibilities of influencing the composition and policies of the Government. Normal legislative procedure was in many instances replaced by

494
The Kroll Opera House, used by Parliament after the Reichstag fire, located on the western side of Königsplatz

495
Sitting of the nazi-
fied Reichstag in
the Kroll Opera
House

emergency decrees issued by the
Reich President. If the Reichstag
objected it was dissolved. On
22 July 1932 Reich Chancellor von
Papen deposed the Prussian Government by decree, thus removing
one of the last republican bulwarks
democracy and in effect depriving
the Prussian Diet of its political
powers.

On the night of 27 February 1933
the Reichstag went up in flames.
The plenary chamber and parts of
the dome burnt down. The question of whether the Nazis were responsible for setting the blaze has
still not been conclusively answered. However, the burning
down of the Reichstag Building
symbolized the end of parliamentary democracy and of the Weimar
Republic. The emergency decree issued on 28 February "to protect
the people and the state", in which
the most important basic rights
were suspended, marked the beginning of the years of Nazi terror and
the National Socialist dictatorship.
The deputies, who, following the
burning down of the Reichstag,
held their few remaining meetings
in the Kroll Opera House opposite
the parliament building, excluded
themselves once and for all from
the legislative process by voting for
the Enabling Law of 23 March
1933. So-called elections to the
Reichstag continued to be held in
the one-party Nazi state, but the
Reichstag's uniformed members
were mere parliamentary decora-
tion for the dictator, Adolf Hitler.

IV. 1945 – 1987: The second democracy

A capital without a Reich

At the end of the war Berlin's parliament buildings, like many parts of the capital and of the German Reich, lay in ruins. The Reichstag Building in particular was severely damaged by bombs and artillery fire in the last years of the war; and on its dome flew the Soviet flag. After the Nazi dictatorship parliamentary democracy in Germany had to be completely rebuilt.

of the Prussian Diet, lay just across the border in East Berlin. Only the Reichstag Building and the part of the city where foreign missions used to be located were in West Berlin.

Reconstruction and renewal

From the very start, the Western sectors of Berlin were included in the process of democratic recon-

The sectoral boundaries which, following Germany's division into two states with different political and social systems, also divided Berlin, cut through the old government quarter, which had already undergone considerable changes under National Socialism. The larger part of that area, including the building

struction. Under the Basic Law, Berlin was represented by its own Members of Parliament in the Bundestag, even though, on account of certain rights retained by the Allies, they only had limited voting rights. Between 1955 and 1965 the Bundestag also held several plenary sittings in Berlin. Until the Berlin crisis

496
The main building of the Technical University during reconstruction

497
Plenary sitting
of the German Bun-
destag on 19 Octo-
ber 1949 in the lec-
ture theatre of the
Physics Institute of
the Technical Uni-
versity

498
In 1957 and 1958
the German Bun-
destag convened
in the newly built
Congress Hall

of 1958, neither the GDR nor the
Soviet Union protested. Following
the conclusion of the Four-Power
Agreement in 1971, however, the
presence of the German Bundestag
in Berlin was limited to meetings of
committees and parliamentary
groups.

After long discussions and debates,
the reconstruction of the Reichstag
began in 1961. The German Bundestag decided that it should again
serve as a parliament building and
therefore also have a new plenary
chamber. At the same time it was
decided not to restore the dome or

499
Between 1954 and 1969 the Federal Convention met to elect the Federal President in the Ostpreußenhalle at the foot of the Radio Tower

all parts of the building. The Berlin architect Paul Baumgarten submitted a modern design, on the basis of which construction work was completed in 1971. As the seat of the German Bundestag in Berlin, the renovated Reichstag building was a symbol both of the tradition of parliamentary democracy in Germany and of national unity.

The revolution in the GDR in the autumn of 1989 and the restoration of national unity in October 1990 also opened up new perspectives for parliamentary life in Berlin. The Reichstag Building, was at the cen-

500
The Reichstag Building, rebuilt between 1961 and 1971

501
The redesigned
plenary chamber
of the Reichstag
Building in 1971

502
Computer simula-
tion showing the
new dome of the
Reichstag Building

tre of the celebrations to mark the
day of German unity. Following the
decision of the German Bundestag
to transfer the seat of Parliament
and Government to the capital,
Berlin, and to have Wallot's building converted in a modern parlia-

mentary building by the English architect Sir Norman Foster, the
Reichstag will, after the decades of
National Socialist dictatorship and
the division of Germany, reassume
its old function of housing Germany's national parliament.

Chronology

Around 1800		The French Revolution poses a fundamental challenge to the old political and social structure in central Europe
1803	25.2	Decree of the Reich Deputation, secularisation of all clerical principalities
1806	11.7	Founding of the Confederation of the Rhine
	6.8	Abdication of Emperor Francis II
	14.10	Battles of Jena and Auerstedt
1807	7.7	Peace of Tilsit between France and Prussia
	30.9	Freiherr vom Stein leading minister in Prussia, initiation of reforms
1809	12.10	Prince von Metternich chief minister in Austria
1813	28.2	Prussian-Russian military pact signed at Kalisch
	16 – 19.10	Battle of Leipzig
1814	30.3	Occupation of Paris, Napoleon is exiled to Elba
	18.9	Opening of the Congress of Vienna
1815	1.3	Landing of Napoleon in France
	8.6	Signing of the Federal Act, founding of the German Federation
	18.6	Napoleon defeated at Waterloo, sent into exile on St. Helena
	26.9	Signing of Holy Alliance between Russia, Prussia and Austria
1816	6.11	Opening of the Federal Assembly in Frankfurt am Main
1817	18.10	Wartburg Festival of the German student fraternities
1818/1820		Modern constitutions in Bavaria, Baden, Württemberg and Hesse-Darmstadt
1819	23.3	Conservative writer August von Kotzebue murdered by German student Karl Ludwig Sand
	6 – 31.8	Carlsbad Conference, suppression of liberal and national movements
1820	24.5	Signing of the Acts of Vienna, extension of the Federal Act of 1815
1830	27 – 29.7	July Revolution in France, spreading of unrest to Brunswick, Hanover, Kurhessen and Saxony
1832	27 – 30.5	Hambach Festival

1833	4.4	Storming of the Frankfurt Guard by students and citizens
1834	1.1	The treaty establishing the German Customs Union comes into force
1835	7.12	Opening of the first German railway between Nuremberg and Fürth
1837	1.11	Repealing of the state constitution in Hanover, protest and dismissal of seven Göttingen professors
1844	June	June uprising of Silesian weavers
1847	3.2	Convocation of the United Diet in Prussia
	June	Establishment of the League of Communists in London by Karl Marx and Friedrich Engels
	12.9	Meeting of South German democrats in Offenburg
	10.10	Meeting of moderate west and south German liberals in Heppenheim
1848	22 – 24.2	Revolutionary unrest in Paris, abdication of King Louis Philippe
	27.2	A People's Assembly in Baden, meeting near Mannheim, drafts the "March Demands"
	7.3	First revolutionary meetings in Berlin
	13 – 15.3	Uprisings in Vienna, resignation of Prince von Metternich
	18.3	Unrest and street riots in Berlin
	21.3	Proclamation by King Frederick William IV of Prussia "To my People and to the German Nation"
	29.3	Appointment of the liberal ministers Ludolf Camphausen and David Hansemann in Prussia
	31.3 – 3.4	Assembly of the *Vorparlament* in the Paulskirche in Frankfurt, decision taken on the setting up of a German National Assembly
	12.4	Start of the Republican uprising in Baden, led by Friedrich von Hecker and Gustav von Struve
	15.5	A second uprising in Vienna forces the setting up of a Reichstag
	18.5	Meeting of the German National Assembly in the Paulskirche in Frankfurt
	29.6	Creation of a temporary central government, election of Archduke John of Austria to the post of Imperial Administrator

1848	26.8 – 16.9	Under pressure from the great powers, Prussia signs the armistice of Malmö which settles the conflict with Denmark over Schleswig-Holstein; the National Assembly in Frankfurt initially rejects the armistice but is eventually forced to accept it
	6/7.10	Third uprising in Vienna
	31.10	Reconquest of Vienna by Imperial troops
	2.11	Appointment of the conservative Brandenburg ministry in Prussia
	21.11	Prince zu Schwarzenberg becomes head of the Imperial Ministry in the Habsburg Monarchy
	2.12	Abdication of the Austrian Emperor Ferdinand I, accession to the throne of his nephew Francis Joseph I
	5.12	Dissolution of the Prussian National Assembly, granting of a constitution
	21.12	Passing of the law on the fundamental rights of the German People by the Frankfurt National Assembly
1849	4.3	Dissolution of the Austrian Reichstag, granting of a constitution
	27/28.3	Passing of a constitution for the German Reich in the Paulskirche in Frankfurt, election of Frederick William IV of Prussia as German Emperor
	28.4	Rejection of the German Emperor's crown by the Prussian King
	May – July	Campaign for a Reich constitution, uprisings in Saxony, Breslau and Baden are violently suppressed
	26.5	Three Kings' Alliance between Prussia, Saxony and Hanover; passing of the "Erfurt Reich Constitution" based on the Prussian policy of union
	6 – 18.6	Meeting of the "Rump Parliament" in Stuttgart
	20.12	Resignation of the Imperial Administrator, Archduke Johann
1850	31.1	Implementation of the Prussian Constitution imposed from above
	1.9	Reopening of the Bundestag in Frankfurt
	29.11	Treaty of Olmütz, end of the Prussian policy of union
1854/1856		Crimean War between England, France and Russia; Austria and Prussia remain neutral
1858	7.10	William I of Prussia takes over the regency for his mentally-ill brother Frederick William IV; beginning of the "New Era"
1859	3.5 – 11.7	Piedmont and France go to war against Austria

1859	16.9	Founding of the German National Association as an organisation for the supporters of a "Little German" nation-state under Prussian leadership
1861	2.1	Death of Frederick William IV, accession to the throne of William I
	26.2	February Patent, constitution for the Austrian Monarchy
	6.6	Founding of the German Progressive Party
1862	29.3	Signing of the Franco-Prussian Trade Treaty
	24.9	Appointment of Otto von Bismarck as Prussian Prime Minister; the constitutional conflict over the reform of the army deepens
	28.10	Founding of the German Reform Association as an organisation for the proponents of a "Greater German" nation-state
1863	23.5	Founding of the General Association of German Workers in Leipzig under the leadership of Ferdinand Lassalle
	16.8 – 1.9	Congress of princes in Frankfurt
1864		Prussian-Austrian war against Denmark over Schleswig-Holstein
1865	14.8	Treaty of Gastein between Prussia and Austria on the administration of Schleswig-Holstein
1866	21.6 – 26.7	War between Prussia and Austria
	3.7.	Battle of Königgrätz/Sadowa
	23.8	Peace Treaty of Prague: dissolution of the German Confederation, recognition of Prussia's dominant position in Germany
	3.9.	Passing of the Indemnity Bill by the Prussian Lower House, settling of the constitutional conflict
	17.11.	Founding of the National Liberal Party
1867	12.2	Elections to the Constituent Reichstag of the North German Confederation
	12.6	Austro-Hungarian settlement
	21.12	"December Laws" in Austria, beginning of a liberal era
1869	7 – 9.8	Founding of the Social Democratic Workers' Party in Eisenach, led by August Bebel and Wilhelm Liebknecht
1870	13.7	Ems Telegram
	18.7	Proclamation of the doctrine of papal infallibility by the First Vatican Council
	19.7	France declares war on Prussia

1870	2.9	French army surrenders at Sedan, Emperor Napoleon III imprisoned
	19.9	Start of the siege of Paris
1871	18.1	Proclamation of the German Empire at Versailles
	10.5.	Peace Treaty of Frankfurt am Main; ceding of Alsace-Lorraine to Germany and payment of war reparations of five thousand million francs; start of the "cultural struggle" in Prussia and in the German Empire
1873	9.5	Collapse of the Vienna stock exchange, start of the "Great Depression"
	22.10	Triple Alliance between Austria-Hungary, Russia and the German Empire
1875	April – May	"War in Sight" crisis
	22 – 27.5	Supporters of Lassalle and Marx join forces in Gotha to form the "Socialist Workers' Party"
1876	15.2	Founding of the Central Association of German Industrialists
1878	May	Emperor William seriously wounded in an assassination attempt
	13.6 – 13.7	Congress of Berlin
	18.10	Passing of the Anti-Socialist Law by the Reichstag
1879	12.7	Passing of the Protective Tariffs Law by the Reichstag
	7.10	Dual Alliance between the German Empire and Austria-Hungary
1880	14.7	The passing of the first more lenient laws heralds the end of the "cultural struggle" in Germany
1883	15.6	German Reichstag passes the law on sickness insurance
1884	27.6.	Introduction of accident insurance in Germany; acquisition of German colonies in South-West Africa, Togo and Cameroon
1885		Acquisition of German East Africa
1887	18.6	Signing of the Reinsurance Treaty between Russia and the German Empire
1888	9.3	Death of Emperor William I; accession to the throne of his terminally ill son Frederick III
	15.6	Death of Frederick III; accession to the throne of his eldest son William II
1890	25.1	The Reichstag rejects any extension of the Anti-Socialist Law; it expires on 30.9.1890

1890	20.3	Resignation of Otto von Bismarck as Reich Chancellor and Prussian Minister-President; under his successor, General Leo von Caprivi, a "new course" in social and tariff policy is charted
	27.3	German-Russian Reinsurance Treaty not extended
	1.7	Helgoland-Zanzibar Treaty, balancing of Anglo-German colonial interests
1891	1.7	Founding of the Pan-German Association in Berlin
1893	18.2	Founding of the Agrarian League as the organization of large landowners east of the Elbe
1894	26.10	Dismissal of Chancellor Geery Leo von Caprivi in connection with the "subversion bill" directed against the SPD; succeeded by Prince Hohenlohe-Schillingfürst
1895	21.6	Opening of the Emperor William Canal (North Sea-Baltic Canal)
1896	1.7	Civil Code passed by the Reichstag; it comes into force on 1.1.1900
1900	17.10	As successor to Prince Hohenlohe, Foreign Secretary Bernhard von Bülow becomes new Reich Chancellor
1905/1906		First Moroccan crisis between France and the German Empire
1908	Oct./Nov.	Daily Telegraph affair, strengthening of the Reichstag's position
1909	14.7	As successor to the retired Reich Chancellor Bernhard von Bülow, Theobald von Bethmann Hollweg becomes new head of government
1911		Second Moroccan crisis
1912	12.1	For the first time at Reichstag elections, the Social Democrats become the strongest party
1914	28.6	Assassination of the heir to the Austrian throne, Archduke Franz Ferdinand, by Serbian nationalists in Sarajevo
	28.7	Austria-Hungary declares war on Serbia
	30.7	General mobilisation by Russia
	1.8	German mobilisation; Germany declares war on Russia
	3.8	Germany declares war on France
	4.8	Great Britain responds to the violation of Belgian neutrality by German troops by declaring war on the German Empire
	4.8	Approval of war loans by all parties in the Reichstag including the SPD

1914	26 – 31.8	Battle of Tannenberg, decimation of the Second Russian Army
1916	21.2 – July	Battle of Verdun
	29.8	von Hindenburg and Ludendorff assume supreme command of the army
1917	9.1	German Headquarters decides on unrestricted submarine warfare
	8.3	Outbreak of revolution in Russia, abdication of Tsar Nicholas II
	6.4	USA declares war on the German Empire
	6 – 8.4	Inaugural party meeting of the Independent Social Democratic Party in Gotha
	14.7	Resignation of Reich Chancellor Theobald von Bethmann Hollweg under pressure from the supreme army command
	19.7	Reichstag passes the "Peace Resolution" calling for a negotiated peace; formation of a cross-party group by the Centre, the SPD and left-wing liberals
	6 -7.11	October Revolution in Russia, Bolshevik putsch
	15.12	Armistice between Russia and the German Empire
1918	28.1	Mass strikes in Berlin and other German cities
	3.3	Peace Treaty of Brest-Litovsk
	29.9	Supreme army command calls for the offer of a cease-fire
	3.10	Establishment of a new Reich government under Prince Max von Baden which also includes representatives of the majority parties
	24 – 28.10	Constitutional reform; the Reich executive becomes more accountable to Parliament
	28.10	Outbreak of German naval mutiny
	3 – 4.11	Sailor's mutiny in Kiel
	6 – 8.11	The revolutionary movement spreads to the rest of the Empire
	9.11	Proclamation of a republic by the Social Democrat Philipp Scheidemann
	10.11	Establishment of the Council of Peoples' Representatives from the ranks of the SPD and USPD
	15.11	Stinnes-Legien agreement between employees and employers
	16 – 20.12	Reich Congress of Workers' and Soldiers' Councils in Berlin

1918	23.12	Mutiny of the People's Naval Division in Berlin
	29.12	The USPD members walk out of the Council of Peoples' Representatives
	31.12	Founding of the KPD
1919	5 – 12.1	Spartacus uprising in Berlin
	15.1	Murder of Rosa Luxemburg and Karl Liebknecht
	19.1	Election of a National Assembly
	11.2	Social Democrat Friedrich Ebert elected as Reich President by the National Assembly in Weimar
	13.2	Formation of the Scheidemann Government; Weimar coalition of SPD, Centre party and DDP
	1 – 3.5	Suppression of the Soviet republic in Munich
	16.6	Ultimatum to the German government demanding its acceptance of the Peace Treaty
	28.6	Signing of the Treaty of Versailles
	11.8	Promulgation of the Weimar Constitution
1920	13 – 17.3	Kapp-Lüttwitz putsch in Berlin
	March/April	Communist uprising in the Ruhr and in central Germany
	6.6	Reichstag election; the parties of the Weimar coalition lose their majority
1921	20.3	Plebiscite in Upper Silesia
	26.8	Assassination of Centre politician Matthias Erzberger by rightwing radicals
1922	16.4	Treaty of Rapallo between the USSR and the German Empire
	24.6	Assassination of Reich Foreign Minister Walther Rathenau by right-wing extremists
1923	11.1	Occupation of the Ruhr by French and Belgian troops
	13.1	Announcement of passive resistance against the Ruhr occupation
	26.9	Abandonment of the Ruhr struggle by the Stresemann government; declaration of a state of emergency in Bavaria; the Reich government responds by declaring a state of emergency in the Reich as a whole
	19.10 – 18.2.24	Conflict between Bavaria and the Reich
	22 – 23.10	Attempted communist uprising in Hamburg
	29.10	Action taken by the Reich against SPD, KPD in Saxony
	8 – 9.11	Hitler putsch in Munich

1923	15.11	New currency; end of inflation
	23.11	Collapse of the Stresemann government
1924	July/August	Acceptance of the Dawes Plan by the London Reparations Conference and by the Reichstag
	7.12	Reichstag election; gains by the SPD and the middle-class centre, start of a period of relative stability in the Weimar Republic
1925	28.2	Death of Reich President Friedrich Ebert, election of General Field Marshall Paul von Hindenburg as his successor
	1.12	Signing of the Locarno Treaty
1926	24.4	Signing of the Treaty of Friendship and Neutrality with the Soviet Union in Berlin
	10.9	Entry of Germany into the League of Nations
1928	28.6	Formation of the Grand Coalition between the SPD, Centre, DDP and DVP under the Social Democratic Chancellor Hermann Müller
1929	7.6	Young Plan finally settles the reparation problem
	3.10	Death of Foreign Minister Gustav Stresemann
	25.10	"Black Friday" in New York; beginning of the world economic crisis
1930	27.3	Collapse of the Müller government over the question of financing unemployment benefits
	30.3	Appointment of Centre politician Heinrich von Brüning to the post of Chancellor at the head of a minority government
	30.6	French troops leave the Rhineland ahead of schedule
	16.7	First Emergency Decree by the Reich President in the interests of "economic and financial security"
	14.9	Reichstag election: NSDAP landslide
1931	11.10	Formation of the Harzburg Front between the NSDAP, DNVP and the *Stahlhelm*
1932	10.4	Re-election of Reich President Paul von Hindenburg
	30.5	Resignation of the Brüning Government
	1.6	Formation of a right-wing cabinet under Franz von Papen
	20.7	Action taken by the Reich against Prussia; the government, headed by the Social Democrats, is overthrown
	31.7	Reichstag elections: NSDAP becomes the strongest party

1932	6.11	New Reichstag elections: loss of support for the National Socialists
	17.11	Resignation of the von Papen cabinet
	3.12	General Kurt von Schleicher appointed Reich Chancellor
1933	28.1	Resignation of Chancellor Kurt von Schleicher
	30.1	Adolf Hitler appointed Reich Chancellor
	27.2	Reichstag fire
	28.2	"Reich President's Decree on the Protection of the People and the State"
	5.3	Reichstag election: majority for the NSDAP and its coalition partner the DNVP
	23.3	The Reichstag approves the Enabling Act, despite the opposition of the SPD
	31.3	First law to "coordinate" the *Länder*
	1.4	Organised boycott of Jewish businesses
	7.4	Second law to "coordinate" the *Länder*
	2.5	Disbanding of trade unions
	June/July	Disbanding of all parties with the exception of the NSDAP
	20.7	Concordat between the German Reich and the Vatican
	14.10	Germany leaves the League of Nations
1934	30.6	"Röhm putsch", elimination of the SA leadership, General Kurt von Schleicher murdered
	2.8	Death of Paul von Hindenburg, swearing of an oath of allegiance by the *Wehrmacht* to the "Führer and Reich Chancellor" Adolf Hitler
1935	13.1	Plebiscite in the Saarland on the issue of its return to the Reich
	16.3	Reintroduction of compulsory national service
	15.9	"Nuremberg Laws", Jewish population deprived of their rights
1936	7.3	German troops march into the demilitarised Rhineland
	1.8	Opening of the Olympic Games in Berlin
1936	25.10	German-Italian Treaty, "Berlin-Rome Axis"
	25.11	Anticomintern Pact between Germany and Japan
1938	12.3	German troops march into Austria
	29.9	Munich Treaty on the ceding of the Sudetenland to the German Empire

1938	9.11	*Reichskristallnacht*, organised riots against the German Jews
1939	15.3	German troops invade Czechoslovakia, the Reich Protectorate of Bohemia and Moravia established
	23.3	The Memel territories given back to the German Reich
	23.8	Signing of the German-Russian Non-Aggression Pact
	1.9	German invasion of Poland
	3.9	Great Britain and France declare war on the German Reich
1940	9.4	Occupation of Denmark, invasion of Norway
	10.5	German attack on Belgium, the Netherlands, Luxembourg and France
	22.6	Signing of the Franco-German ceasefire in Compiègne
1941	22.6	Germany attacks the Soviet Union
	11.12	Germany declares war on the USA
1942	20.1	"Wannsee Conference", announcement of the "final solution of the Jewish Question"
1943	14 – 25.1	Casablanca Conference between Franklin D. Roosevelt and Winston Churchill, demand for "unconditional surrender"
	31.1 – 2.2	Surrender of the German Sixth Army at Stalingrad
1944	6.6	Allied landing in north-western France
	20.7	Assassination attempt on Hitler by Count Claus von Stauffenberg; attempted coups d'etat in Berlin and Paris
1945	4 – 11.2	Yalta Conference
	12.4	Death of American President Franklyn D. Roosevelt
	25.4	Meeting of American and Soviet troops near Torgau on the Elbe
	30.4	Adolf Hitler commits suicide
	7 – 9.5	Signing of the German surrender in Reims and Berlin-Karlshorst
	10.6	Command No 2 of the SMAD; licensing of parties and trade unions
	11.6 – 5.7	Founding of the KPD, SPD, CDU and LDP in Berlin
	1 – 4.7	Withdrawal of British and American troops from Saxony, Thuringia and Mecklenburg; Western troops enter Berlin
	14.7	Founding of the "United Front of Antifascist Democratic Parties" in Berlin

1945	17.7 – 2.8	Potsdam Conference
	Aug./Sept.	The licensing of political parties begins in the western zones of occupation
1946	20 – 27.1	First local elections in the American zone
	7.3	Founding of the "Free German Youth"
	21/22.4	Amalgamation of the KPD and SPD to form the SED in the Soviet zone of occupation and East Berlin
	30.6	Plebiscite in Saxony on the expropriation of "war criminals and active Nazis"
	6.9	Speech by US Foreign Minister James F. Byrnes in Stuttgart
	1.10	Passing of sentences in the Nuremberg War Crimes Trials
	20.10	Elections to the state parliaments in the Soviet zone
	2.12	Washington Treaty on the economic unification of the British and American zones
1947	25.2	Formal dissolution of the state of Prussia by the Allied Control Council
	10.3 – 24.4	Moscow foreign ministers' conference of the four victorious allies
	5.6	Announcement of a programme for the economic reconstruction of Europe by US Foreign Minister George C. Marshall
	6 – 7.6	Conference of minister-presidents in Munich
	10.6	Economic Council of the Bizone set up in Frankfurt am Main
	14.6	"German Economic Commission" established in the Soviet zone
	25.11 – 15.12	London foreign ministers' conference of the four victorious allies
1948	23.2 – 6.3 and	Six Power Conference in London, adoption of the
	20.4 – 2.6	recommendations on the founding of a West German state
	20.3	Last meeting of the Allied Control Council
	20./21.6	Currency reform in the western zones
	24.6	Start of the Berlin airlift
	1.7	Handing over of the "Frankfurt Documents" to the West German minister-presidents
	10 – 23.8	Herrenchiemsee constitutional conference
	1.9	Setting up of the Parliamentary Council in Bonn

1949	4.5	Jessup-Malik Agreement on the lifting of the Berlin blockade on 12.5.1949
	15 – 16.5	Elections to the Third German People's Congress in the Soviet zone, first elections on the single-list system
	23.5	Promulgation of the Basic Law for the Federal Republic of Germany
	14.8	Election of the first German Bundestag
	7.9	Constituent sitting of the German Bundestag
	12.9	Election of Theodor Heuss (FDP) as Federal President
	15.9	Election of Konrad Adenauer (CDU) as Federal Chancellor
	21.9	Statute of occupation comes into effect
	7.10	Establishment of the German Democratic Republic
	11.10	Election of Wilhelm Pieck (SED) as President of the GDR
	22.11	Petersberg Treaty ends dismantling
1950	16.1	End of food rationing in the Federal Republic
	8.2	Ministry of State Security established in the GDR
	15.6	Bundestag decides in favour of the Federal Republic's accession to the Council of Europe
	25.6	Start of the Korean War
	29.9	GDR joins the Council for Mutual Economic Assistance (Comecon)
1951	10.4	Bundestag passes the law on codetermination in the steel and coalmining industries
	18.4	Signing of the European Coal and Steel Community Treaty in Paris
1952	26.5	Signing of the Bonn Conventions
	27.5	Signing of the European Defence Community (EDC) Treaty in Paris
	9 – 12.7	Decision by the Second Party Congress of the SED concerning the "planned building of Socialism in the GDR"
	23.7	Division of the *Länder* in the GDR into 14 districts and 217 counties
	10.9	Signing of the Reconciliation Treaty between Israel and West Germany
1953	5.3	Death of Josef Stalin
	17.6	Uprising in East Berlin and East Germany
	27.7	Ceasefire in Korea

1954	25.3	Declaration by the USSR recognizing the sovereignty of the GDR
	23.10	Signing of the Treaty of Paris allowing the Federal Republic to join NATO and permitting German rearmament, following the rejection of the EDC Treaty by the French National Assembly
1955	5.5	Paris Treaty comes into force, sovereignty for the Federal Republic
	14.5	Founding of the Warsaw Pact, including the GDR
	9 – 13.9	Visit by Chancellor Konrad Adenauer to Moscow
	20.9	Confirmation of the "full sovereignty" of the GDR
	23.10.	Plebiscite in the Saarland, rejection of European status
1956	18.1	Decision by the People's Chamber to set up a "National People's Army"
	20/23.2	FDP forces the collapse of the Arnold government in North Rhine-Westphalia, division in the FDP group, FDP leaves the Federal Government
1957	1.1	Incorporation of the Saarland into the Federal Republic
	22.1	Bundestag passes the Pension Reform Law
	25.3	Signing of the Treaty of Rome establishing the European Economic Community
	15.9	Bundestag election, absolute majority for the CDU/CSU
1958	29.5	Abolition of ration cards in the GDR
	10.11	"Berlin Ultimatum" issued by the Soviet Union
1959	1.7	Election of Heinrich Lübke as Federal President
	13 – 15.11	SPD Godesberg Conference, adoption of a new programme
1960	30.6	Bundestag speech by Herbert Wehner, acceptance by the SPD of rearmament and Western integration
	12.9	Following the death of Wilhelm Pieck, the Council of State of the GDR is established under the chairmanship of Walter Ulbricht
1961	13.8	Building of the Berlin Wall
1962	14 – 28.10	Cuba Crisis
	Oct./Nov.	Spiegel Affair, resignation of Federal Defence Minister Franz-Josef Strauss
1963	22.1	Signing of the Franco-German Friendship Treaty in Paris
	24 – 25.6	Economic conference of the SED and the Council of Ministers concerning the "New Economic System of Planning and Guidance"

1963	15./16.10.	Resignation of Chancellor Konrad Adenauer, election of Economics Minister Ludwig Erhard as his successor
	17.12.	First agreement on crossborder travel between the GDR and the West Berlin Senate
1964	24.9	Willi Stoph becomes chairman of the GDR Council of Ministers following the death of Otto Grotewohl
1965	24.2	Walter Ulbricht's state visit to Egypt
1966	27.10	FDP ministers resign from the Ludwig Erhard Cabinet
	1.12	Formation of a Grand Coalition between CDU/CSU and SPD under Chancellor Kurt Kiesinger
1967	31.1	Establishment of diplomatic relations between West Germany and Romania, relaxation of the Hallstein Doctrine
	14.2	Start of the process of "concerted action" chaired by Economics Minister Friedrich Schiller
	20.2	Law on "citizenship" of the GDR
	8.6	Passing of the Stability Law by the Bundestag
1968	6.4	Plebiscite on the new GDR constitution
	11 – 17.4	Murder of the student leader Rudi Dutschke, "Easter Riots" in Berlin and other West German cities
	30.5	Bundestag passes emergency legislation
	21.8	Troops of the Warsaw Pact invade Czechoslovakia
1969	5.3	Election of Gustav Heinemann (SPD) as Federal President
	28.9	Bundestag election, considerable gains made by the SPD
	21/22.10	SPD Chairman Willy Brandt elected Chancellor, formation of an SPD/FDP Federal Government
	28.11	The Federal Republic signs the Non-proliferation Treaty
1970	19.3	Meeting between Chairman of the GDR Council of Ministers Willi Stoph and Federal Chancellor Willy Brandt in Erfurt
	21.5	Return visit by Willi Stoph to Kassel
	12.8	Signing of the German-Soviet Non-Aggression Pact in Moscow
	7.12	Signing of the German-Polish Treaty in Warsaw
1971	3.5	Erich Honecker replaces Walter Ulbricht as Secretary General of the SED Central Committee
	3.9	Signing of the Four Power Agreement on Berlin
	10.12	Chancellor Willy Brandt receives the Nobel Peace Prize

1972	27.4	CDU/CSU fails in an attempted vote of no confidence against Chancellor Willy Brandt
	17.5	Ratification of the Moscow and Warsaw Treaties by the Bundestag
	26.5	Signing of transport agreement between the GDR and the Federal Republic
	19.11	Bundestag elections: SPD and FDP gain a clear majority
	21.12	Signing of the Basic Treaty between the GDR and the Federal Republic in East Berlin
1973	18.9	The Federal Republic and the GDR become members of the United Nations
	October	Start of the global oil crisis; Arab oil-producing nations restrict supplies and raise prices
1974	6.5	Resignation of Chancellor Willy Brandt
	15.5	Election of Foreign Minister Walter Scheel (FDP) as Federal President
	16./17.5	Election of Finance Minister Helmut Schmidt (SPD) as Chancellor, renewal of the SPD/FDP Coalition
	4.9	Establishment of diplomatic relations between the GDR and the USA
1975	1.8	Signing of the CSCE Final Act in Helsinki
1976	3.10	Bundestag election: a narrow victory for the SPD/FDP Coalition
	16.11	Wolf Biermann deprived of East German citizenship
1977	7.4	Murder of Federal Prosecutor-General, Siegfried Buback
	30.7	Murder of the banker, Jürgen Ponto
	5.9 – 19.10	Kidnap and murder of the president of the employers' federation, Hanns-Martin Schleyer; hijack of a Lufthansa plane; liberation of the hostages in Mogadishu; suicide of the terrorists Baader, Ensslin and Raspe
1978	16/17.7	World Economic Summit of the seven leading Western industrialized countries in Bonn
1979	23.5	Election of Karl Carstens (CDU) as Federal President
	7 – 10.6	First direct elections to the European Parliament
	12.12	Decision to increase deployment of nuclear missiles taken by NATO Council of Ministers
	27.12	Soviet invasion of Afghanistan
1980	30.6/1.7	Visit by Chancellor Helmut Schmidt to Moscow
	5.10	Bundestag election: SPD and FDP strengthen their majority

1981	10.10	Peace demonstration in Bonn
	11 – 13.2	Visit by Chancellor Helmut Schmidt to East Germany
1982	17.9	Collapse of the SPD/FDP coalition, resignation of FDP ministers
	1.10.	Replacement of Chancellor Helmut Schmidt and the SPD minority government by a CDU/CSU/FDP coalition under Chancellor Helmut Kohl
1983	6.3	Bundestag elections: the CDU/CSU and the FDP obtain an absolute majority, together polling 55 % of the second votes, and are able to continue their coalition; the Greens win 28 seats and are represented in the Bundestag for the first time
	29.3	The German Bundestag re-elects Helmut Kohl as Federal Chancellor
	21/22.11	Bundestag debate on NATO's dual-track decision and force modernization
1984	May/July	Strikes for the 35-hour week in the engineering and printing industries
	23.5	Richard von Weizsäcker, Governing Mayor of Berlin, is elected Federal President
1985	2/5.5	World Economic Summit in Bonn
	5.5	US President Ronald Reagan visits Bergen-Belsen and Bitburg
	2/3.12	EC summit on reform of the European Community and the accession of Spain and Portugal
1986	January	The Neue Heimat scandal, involving a co-operative building association owned by the trade unions, reaches its climax
	26.4	Accident at the Chernobyl nuclear reactor in the Soviet Union
1987	25.1	Bundestag elections: the CDU/CSU and the FDP retain their majority and again form the Federal Government
	7/11.9	Erich Honecker, Chairman of the Council of State of the GDR, visits the Federal Republic of Germany
1988	27/28.6	The heads of state and government of the European Community decide at a summit meeting in Hanover to complete the internal market of the Community by 1 January 1993
	27/29.9	Annual meeting of the International Monetary Fund (IMF) and the World Bank in Berlin
1989	23.5	The Federal Convention re-elects Richard von Weizsäcker as Federal President

1989	24.5	40th anniversary of the founding of the Federal Republic of Germany and of the entry into force of the Basic Law
	7.10	40th anniversary of the founding of the German Democratic Republic
		Mass demonstration in Leipzig for reform and democracy
	18.10	Erich Honecker is replaced as General Secretary of the SED
	9.11	Opening of the Berlin Wall, GDR citizens may travel freely
	30.11	Alfred Herrhausen, spokesman of the board of directors of Deutsche Bank, is murdered
1990	18.3	First democratic elections to the People's Chamber of the GDR
	1.7	Economic, monetary and social union comes into force between the Federal Republic and the GDR
	23.8	People's Chamber of the GDR declares that the GDR will accede to the Basic Law on 3 October 1990
	3.10	Accession of the GDR to the Federal Republic of Germany
	2.12	First all-German elections to the Bundestag; the CDU/CSU and the FDP retain their majority and form the Federal Government
1991	17.1 – 3.3	War waged by Allied forces against the Iraqi occupation of Kuwait
	1.4	Detlev Karsten Rohwedder, President of the Berlin Treuhand privatization agency, is murdered
	20.6	The Bundestag decides by 337 to 320 votes to transfer parliament and the government to the capital, Berlin
	20 – 28.6	Slovenia and Croatia declare independence, civil war begins in Yugoslavia
	19/22.8	In the Soviet Union a putsch organized by conservative forces to put an end to President Mikhail Gorbachev's reform policy fails due popular resistance
	17 – 23.9	Attacks against asylum-seekers in Hoyerswerda in Saxony and in other towns
	8.12	Break-up of the Soviet Union, establishment of the Commonwealth of Independent States in Minsk
	9 – 10.12	EC summit meeting in Maastricht, signing of the treaties on economic and monetary union and political union

1992	27.4	Foreign Minister Hans Dietrich Genscher resigns after 18 years in office
	3.6	UN Conference on Environment and Development in Rio de Janeiro
	29.7	Erich Honecker is extradited from Russia to Germany to face trial for the fatal shootings at the Berlin Wall; the trial begins on 12 November
	22.11	Three people die in an arson attack by right-wing extremists on a house in Mölln, near Hamburg
	6.12	The coalition partners, the CSU/CSU and FDP, together with the SPD opposition, agree to reorganize asylum procedures and amend Article 16 of the Basic Law on the right to asylum
1993	1.1	Completion of the European Single Market
	3.5	The SPD chairman and Minister President of Schleswig-Hostein, Björn Engholm, resigns after making a false statement concerning the Barschel-Pfeiffer affair of 1987
	22.7	German troops are deployed for the first time as UN peace-keeping troops at Belet-Huen in Somalia
	3 – 4.10	In Moscow the putsch launched by Parliamentary Speaker Ruslan Khasbulatov and Vice-President Alexander Rutskoi against President Boris Yeltsin is violently crushed
	28.10	Frankfurt am Main is chosen as the headquarters of the European Monetary Institute by the EU heads of state and government
	1.11	The Maastricht Treaty on European Union, signed two years previously, enters into force
1994	23.5	Roman Herzog, President of the Federal Constitutional Court, is elected Federal President
	29.5	Death of Erich Honecker in Chile
	16.10	Elections to the Bundestag: CDU/CSU and FDP retain their majority by a small margin, PDS wins seats in the new *Länder*
1995	30.6	The Bundestag decides to deploy units of the Federal Armed Forces to protect the UN rapid reaction force in Bosnia-Herzegovina
	16.11	Oskar Lafontaine, Minister-President of the Saarland, is elected SPD party chairman in a contested vote at the SPD federal party conference in Mannheim, thus replacing Rudolf Scharping
1996	5.5	The proposed unification of the *Länder* of Berlin and Brandenburg is rejected in a referendum

AEG-Telefunken, Zentralbibliothek
Berlin
174

Erich Anders, Hamburg
294

Archiv Museum der Arbeit, Hamburg
386

Archiv für Kunst u. Geschichte, Berlin
75, 113, 214, 226, 279, 295, 482,
488, 490

Archiv Gerstenberg, Wietze
16, 23, 26, 38, 39, 44, 53, 76, 79,
86, 88, 99, 110, 112, 119, 128,
129, 130, 131, 132, 136, 139, 140,
141, 143, 148, 164, 166, 167, 169,
170, 173, 177, 183, 185, 187, 209

Archiv der sozialen Demokratie
(AdsD), Bonn-Bad Godesberg
168, 180, 221, 324

Associated Press, Frankfurt Main
465, 471

Bayerisches Hauptstaatsarchiv,
Munich
108

Bayerische Staatsbibliothek, Munich
257, 261, 299

Berlin und seine Bauten
489

Berlinische Galerie
493

Bildstelle VfWD
362

Bundesarchiv, Außenstelle
Frankfurt/Main
24, 90, 91

Bundesarchiv Koblenz
92, 93, 95, 184, 190, 196, 208,
210, 212, 251, 252, 260, 262, 267,
286, 297, 302, 308, 310, 356, 364,
370, 373, 375, 376, 381, 388, 392,
423, 424, 443,

Bundeskriminalamt
428

Collection, The Museum of Modern
Art, New York
231

Michael S. Cullen, Berlin
479

Kurt Desch Verlag, Munich
180

Deutsche Presse-Agentur, Bildarchiv
193, 314, 316, 326, 327, 328, 335,
342, 343, 358, 363, 366, 377, 379,
383, 410, 411, 413, 418, 419, 422,
427, 432, 437, 438, 457

Deutscher Bundestag
1, 7, 11, 35, 40, 56, 84, 155, 162,
199, 200, 215, 238, 265, 322, 365,
369, 378, 390, 391, 393, 429, 434,
435, 454, 461, 462, 463, 472, 473,
474, 475, 477, 478, 480, 481, 484,
485, 486, 487, 492, 495

Deutsches Historisches Museum,
Berlin
175, 201, 202, 203, 204, 205, 253,
277, 305, 321, 340, 351, 372, 387,
389

Deutsches Museum, Munich
172

Gerhard Gäbler, Leipzig
441

Geheimes Staatsarchiv Preußischer
Kutlurbesitz, Berlin
116, 147

v. Gerlach-Parsow, Hohenstein
135

Germanisches Nationalmuseum,
Nuremberg
32, 61, 64, 85, 105

Generallandesarchiv Karlsruhe
58, 59, 60

Geschwister-Scholl-Archiv, Munich
274

G+J Berliner Zeitung Verlag GmbH
& Co
329, 330, 333, 355, 403, 404, 414,
425, 430, 453

Goethe-Museum, Düsseldorf
13

Claus-Peter Groß, Tegernsee
179, 336

Wolfgang Haut, Nidderau
459

Heimatmuseum Ludwigsburg
31

Heimatmuseum Weißenhorn
66

Rudolf Herz, Munich
269

Historisches Museum der Stadt
Frankfurt/Main
27, 49, 63, 94, 142, 293

Historisches Museum, Pfalz
65

Heinrich Hoffmann, Munich
254, 300

Hanns Hubmann
336

Hulton Deutsch, London
331

Colorfoto Hans Hinz, Basel
195

Imperial War Museum, London
317

Interfoto Friedrich Rauch, Munich
347

Internationaal Institut voor Sociale
Geschiedenis, Amsterdam
133

Jürgens, Cologne
445

Keystone-Pressedienst
380, 431, 456

Kladderadatsch
138

Barbara Klemm, Frankfurt/Main
426, 452, 460

Kunsthistorisches Museum, Vienna
2

Kunstmuseum Basel
55

KZ-Gedenkstätte, Dachau
272

Landesarchiv Berlin
103, 192

Landesbildstelle Berlin
15, 114, 125, 171, 186, 189, 191,
194, 197, 198, 206, 207, 222, 323,
237, 255, 285, 290, 341, 382, 400,
407, 476, 478, 483, 494, 496, 497,
498, 499, 500, 501

Landesmuseum Mainz
12

Klaus Lehnarz, Berlin
440

Leipziger Illustrierte
36, 45, 68, 71, 72, 73, 74, 78, 80,
82, 83, 87, 89, 96, 97, 98, 100,
102, 104, 106, 107, 111, 115, 126,
127

Maschinenfabrik Augsburg-Nuremberg AG (MAN), Augsburg
124

Klaus Mehner
451

Klaus Morgenstern, Berlin
415

Museum der Stadt Regensburg
3, 4

Naumann-Stiftung
320

Politisches Archiv des Auswärtigen Amtes, Bonn
149, 176

Presse- und Informationsamt der Bundesregierung, Bundesbildstelle, Bonn
239, 339, 344, 352, 353, 360, 367, 368, 397, 398, 401, 402, 405, 409, 420, 455, 458, 502

Privatbesitz
20

Propyläen Verlag, Berlin
19

Reichsgesetzblatt
259, 291

Réunion des Musées Nationaux, Paris
14

Klaus Rose
417

Sammlung der Deutschen Akademie der Künste
25

Gerhard Schoenberner, Berlin
273

Dr. Erich Schwan, Darmstadt
151

Der Spiegel
394

Staatliche Graphische Sammlungen, Munich
18

Staatliche Museen Preußischer Kulturbesitz, Nationalgalerie Berlin
48

Staatliche und Städtische Kunstsammlung Kassel
46, 62

Staatsbibliothek Preußischer Kulturbesitz, Bildarchiv, Berlin
6, 10, 33, 34, 41, 42, 51, 52, 101, 118, 120, 121, 122, 134, 137, 144, 145, 146, 150, 152, 154, 156, 157, 158, 159, 160, 161, 163, 165, 178, 181, 182, 204, 227, 245, 246, 248, 249, 250, 259, 276, 292, 301, 313, 334, 338, 395, 491

Stadtarchiv Augsburg
9

Stadtarchiv Frankfurt/Main
81, 280, 281, 289

Stadtarchiv Hamburg
17, 47, 50

Stadtarchiv Heidelberg
70

Stadtarchiv Constance
69

Stadtarchiv Munich
37, 264, 283, 284, 298

Stadtarchiv Nuremberg
357

Städtisches Museum Wetzlar
5

Städtisches Reiss-Museum
30, 54

Stadtmuseum Berlin
22, 43, 77, 153, 448

Stadtmuseum Munich
8, 28, 57

Stiftung Bundeskanzler-Adenauer
325

Stiftung der Parteien und Massenorganisationen der DDR im Bundesarchiv
318, 332, 337, 345, 346, 350, 374

Stiftung Deutsche Kinemathek
234

Horst Sturm, Berlin
408

Süddeutscher Verlag, Bilderdienst,
Munich
213, 223, 224, 229, 247, 256, 266,
268, 271, 275, 287, 304, 306, 309,
312, 349, 354, 359, 385, 439, 449,
464, 466, 467, 468, 469,470

Walter Tuphorn, Höchstadt/Aisch
307

Ullstein Bilderdienst, Berlin
211, 216, 217, 218, 219, 220, 225,
228, 230, 232, 233, 235, 236, 240,
241, 242, 243, 244, 263, 270, 278,
282, 303, 311, 315, 319, 361, 371,
396, 412, 416, 421, 433, 436, 446,
447, 450, 454

Universitätsbibliothek der Freien
Universität Berlin
29

Universitätsbibliothek der Technischen Universität Berlin
117, 123

Volkswagenwerk AG, Wolfsburg
348

Wehrgeschichtliches Museum Rastatt
109

Werksarchiv Krauss-Maffei, Munich
288

Yad Vaschem
296

ZENIT, Berlin
444

Gerhard Zwickert, Berlin
442

Paula Abraham, Berlin
ABZ/Haeckel, Berlin
Konrad-Adenauer-Stiftung, Bonn
AEG-Telefunken, Berlin
Agentur für Bilder zur Zeitgeschichte
Wolfgang Albrecht, Berlin
Erich Anders, Hamburg
Jörg P. Anders, Berlin
Amerika-Gedenkbibliothek, Berlin
Archiv der Deutschen Burschenschaft, Frankfurt/Main
Archiv Gerstenberg, Wietze
Archiv der sozialen Demokratie
(AdsD), Bonn-Bad Godesberg
Archiv für Kunst und Geschichte,
Berlin
Archiv Museum der Arbeit, Hamburg
argus/Hamburg
Associated Press GmbH, Frankfurt/Main
Augustinermuseum der Stadt Freiburg i. Breisgau
Auswärtiges Amt, Bonn

Badisches Generallandesarchiv,
Karlsruhe
Heinrich Bauer-Verlag
Bauhaus-Archiv, Berlin
Fred Bayer, Berlin
Bayer AG, Leverkusen
Bayerische Staatsbibliothek, München
Bayerisches Hauptstaatsarchiv,
München
Berliner Morgenpost, Berlin
Berliner Post- und Fernmeldemuseum
Berliner Verkehrs-Betriebe (BVG)
Berlinsche Galerie
Bezirksamt Tiergarten, Abt. Bauwesen, Berlin
Bildstelle VfWD
Manfred Bleif, Berlin
Herbert Bode, Bonn
Karl-Heinz Buller, Berlin
Bundesarchiv, Außenstelle Frankfurt/Main
Bundesarchiv Koblenz
Bundeskriminalamt Wiesbaden
Bundesministerium für Verteidigung, Bonn

Bundesministerium für Wirtschaft,
Bonn
Bundespostmuseum,
Frankfurt/Main
Bundespräsidialamt, Bonn
Burda-Verlag
Burschenschaft Teutonia zu Jena in
Berlin

CDU, Bonn
Collection, The Museum of Modern
Art, New York
Michael S. Cullen, Berlin

Kurt Desch Verlag, Munich
Gerd Deutsch, Berlin
Deutsche Bank AG, Frankfurt/Main
Deutsche Bundesbank,
Frankfurt/Main
Deutsche Presse-Agentur, Bildarchiv Berlin
Deutscher Bundestag
Deutsches Bergbau-Museum, Bochum
Deutsches Historisches Museum,
Berlin
Deutsches Museum, Munich

EUROPA GmbH.

FDP, Bonn
Margarete Feist, Berlin
Frankfurter Allgemeine, Frankfurt/Main
Friedrich-Ebert-Stiftung, Bonn

Gerhard Gäbler, Leipzig
Prof. Dr. Lothar Gall, Frankfurt
Geheimes Staatsarchiv Preußischer
Kulturbesitz, Berlin
Generallandesarchiv Karlsruhe
v. Gerlach-Parsow, Hohenstein
Germanisches Nationalmuseum,
Nuremberg
Geschwister-Scholl-Archiv, Munich
Goethe-Museum, Düsseldorf
Karl Greiser
Prof. Claus-Peter Groß, Rottach-
Egern
Großherzogliche Privatsammlungen, Darmstadt
Gruner und Jahr AG + Co, Hamburg

G+J Berliner Zeitung Verlag GmbH
& Co, Berlin

Horst Haitzinger
Hamburger Kunsthalle
Irmin Hammelbacher, Munich
Wilma Hauck, Berlin
Wolfgang Haut, Nidderau
Hauptstaatsarchiv Stuttgart
Hilde Havel, Berlin
Heimatmuseum Ludwigsburg
Heimatmuseum Weißhorn
Historisches Museum Pfalz
Gisela Hegenwald-Goetze
Brigitte Heligoth
Rudolf Herz, Munich
Herzog-August-Bibliothek Wolfen-
büttel
Dr. Hans-Jürgen Heß, Berlin
Hessische Landes-Hochschul-
bibliothek, Darmstadt
Hessische Landesbibliothek,
Wiesbaden
Hessisches Landesmuseum, Darm-
stadt
Ursula Heuss-Wolff
Colorfoto Hans Hinz, Basel
Historisches Museum der Stadt
Frankfurt/Main
Historisches Museum Pfalz
Hoesch Werke AG, Dortmund
Heinrich Hoffmann, Munich
Hanns Hubmann, Kröning
Burghard Hüdig
Hulton Deutsch, London

Imperial War Museum London
Industriegewerkschaft Metall,
Frankfurt/Main
Institut für Zeitgeschichte, Munich
Institut für Zeitungsforschung,
Dortmund
Interfoto Friedrich Rauch, Munich
International Instituut voor Sociale
Geschiedenis, Amsterdam
Internationales Zeitungsmuseum
der Stadt Aachen

Jürgens, Cologne

Elfriede Kante, Berlin
Hilde Kaspar, Berlin
Keystone-Pressedienst

Barbara Klemm
Helga Kneidl, Hamburg
Kladderadatsch
Stefan Kresin, Heidelberg
Fritz Krüger, Berlin
Friedrich Krupp GmbH, Essen
Kunstbibliothek der Staatlichen
Museen Preußischer Kulturbesitz,
Berlin
Kunstgewerbemuseum, Staatliche
Museen Preußischer Kulturbesitz,
Berlin
Kunsthistorisches Museum, Vienna
Kunstmuseum Basel
Martin Kupke, Berlin
KZ-Gedenkstätte Dachau

Landesarchiv Berlin
Landesbildstelle Baden
Landesbildstelle Berlin
Landesbildstelle Karlsruhe
Landeshauptstadt Munich
Landesmuseum Mainz
Leipziger Illustrierte
Klaus Lehnarz, Berlin

Märkisches Museum
Sammlung Flensburg-Mürwik
Maschinenfabrik Augsburg-Nurem-
berg (MAN), Augsburg
Wilfried Matthias, Bronzekunst-
werkstatt, Berlin
Klaus Mehner
Klaus Morgenstern, Berlin
Museen der Stadt Vienna
Museum für Hamburgische Ge-
schichte, Hamburg
Museum der Stadt Regensburg
Preußischer Kulturbesitz, Berlin
Museum Wiesbaden

Neue Theaterkunst, Berlin
Detlev Niemann, Hamburg
Herbert Nitert, Berlin

Ilsemarie Ollk, Berlin
Olympia Werke AG, Wilhelmshaven

Parlamentsarchiv Bundeshaus,
Bonn
Willi Peiter, Diez
Pix-Features

Politisches Archiv des Auswärtigen Amtes, Bonn
Pressedienst Glaser, Berlin
Pressofoto Lehnartz
Presse- und Informationsamt der Bundesregierung, Bundesbildstelle, Bonn
Preußischer Kulturbesitz, Berlin
Propyläen Verlag, Berlin
Prof. Hubertus Protz, Berlin

Tamara Raaman, Jerusalem
Dr. Christoph Rabenstein, Bayreuth
Réunion des Musées Nationaux, Paris
Ringier Dokumentationszentrum, Zürich
Klaus Rose, Iserlohn
Ruhrland- und Heimatmuseum der Stadt Essen

Sammlung der Deutschen Akademie der Künste
Alfred Schaefer, Berlin
Schiller-Nationalmuseum, Marbach
Elisabeth von Schlegell, Berlin
Margret Schmitt, Berlin
Andreas Schoelzel, Berlin
Gerhard Schoenberner, Berlin
Wolf Schöne
Harald H. Schröder FFM
Margarete Schuppmann, Berlin
Dr. Erich Schwan, Darmstadt
Senatsbibliothek Berlin
Sven Simon, Hamburg
Spiegel-Verlag, Hamburg
Axel-Springer-Verlag
Staatliche Graphische Sammlungen, Munich
Staatliche Schlösser und Gärten
Staatliche und Städtische Kunstsammlung Kassel
Staatsbibliothek Bamberg
Staatsbibliothek Preußischer Kulturbesitz, Berlin
Staatsbibliothek Preußischer Kulturbesitz, Bildarchiv, Berlin
Staats- und Universitätsbibliothek Hamburg
Stadtbibliothek Mainz
Stadtarchiv Augsburg
Stadtarchiv Frankfurt/Main
Stadtarchiv Hamburg

Stadtarchiv Heidelberg
Stadtarchiv Constance
Stadtarchiv Mannheim
Stadtarchiv Munich
Stadtmuseum Berlin
Stadtmuseum Munich
Städtisches Museum Wetzlar
Städtisches Reiss-Museum
Stiftung Bundeskanzler-Adenauer-Haus, Rhöndorf
Stiftung Deutsche Kinemathek, Berlin
Stiftung der Parteien und Massenorganisationen der DDR im Bundesarchiv, Berlin
Stiftung Haus der Geschichte der Bundesrepublik Deutschland, Bonn
Horst Sturm, Berlin
Stuttgarter Nachrichten
Süddeutscher Verlag, Bilderdienst, Munich

Walter Tuphorn, Höchstadt/Aisch

Ullstein Bilderdienst, Berlin
Universitätsbibliothek der Freien Universität Berlin
Universitätsbibliothek der Technischen Universität Berlin

Verkehrsmuseum Nuremberg
Verwaltung der Staatlichen Schlösser und Gärten, Berlin
Volkswagenwerk AG, Wolfsburg

Wehrgeschichtliches Museum Rastatt
Gertrud Weinhold, Berlin
Detlef Weiß, Berlin
Werner-von-Siemens-Institut, Munich
Westfälisches Landesmuseum für Kunst und Kulturgeschichte, Münster

Wolfgang Zierau, Berlin
Günter Zint
ZENIT, Berlin

Conceptual planning and
catalogue:
Prof. Dr. Lothar Gall
Priv.-Doz. Dr. Dieter Hein

Organizer:
Deutscher Bundestag

Layout and visual design:
Prof. Claus-Peter Groß
Margret Schmitt

Production:
Grapach GmbH, Dahlwitz-Hoppe-
garten
Heimann + Co., Berlin
Museumstechnik GmbH, Berlin
Wilhem Noack, Berlin

Photo reproductions:
Wolfgang Schackla, Berlin

Dioramas:
Heinz Bert Dreckmann, Berlin

Film and slide show:
Anita AV-Produktion
Joachim Baumann, Berlin
R.C.F. Film GmbH, Berlin

Catalogue design:
Margret Schmitt

Catalogue translated by:
Language Service of
the German Bundestag
Michael Fox
Sylvia Hofheinz
Hillary Crowe
Astrid Stephen
Penella Thompson

Catalogue printed by:
Gotha-Druck, Wechmar

Cafeteria

Lift

Level 4

VIII. The Path to the Present

Level 3

VII. The Divided Germany

Level 2

V.   The Weimar Republic

VI.   The Third Reich

Level 1.1

III.   The Industrial Revolution
       and the Founding of the Empire

IV.   Imperial Germany

Level 1

I.   From the World of Estates to
       the World of the Bourgeoisie

II.   The Revolution of 1848/49

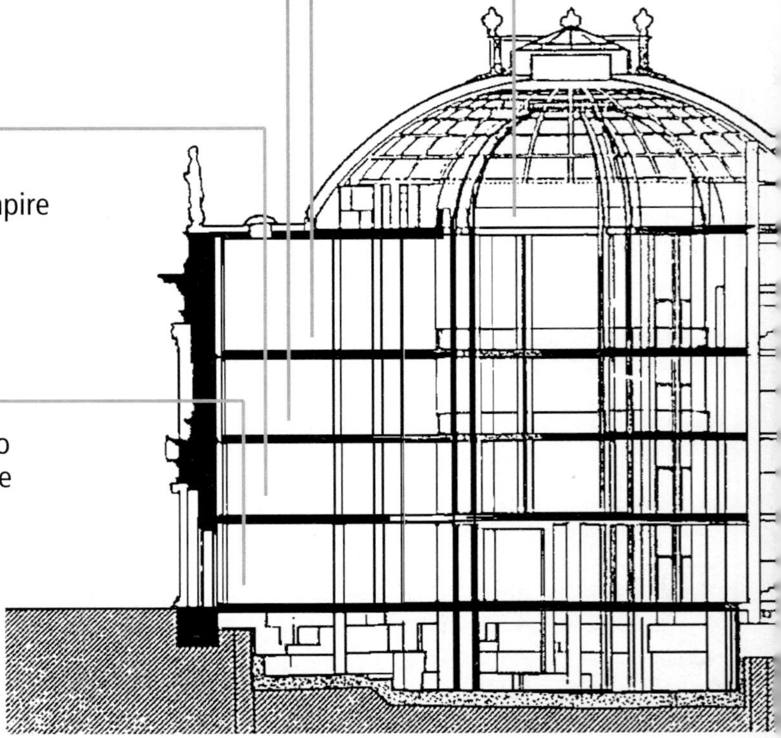

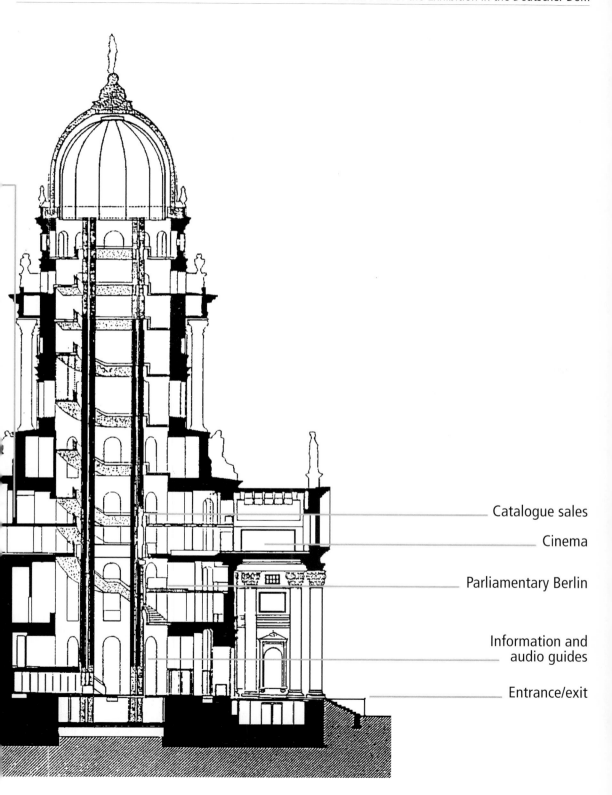

Catalogue sales

Cinema

Parliamentary Berlin

Information and
audio guides

Entrance/exit